UPON THIS ROCK

BOOKS BY FRANK G. SLAUGHTER

Modern Medical Novels:

DEVIL'S HARVEST

TOMORROW'S MIRACLE

EPIDEMIC!

DAYBREAK

SWORD AND SCALPEL

THE HEALER

EAST SIDE GENERAL

A TOUCH OF GLORY

BATTLE SURGEON

AIR SURGEON

SPENCER BRADE, M.D.

THAT NONE SHOULD DIE

Historical Novels:

PILGRIMS IN PARADISE

LORENA

THE MAPMAKER

THE WARRIOR

FLIGHT FROM NATCHEZ

APALACHEE GOLD

STORM HAVEN

FORT EVERGLADES

THE STUBBORN HEART

DIVINE MISTRESS

SANGAREE

THE GOLDEN ISLE

IN A DARK GARDEN

Non-Fiction:

DAVID: WARRIOR AND KING

THE LAND AND THE
PROMISE

THE CROWN AND THE CROSS

IMMORTAL MAGYAR

MEDICINE FOR MODERNS

THE NEW SCIENCE
OF SURGERY

Biblical Novels:

UPON THIS ROCK

THE CURSE OF JEZEBEL

THE THORN OF ARIMATHEA

THE SCARLET CORD

THE SONG OF RUTH

THE GALILEANS

THE ROAD TO BITHYNIA

UPON

A NOVEL OF SIMON PETER,

THIS ROCK

PRINCE OF THE APOSTLES

By Frank G. Slaughter

Coward-McCann, Inc. NEW YORK

*This book is affectionately dedicated
to my grandson,*

FRANK G. SLAUGHTER, III

"... THOU ART PETER, AND UPON THIS ROCK I WILL BUILD MY CHURCH."

Matthew 16:18

CONTENTS

AUTHOR'S PREFACE

SINCE 1948, when I began a period of intensive research in preparation for writing my first biblical novel, *The Road to Bithynia*, I have been intrigued by the challenge inherent in the character of Simon Peter to a novelist attempting to depict New Testament events as they no doubt occurred. A constant study of the biblical field since that time has now produced ten books and convinced me that Simon Peter was not the man who is ordinarily described from the pulpit. There he is often characterized as a bumbling, unlettered and vacillating fisherman whose faith often wavered and who denied our Lord—solely to save himself.

This man is not the Simon Peter I first met on the road to Bithynia, or the Simon Peter I have come to admire and revere through the years. He is not the solid Rock upon which Jesus said he would build his church or the fearless apostle who stood before the Sanhedrin and denounced those who crucified his Master. And he is certainly not the great leader who humbled himself at Antioch and let the Apostle Paul step ahead of him in carrying the good news of Christ's crucifixion and resurrection to a waiting world.

The Simon Peter I have come to know and love is the man whose story is told in the pages that follow. Since no man is an island and his every act is as much a product of the actions of others as of his own will, I have divided the story into parts according to the men who most affected Peter's life at that time. The background sources are scriptural, contemporary historical, archeological, and to a very small degree, the traditional material found in the writings of the early church fathers.

In general I have followed the chronology of Luke, since he was also the author of the Acts of the Apostles. As to the controversy which has raged for centuries over whether Simon Peter lived for some time at Rome and was martyred there, I am convinced after an extensive study that the truth has been best expressed by Dr. Oscar Cullman—perhaps the foremost authority on Peter in the world today—in the concluding pages of his definitive study, *Peter: Disciple, Apostle, Martyr* (The Westminster Press), that Peter probably "died as a martyr under Nero." And certainly few would differ with Dr. Cullman when he says of Simon Peter: "On him Christ, who is himself the cornerstone, will keep building his Church as long as there is such a Church on earth."

Frank G. Slaughter

Jacksonville, Florida

Book One

JUDAS OF GALILEE

"... Judas of Galilee in the days of the taxing, and drew away much people after him: he also perished; and all, even as many as obeyed him, were dispersed."

THE ACTS 5:37

I

ERUSALEM was always exciting for a Galilean, and
never more than during the great religious feasts, or
festivals, attended by every pious Jew as often as he
could afford the cost of the journey. For Simon of Bethsaida,
the occasion that had brought him to the Holy City this fine
spring day was especially momentous; it marked his thirteenth
birthday, when he put away boyhood and became personally
responsible for obedience to the Laws of Moses.

Already almost as tall as an average man, Simon's body
was sturdy, his shoulders broad, and his arms powerful from
handling the heavy nets used by fishermen upon the Sea of
Galilee, the lovely harp-shaped lake lying several days' journey northeastward of Jerusalem. Though relatively isolated
from the Holy City, Galilee was far from being backward,
for several of its most populous cities were traversed by the
"Way of the Sea." This ancient caravan trail from Damascus
and the cities of the East to the fabled land of Egypt to the
south had been in existence for several thousand years, and
from travelers moving along it, the Galileans learned a great
deal about happenings, not only in Israel, but in the whole
Roman Empire during this turbulent period in Hebrew
history.

The present crisis had begun with the death of Herod the
Great, the tyrant who had extended the boundaries of Israel
almost to the full length and breadth reached by the great
kingdoms of David and Solomon in the most glorious days
the nation had ever known. For that accomplishment and be-

cause he professed to worship the Most High and had built the most magnificent temple in all of Israel's history, Herod could have been loved by his people even though he was an Idumean and not a Hebrew. But he had also been cruel beyond belief, executing his own sons when he fancied that they coveted his throne, as well as his beautiful wife Mariamne, a princess in the royal Hasmonean house that traced its lineage back to Judas Maccabeus. For those and many other crimes, the Israelites could not forgive Herod, and a seething caldron of hate had boiled just below the surface during the latter years of his reign.

Hard on the news of Herod's death had come the announcement that according to his will the kingdom would be divided between three of his sons—Antipas, Philip and Archelaus. When each then sought to outdo the other in currying favor with the emperor at Rome, hoping to enlarge his own share at the expense of his brothers, the people became first alarmed and then ripe for rebellion. For with the kingdom divided and each section under the rule of a petty tyrant who had spent most of his life in Rome—as had all of Herod's sons—the Jews saw their identity as a nation threatened, their future as a separate people in serious jeopardy, and the end of the messianic hope promised by great prophets such as Isaiah.

Two climactic events occurring in rapid sequence had brought the political climate to a point of violent upheaval. One was the departure of Herod's sons for Rome, each to plead his own cause with Augustus. The second, and most alarming, was the arrival in Jerusalem of Sabinus, Procurator Fiscal of Syria, with the announced intention of seizing the magnificent treasures of the temple, ostensibly as taxes in the name of the emperor, but actually largely for his own personal enrichment.

News of the threat to Israel's sacred treasure had raced through the land like flames through a wheat field at harvesttime, and from Beersheba in the south to the ancient tribal center of Dan in the foothills of Mount Hermon near the sources of the Jordan, angry Jews had converged upon Jerusalem. The excuse for the gathering of such a great number was the Feast of Pentecost, marking the beginning of summer some fifty days after the Passover. But many came prepared to fight for their national identity and for the great golden-domed temple that was the wellspring of their faith.

Simon of Bethsaida had been promised a visit to Jerusalem in autumn when the Feast of Booths or Tabernacles celebrated the grape harvest with singing, dancing and sacrificing the first fruits in thanksgiving to the Lord. But, two journeys to Jerusalem in a single year were far beyond the means of a Galilean fisherman, and when a group of men from the teeming centers of the lake region had embarked upon the almost week-long journey southward, planning to protest the action of Sabinus, Simon and his father Jonas had accompanied them.

It had been nearly dark the evening before when the company of Galileans made camp on the slope of the Mount of Olives facing the Holy City. Simon had not been able to see much except the looming shadows of the walls and the torches of the sentinels at their posts upon the battlements. Excited by his first visit to Jerusalem and the finally accomplished fact of reaching his religious majority at thirteen—plus the prospect of what could be a holy war if the Roman procurator fiscal tried to seize the temple treasures—Simon had slept little that night. Well before dawn he was awake and perched atop a rocky promontory from which he would have an unobstructed view of the city as it was revealed by the dawn's light.

II

The spring rains—the *moreh*—had carpeted the hillsides around Jerusalem with green, and wherever the land had not been cleared for pasture, field or vineyard, the tough burnet thorn grew profusely. The tiny blood-red blossoms, which for a short time in spring turned the burnet patches into blankets of scarlet, were gone now. But the bushes were still glossy and green, largely hiding the sharp spikes, and man and beast alike still kept to the paths or the fields, avoiding the cruel thorns that made the burnet such an excellent protection for vineyards and gardens.

On the Mount of Olives, across the brook called Kidron, from the eastern part of Jerusalem and the elevation crowned by the glory of the temple, the fields and vineyards were heavy with the bounty of growing things, and the fragrance of fallow earth penetrated even the heavy fog that hung over the hilltops during the night. As yet, only a faint glow in the east promised the coming of day, but already the sun's rays had begun to dispel the fog, revealing first the tops of the hills and then, as if reaching out with loving fingers to caress man's most magnificent tribute to the glory of God, touching the dome of the great white temple and brushing it with molten gold.

Simon had looked forward to this moment with mounting anticipation ever since his father had promised him the visit to Jerusalem in celebration of attaining religious majority. And as the beauty of the glorious city revered by pious Jews next only to the Most High himself was revealed to his eager gaze, his heart felt as if it would burst within him. Because of its elevated position, the sun's rays revealed first the grim battlements marking the fortress of Antonia, located so close to the temple that the sacred courts could be reached by a walkway from the walls of the fortress. They picked out the figure of a Roman sentry walking his post within the closed gates, the leather soles of his *caligae*, the half boots worn by the legions, thudding upon the stones.

At another time the rhythmic beat of the sentry's tread might have reminded Simon that, for all their glorious history as a people chosen by God to bring the knowledge of his glory and his Law to the world, the Jews were still a subject nation. But this morning he was too excited and too stirred by his first view of Jerusalem to think of that or the threat to the temple treasures posed by the well-known greed and rapacity of Rome's provincial administrators.

The first section of Jerusalem to emerge fully into the sunlight, after the Antonia, was the Mount of Zion, highest of the five hills upon which the city stood. The warming rays revealed the great houses of the rich and nobles, but their owners for the most part were still asleep. Southward from Zion, in what was called the Lower City, lay an area given over largely to the homes of artisans and ordinary workmen. Here the inhabitants were already beginning to bestir themselves, for a man needed the whole period of daylight between the sun's rising and setting to earn bread and a place for his family to sleep. And in the cluster of hovels along the walls on either side of the gates, the beggars who largely inhabited that area were already about, hoping to accost a pious early worshiper on the way to the temple for morning prayers before beginning the day's business.

The boy watching from the hill was not interested in the houses of the poor or the hovels of the beggars today; he had seen more than enough of poverty in Bethsaida. Instead, his eyes were drawn to the heights where the three towers

erected by Herod the Great—Phasael, Hippicus and Mariamne—were just breaking through the fog, although their
anchors upon the solid stone of the ridge beneath were not
yet visible.

"Simon! Simon! Where are you?"

"Here I am, Father," the boy answered, still spellbound by
the panorama of beauty unfolding itself before him.

"Come!" Jonas said. "We are going to the temple to make
the sacrifices."

Simon scrambled down from the rock and raced to the tent
they had erected upon the hillside the night before. His father
was already dressed, so they paused only to seize a handful of
dates and a crust of bread, which they munched as they followed the path leading down to the stone bridge crossing the
Brook Kidron.

Though it was barely light here in the shadow of the city
walls, many people were already upon the road. Some were
pilgrims like themselves, going to the temple for the morning
sacrifice. Others were laborers trudging out to work in the
vineyards and fields, or thorngatherers searching for dead
burnet bushes on the hillsides, to be sold at the end of the day
to the potters, who favored the dry wood because it burned
with a hot flame and left little ash.

At the spring called Gihon, Simon and his father paused to
drink before beginning to ascend the western slope of the
Kidron Valley, leading up to the base of the wall upon the
stony escarpment north of the old City of David. They had
made an engagement in Bethsaida more than a week before to
meet a friend of Jonas's named Aristobulus at the entrance to
the lower level of the temple, the so-called Court of the
Heathen. A merchant from the island of Crete, Aristobulus
was one of the Diaspora, as the Jews outside Israel were

called. Many of these were descendants of Hebrews torn from their homeland centuries earlier and carried off as prisoners of war to Babylon and elsewhere, but not a few had been drawn away to the great cities of the empire by increased opportunities for trade. With his son Barnabas, a boy some three years younger than Simon, Aristobulus was visiting his sister Mary, who lived with her husband in a house in the Lower City near the southern wall.

Streams of people were passing in both directions through the gate by which Jonas and Simon entered the city a little south of the sanctuary area, where the temple stood. The guards at the gate made Jonas stop momentarily while they searched him for hidden weapons, then waved the two on. Simon watched wide-eyed, wondering if they would search him and half hoping they would, but they let him pass.

Inside the walls the city was awakening to life street by street and house by house as the sun brought warmth and drove away the damp chill that hung over the hills at night, even though summer was not far away. Scratching themselves, yawning, calling greetings to neighbors, men went to raise wooden shutters or put away the screens that had closed the shops during the night. Here and there a street vendor called out his wares, and since Jerusalem was largely a city of artisans and traders—outside of the large number of people connected with the running of the temple and its many activities—shopkeepers were already opening their places of business and setting out their stores of merchandise.

Simon's eager gaze spotted a potter moistening clay with water as he kneaded it into a soft, doughy mass to be shaped upon the wheel—kicked by his feet to keep it in motion—into a bowl or an urn. Many were busy shaping small vases to be fired in the kilns and then painted with scenes from the Holy

City, for such articles were much in demand by pious Jews of the Diaspora, to be exhibited in their homes as tokens of their visit to Jerusalem.

In another street he saw metalsmiths arranging hammers, punches, chisels and small anvils that had been carefully put away during the night, for tools were as precious as jewels. Others were pounding thin sheets of silver into the shape of vessels, before taking up the sharp tools needed for the delicate task of engraving.

Workers in leather waxed tough strands of thread for sewing, and whetted carefully guarded needles of Damascus steel, giving them the sharp point needed for penetrating the tough hides from which sandals and boots were made. Tailors, sitting cross-legged like their kind had done as far as men could remember, busied themselves cutting and sewing fabrics that had come by ship, camel or donkey to this cosmopolitan city. In variety the cloth ranged from the almost transparent and very expensive *byssus*, woven a short distance to the south around Hebron, to the tough fabric from the province of Cilicia and the city of Tarsus to the north, a material fashioned from goat's-hair and so highly prized for making tents and sails that it had been given the name of the province itself—*cilicium*.

These and the many other fascinating sights to be seen in the awakening city would have held Simon's attention, but Jonas urged him on, since it was almost time for the morning sacrifices to begin. As they entered the Court of the Heathen, already thronging with people, Simon could not help shivering a little when he read the signs chiseled into the walls in several languages, warning all unbelievers to climb no higher, on pain of death.

As a Jew, Simon was entitled to ascend to the second terrace, but only the priests were allowed upon the topmost level. Jonas spotted Aristobulus and Barnabas waiting near a stairway that descended to the temple markets located beneath the Royal Porch at the southern portico. Joining their friends, Simon and his father hurried down the stairs to purchase an animal for the sacrifice. Simon could not understand Jonas's haste, since the day was before them, but he would never have thought of questioning his father's action, for the Law was very strict concerning obedience to one's parents.

Only a few of the stalls where animals were sold had opened for business this early, for the sacrifices had not yet actually begun. At the booth of a seller of doves, Simon carefully made a selection for this, his first sacrifice, even though he could see that his father was impatient and kept glancing around them, as if afraid someone might interfere. Finally the boy chose a fat dove for which he paid a whole *denarius*— the equivalent of a laborer's daily wage—which he had earned preparing fish for drying in the market at Bethsaida.

At the stall of a moneychanger upon whose wooden cabinet were piled rows of various coins, Aristobulus was changing a Greek coin for the Tyrian shekel which alone could be used in paying the annual tribute required of every adult Jew, whether in Israel or abroad. Many pilgrims did not know the rate of exchange, Simon had heard, and were frequently bilked by the shrewd moneychangers, who shared their gains, it was said, with the priests who allotted them space in the market area. But Aristobulus was a merchant and let the dealer in money gain no more than the small profit on the transaction allowed him by law, with the result that the wails of the moneychanger followed them up the stairway to the upper levels where the two men paid the required tribute to a priest stationed there for that purpose.

The Royal Porch and the Porch of Solomon, where the teachers, or rabbis, daily instructed students and answered the questions of passersby, were roofed over with massive cedar timbers supported by four rows of columns carved from Corinthian marble polished until it shone like gold. Tired from their rapid passage through the city and the temple, Simon would have been happy to rest in the cool, shaded cloister of the porches and listen to the rabbis, but Jonas insisted that they ascend to the second level, from whence they could watch the first of the morning sacrifices.

Here there was much activity as priests in white robes hurried from their quarters to the several altars used for the sacrifices. Already a Levite had kindled the great torch that burned there, ready to ignite the first offering to the Lord. And as the sun showed itself above the eastern hills a band of Levites—who alone might serve the priests and assist in the rituals of the temple—raised their trumpets and sounded the morning call to worship. The notes floated across the cool morning air to the surrounding hillsides where hundreds of pilgrims, camped there rather than pay the high prices charged by the innkeepers and foodsellers of Jerusalem during the religious festivals, were massed for the morning prayers.

At the great altar the priest who was to perform the first sacrifice raised the ritual knife. And as the shining blade flashed downward to slash the throat of the lamb held immobile upon the altar by a Levite, the trumpets sounded once again, marking the full beginning of yet another day. At the same moment, in a burst of exultant thanks to God for his blessings, the music of harps, zithers, and the high, clear notes of ram's-horn trumpets poured down upon the city and floated across the hills, while a choir chanted a hymn of praise.

In their homes or their shops, upon the terraces of the temple, or wherever they were, devout Jews paused at the sound to pray, while the torch ignited the first of the burnt offerings of the day and a black plume of smoke rose skyward when the wood upon the altar caught fire. Hanging like a banner above the temple and the holy altar, it was both a reminder of God's presence and a warning of his anger against those who did not obey him.

Simon would have welcomed the chance to spend the day in the temple, seeing for himself its many parts and the manifold activities of which he had learned in the synagogue school at Bethsaida. There he had been taught to read the scrolls telling of Israel's glorious history, the writings of the prophets, and particularly the body of precepts and customs governing the religious and secular life of Israel—for both were the same—known as the Laws of Moses. But as soon as they had witnessed the opening sacrifice, Jonas hurried him down the stairway to the lower terrace and out into the city once again.

Simon was surprised to see that, in the brief period since they had entered the temple, the streets around it had filled with people. The crowd was strangely quiet, as if waiting for something, and though Simon recognized several of their Galilean friends, Jonas did not pause even for a greeting. The shortest way to the home of Aristobulus' sister in the lower city would have been across the bridge or viaduct leading to an area of rich palaces on the northern heights of what was called the Upper City. But the bridge was solidly massed with people, so Jonas chose a stairway leading to the depths of the Tyropean Valley below. Even then they had to move slowly, for the stairway, too, was crowded with people pushing upward.

Simon started to protest at their hurry, but one look at Jonas's worried face made him hold his tongue. At the foot of the stairway they turned southward through streets that were rapidly filling with people. Simon was beginning to resign himself to his disappointment in being given such a brief glimpse of the temple and its activities, when suddenly the sight of a familiar figure in the street ahead of them put everything else out of his mind. It was a tall man with a lean, craggy face and burning eyes, who stood upon a cart and from this improvised pulpit harangued the people massed about him. These, in turn, greeted almost every word with shouts of approval.

"It is Judas of Galilee, Father!" Simon cried. And quite forgetting that Jonas knew the tall man as well as he, yet would have led them past him, the boy pushed into the crowd.

Jonas had no choice except to turn back, or leave Simon behind, and at once they were all caught up in the surging mass of people surrounding the speaker. Eagerly working his way closer to the man on the cart, Simon did not realize that, in hurrying them all back to the home of Aristobulus' sister, his father had been seeking to avoid the very thing that was happening—for the man called Judas was no ordinary Galilean.

III

Judas of Galilee, with a priest named Sadduc, had been active in the region around the lake where Simon lived, for many months. Leaders of a new political movement or party who called themselves by the name of *Kanna'im*, or Zealots, their avowed purpose was to stir the people to an even greater hatred of Rome than had existed before. In this effort they had been singularly successful, for rebellion came naturally to Judas. His father had been executed by Herod the Great, and Judas himself had spent his adult life as a brigand, robbing caravans in the hill country between the Sea of Galilee and the fertile Plain of Esdraelon. Until the recent surge of resentment against Rome, following the news that Herod's will had divided the nation and that Sabinus was moving southward with a column of troops to seize the temple treasures, most of the Galileans had not considered Judas to be anything more than an outlaw. But as the leader of those who dared to preach rebellion in a time of national indignation, he had become a hero almost overnight, gaining a considerable following even in the Holy City itself.

In Galilee, Jonas, too, had listened to the fiery exhorter, and Simon had been proud when his father had persuaded nearly fifty men from Bethsaida to come to Jerusalem in support of Judas's plan, along with other dissident groups, to forestall the expected attempt of the Romans to seize the treasures of the temple. Jonas's main reason for coming to Jerusalem now concerned Judas's cause, but he had been intent on being certain first that Simon was safe. That plan, however, the boy had foiled when he recognized the Galilean and impetuously joined those listening to him.

"To obey Roman law is to break the Laws of Moses!" Judas was shouting. "The Most High alone is our King. Him we must obey as our fathers obeyed, or be guilty of blasphemy."

Simon eagerly joined in the shout of acclamation. He could see that many of the men openly wore the razor-sharp dagger called a *sicarius*, which had been adopted by the followers of Judas and Sadduc as a symbol of rebellion against Rome, giving them still another popular nickname—"The *sicarii*."

"When Zimri took a woman of the Midianites in the sight of the congregation of Israel," Judas continued, "Phinehas thrust his javelin through them both at one stroke, even though Zimri was the son of a prince in one of the chief houses of the Simeonites. Then the Lord said to Moses, '*Vex the Midianites and smite them!*' And because Phinehas had slain the sinful in the sight of God and the people, the plague was stayed from the house of Israel and victory was ours. Even as Phinehas, we must vex the Midianites of today and regain our own freedom."

"Vex the Midianites!" A man in the front row of the spectators shouted, as if on cue, and the crowd took up the cry, knowing that Midian, in this case, meant Rome itself.

Simon recognized several of the men standing near Judas. They had come with the party from Bethsaida and were close followers—even as his father was—of the fiery Galilean. He felt a thrill at the bravery of Judas in defying Rome here in the Holy City, just as another Judas—called Maccabeus or the "Hammerer"—had stirred his people to rebellion against oppression by hated Syria centuries before. Nor could there be any doubt—at least in the boy's mind—that just as the Lord had marched beside the Hammerer, giving him victory everywhere until the enemies of Israel were sent reeling back, Judas of Galilee had now been sent to lead his people to a new glory as a nation chosen by God for his very own. And like thousands in Galilee and now here in Judea, Simon was ready to see in the lean, burning-eyed figure the messiah Israel so fervently desired to bring the nation once again to its former glory, the great leader which all of the prophets had assured them would arise in their time of greatest need.

"The Lord favors us today," Judas assured his listeners. "Sabinus is shut up in the tower of Phasael, surrounded by our people and cut off from his own troops in the Antonia. The Romans are without leaders, and if we attack now, we shall drive them from our land."

This was strong talk—too strong, Simon saw, for Aristobulus, who was shaking his head doubtfully. But it was not too strong—the boy also saw, with a thrill of pride—for his father. Jonas's eyes, too, had begun to burn with the same fervor that set the boy's pulse racing, and he seemed to have quite forgotten his original intention to avoid the street where Judas and his followers had gathered.

"Vex the Midianites!" Simon shouted, and heard himself joined on every side.

"This is no place for children, Jonas." Aristobulus plucked at his friend's sleeve to gain his attention, and reluctantly Jonas turned his eyes from the speaker.

"We must go," he agreed. "Come, Simon."

"But, Father—" Simon's shocked protest was of no avail, for Jonas was already pushing his way through the milling crowd, and the boy had no choice except to follow, with Barnabas just behind him and Aristobulus bringing up the rear.

"In Galilee, you followed Judas, Father," Simon protested when they were clear of the crowd and moving down a less congested street. "How can you desert him now?"

"An armed rabble is no place for children!" Aristobulus said sharply.

"But I am not a child!"

"Aristobulus is right, Son." Jonas put his arm across the boy's shoulders, already almost as broad as his own. "This is no place for you—or Barnabas."

"Are you going to desert Judas?" Simon cried unbelievingly.

Before Jonas could answer, they had turned into the doorway of Mary's home, and Aristobulus drew Jonas aside immediately for an earnest colloquy, leaving the two boys together. Simon had become very fond of Barnabas, and at another time would have enjoyed hearing again his tales of proud ships that sailed the seas around the island of Cyprus where they lived; ships that were driven by banks of oars and huge sails that caught the wind. But he was much more interested now in listening to the earnest conversation going on between his father and Aristobulus at the end of the room, and surreptitiously moved nearer so he could hear.

"This man Judas is mad to think of attacking the Romans," Aristobulus was arguing. "In Galilee and Judea, you see only a little of Roman might, Jonas. But I have journeyed as far west as Ephesus, and I tell you their soldiers are like the sands of the sea."

"We have no quarrel with the Romans, so long as they leave us alone," Jonas insisted. "When we have driven them out of Israel and established our own kingdom, we will be content."

"Men like Judas of Galilee feed on power," Aristobulus warned. "Give him a taste of it by defeating a few Roman soldiers here in Jerusalem, and he will believe he can defeat them elsewhere. There will be no end then, except destruction for all of you."

"But the Lord fights on our side," Jonas protested. "He has promised us a leader in our time of need."

"The Messiah spoken of by the prophets?"

"Yes."

"How do you know this is the time? Or Judas the man?"

"With the kingdom divided and heathen seizing the treasures of the temple, what better time could there be?"

Aristobulus shrugged. "Then you really do believe Judas is the Messiah?"

"Surely you saw it in his eyes and in his voice just now," Jonas said. "But I will tell you more. Judas has not only named himself the Expected One, but he promises to restore Israel to the glory that was ours in the time of David and Solomon."

"You may have heard a messiah this morning but I heard only a rabble rouser," Aristobulus said, a little shortly. "One who will yet cause thousands to be nailed to Roman crosses and lose for you what freedom you already have."

"You have lived too long among the Greeks, Aristobulus." Jonas shook his head sadly. "But we must not quarrel over this; we have been friends too long."

"I will not try to change you," Aristobulus agreed. "But be careful because of the boy, Jonas. I saw his eyes just now when he was watching Judas of Galilee. Simon is already as large as many grown men—but he is still too young to hang from a cross."

Simon could hold his peace no longer. "I can fight, Father," he insisted. "In Bethsaida, no boy my age can stand against me."

Jonas smiled and rumpled the boy's dark hair with his hand. But when his face grew sober, Simon's heart began to sink, for he had seen that look before.

"Today you made your first sacrifice in the temple, Simon, so it is your responsibility now to obey the Law," Jonas said. "Do you remember the fifth in the Commandments given by God to Moses upon the mountain?"

"Yes, Father."

"Then repeat it for me."

"*Honour thy father and thy mother, that thy days may be long upon the land which the Lord thy God giveth thee,*" Simon repeated dutifully.

"The men of Bethsaida expect me to lead them, so I must join Judas and the others," Jonas said. "Promise me that you will stay with Aristobulus and Barnabas."

"No one will be safe inside the walls if fighting breaks out," Aristobulus said quickly. "We will go to your camp on the Mount of Olives, Jonas."

"That would be best," Jonas agreed, and turned back to Simon. "Will you give me your promise to obey Aristobulus as you would me, Simon?"

"Yes, Father." They were the hardest words the boy had

ever been forced to speak, but he was bound to obey upon pain of committing a deadly sin by breaking the Law. When his father gave him a quick embrace of farewell, he fought hard to keep back the tears of disappointment.

"If I should not return, take Simon to Capernaum and leave him with Zebedee on your way north to Antioch," Jonas directed Aristobulus. "He can easily get to Bethsaida from there."

"I will guard the boy as if he were my own," the Cypriot promised. "And I will pray for you, Jonas."

"Father!" It was a cry of anguish but Jonas was gone without looking back.

Blindly, Simon turned his face to the wall, trying to hide his tears, but when he felt a comforting arm about his shoulders he buried his head against Aristobulus' breast and sobbed bitterly until no more tears would flow.

IV

It was only a little after midday when exciting news raced through the streets. Sabinus—the story said—apprehensive at the gathering of so many people in Jerusalem, had sent a message to the fortress of Antonia and the Roman garrison there, ordering them to attack the temple. The temple guards, being Jews and not Romans, had obeyed the orders of the high priest, denying the Romans the treasure they sought to seize, and fighting was already said to be going on.

In the face of this disturbing news, Aristobulus wasted no time in indecision. "We must go at once to the camp of the Galileans on the Mount of Olives," he told the others. "If

Sabinus does not get the treasure, he will burn Jerusalem. It is an old Roman trick."

Less than an hour later, Simon, Mary, her husband, Aristobulus, and Barnabas joined a stream of refugees pouring through the Essene Gate near the southwest corner of the city's walls. No soldiers guarded the entrance—mute evidence that all Roman troops in the city were already involved in the attack upon the temple and a chilling omen for the success of those who sought to defend it. The gate gave access to a road leading eastward through the Valley of Hinnom, south of the city wall. It was an area ordinarily shunned by devout Jews because it was largely covered by the tombs of the dead, but few troubled themselves about defilement today. Most of those leaving Jerusalem were pilgrims who, like Aristobulus, knew something of Rome's awesome power and the utter futility of rebellion.

Where the Valley of Hinnom joined that in which the Brook Kidron flowed, Aristobulus and his party turned northward beside the city's east wall, moving toward the Mount of Olives and the road leading to Bethany and Jericho. They were near the walls now, though well below them, and could plainly hear from the heights where the temple stood the sounds of conflict, the clash of metal against metal, and the screams of the wounded.

The waters of the brook were tinged with red, but not yet from the battle raging on the walls above. Sluices beneath the altars of the temple emptied through stone-lined conduits into Kidron, and for most of the day the swift current was stained with the blood of the sacrifices, clearing only at night after the altars had been sluiced clean in preparation for another dawn. Judging from the screams of pain and the clash of arms from the walls above, however, it seemed likely that the water would run red for a much longer period today.

Simon's disappointment at not being allowed to take part in the exciting battle going on in the city had changed now to apprehension for his father, as refugees streaming through other gates of the city told of events taking place within the sanctuary area, the center of conflict. All the accounts agreed on one point: the attack upon the temple was not only backed by the regular garrison of Jerusalem and a column of legionnaires which had accompanied Sabinus to Judea, but also by a rabble of thieves and beggars the Roman procurator had hired and armed, turning them against their own people with the promise of freedom to loot the shops of the city when the fighting was over.

The sounds of battle on the heights above grew louder as Simon and his companions moved along the bank of the brook toward the section of the wall nearest to the temple. Simon kept his eyes upon the ramparts defending the temple itself, expecting at any moment to hear a trumpet of ram's-horn sound the victory note. Occasionally he saw men struggling upon the walls, but could tell nothing about how the tide of battle was going. Then suddenly a scream of pain sounded directly overhead and a body hurtled downward, turning in the air as the dying man instinctively flailed out with his arms in a desperate attempt to break his fall. Women screamed as the crowd on the road pushed frantically back, lest the falling body strike in their midst. Simon was so frozen with horror at his first sight of violent death, however, that he stayed rooted to the spot. And when the body struck the rocky path almost at his feet, some of the blood from the breast of the dead man's robe—where a Roman spear had penetrated his heart—actually splashed upon the boy's sandals.

"Simon!" The anxious voice of Aristobulus finally forced him to tear his gaze from the corpse, but just then another body came plummeting down from the sanctuary area, where according to the excited stories of the refugees, the Roman garrison was repelling the attack of the now enraged populace with the skill and ruthlessness of professional soldiers. And numb with horror, Simon stumbled across the brook on the arching stone bridge to hurry on after Aristobulus and the rest of the party.

"The Romans are burning the temple!" It was a woman's voice shocked with horror by the desecration she was witnessing. And as thousands of pilgrims and refugees turned to look up at the temple, a wall of flame raced along the porches of the golden-domed structure, quickly hiding it in a dense pall of flame and smoke. Only hours later did refugees coming from Jerusalem bring the story of what had really happened that terrible morning. Meanwhile, to those watching from the hill, it seemed that the whole city was being destroyed.

Alarmed by the increasing number of Jews thronging the streets of Jerusalem—it was reported—the Procurator Sabinus had ordered the troops he had brought with him to attack the temple and seize the treasure. But when the attackers neglected to secure the wooden roofs of the temple courts, the guards stationed there had rained down spears, arrows and even stones torn from the walls of the buildings, upon the heads of the luckless invaders, driving them back.

In desperation, Sabinus had called upon the Jerusalem garrison stationed in the Antonia for help, and the trained, ruthless legionaires had taken charge at once. Their first move had been to set fire to the highly inflammable roof timbers of the temple courts, driving back the defenders who thus lost a place of vantage and were quickly ringed in by a wall of fire that either burned them to death or forced them to flee, only to be impaled upon the weapons of the waiting Roman troops when they emerged from the wall of flame.

With the temple guards, the only skilled soldiery inside the city besides themselves, put to rout, the Roman garrison had methodically beaten back the untrained Jews, most of whom were without effective weapons, when they tried to help the guards trapped within the temple. Meanwhile, the troops commanded by Sabinus had rallied to occupy the sanctuary area as soon as the flames were extinguished, establishing themselves behind a stout wall that stretched across one end of the Court of the Gentiles.

The wall had been built originally to make sure that the temple guards would always have a fortress from which to fight in case of attack. Instead, it had trapped them there with no route of escape from the fiery wall of death created by the burning timbers of the porches. And with the entire citadel now in the hands of the Romans, the attempt by the largely untrained men from Galilee and elsewhere in Israel to recapture it had failed.

Resistance had by no means ceased within the city, however, according to the reports of those fleeing from it. And with almost the entire population now siding against the Romans who had desecrated the temple, Sabinus and his forces were actually prisoners within the walls. Throughout the afternoon, reports of the fighting continued, and when the fires gradually died away, those watching from the nearby Mount of Olives could see that, although the wooden roof timbers of the temple courts had been destroyed, the main part of the structure itself was but little damaged.

Simon was eating a frugal evening meal of cheese and bread shortly after dark when he saw a familiar figure wearily ascending the hillside. Jonas's clothes were torn and the collar of his robe was stained with blood from a cut upon his cheek. He had taken no food since morning, and while he ate rapidly he gave them a terse résumé of what had been happening inside the city.

"Then it is true that they have taken the temple?" Simon asked when his father paused to drink wine from a small skin.

"They hold the inner fortress, and the treasures are in their hands. But Jerusalem is still ours."

"But if they have the temple, everything is lost!"

"What happened today was just the beginning," Jonas assured his listeners. "If we had possessed weapons, we could have overcome them, but the only arms besides those of the Romans were in the hands of the temple guards, and they were burned alive or killed as they sought to escape. So long as Sabinus and his troops remain in the temple area, they are safe. If they try to leave, the people will stone them to death from the rooftops."

"But the Romans are certain to send reinforcements as soon as they learn what has happened," Aristobulus said.

"Judas expects that," Jonas agreed. "But he is taking steps to prevent it."

"What steps?"

"Runners have been sent out to Judea, across the Jordan into Peraea and into Galilee, calling upon everyone to march upon Jerusalem. As soon as we can supply the people with weapons, we will have an army that even the legions cannot turn back."

"Where will you find arms?"

"We march north tonight to seize the arsenal at Sepphoris. It contains more than enough weapons to arm the whole country."

"Will Judas lead the attack on Sepphoris?" Simon asked eagerly.

"Yes," his father said. "He knows the country well and the Roman garrison is small. If we move fast, they will not have heard about what happened here at Jerusalem, and we should have no trouble in taking the city. Then all of Galilee, Peraea and probably even Samaria will rise with us and we will have ample arms to supply them. Even Rome cannot subdue an aroused nation."

"Judas must truly be the Messiah!" Simon cried. "Surely no greater time of need could occur than now, and no greater leader to make us free!"

"No one can doubt it now," Jonas agreed. "As soon as the weapons are in our hands, we will lead a victorious army against whom not even the Romans can stand."

Aristobulus said nothing, but Simon could see that he was not convinced.

"Are you still determined to leave Jerusalem, Aristobulus?" Jonas asked.

"Yes."

"Do you mind leaving Simon at the house of Zebedee in Capernaum?"

"I will take care of him," Aristobulus promised, gripping his friend by the arm in the Roman fashion of farewell. "And God go with you, Jonas."

This time Simon did not cry as he told his father goodbye. From Capernaum to Sepphoris was less than a day's journey across the hills of central Galilee. Once Aristobulus and Barnabas had left him at the house of Zebedee, it would be an easy matter to slip away for the short journey. And even if he missed the fighting at Sepphoris, strong backs would be needed to carry the weapons to Jerusalem, where the real battle would undoubtedly take place.

V

Anxious to get those under his care safely away from Jerusalem, Aristobulus insisted that they depart for Capernaum the next morning. They made camp that afternoon outside Jericho, on the edge of the *ghor*, the deep cleft in which the River Jordan flowed to the Dead Sea, only a few miles to the south. From Jericho, they moved northward the next day, following the Jordan through a fertile plain famous for its fruit and grain, extending along the river's course almost to the southern end of the Sea of Galilee.

Everywhere they found the people in a ferment of anger against the Romans for daring to defile the temple. And at Scythopolis—site of the ancient city of Beth-shan and a way station upon a direct caravan route between Ptolemais, or Accho, on the Phoenician coast and the Greek cities of the Decapolis east of the Jordan—they heard news that made Simon's heart leap with joy.

By daring to make a lightning march directly through the district of Samaria—ordinarily avoided by Jews because of a long-standing enmity between them and the Samaritans— Judas the Galilean had surprised the Roman garrison at Sepphoris, capturing the city and the large arsenal of weapons stored there. Now, according to the reports, men from Galilee were pouring into Sepphoris from all directions, to reinforce Judas in preparation for the march southward to liberate Jerusalem from its Roman conquerors.

At Capernaum, Simon bade goodbye to Aristobulus and Barnabas, who were planning to travel northward to Antioch in the valleys of the Leontes and Orontes rivers lying between Mount Lebanon and Mount Hermon. The boy was almost as much at home in the house of Zebedee at Capernaum as he was in Bethsaida, only a few miles to the northeast, and he could have finished his journey in one of Zebedee's boats if he had wished. But the glowing reports of the victory at Sepphoris had crystallized his determination to join the forces gathering there. He divulged this plan only to Zebedee's oldest son, John, who was a few years younger than he, first swearing his friend to secrecy with a blood-curdling oath such as young boys love.

Groups of men were constantly passing through Capernaum, moving toward the great center at Sepphoris or southward to join the fighting which had also broken out around Jericho, at Emmaus and other towns near Jerusalem. Simon watched until he saw a group from Bethsaida, followed by a band of youths who made up for their lack of fighting experience by their enthusiasm for the cause and its leaders. Many in the band were his friends, and when he fell in behind the group, as if he had come with them all the way from Bethsaida, none tried to stop him.

Every few miles, other recruits joined the excited Galileans, many of them with glowing tales of fighting in widely separated areas. The Roman garrison defending the town of Betharamtha in the shadow of Mount Nebo—from whose summit the dying Moses had been allowed to glimpse the Promised Land—was reported to have been cut to pieces. At Emmaus, a former shepherd named Arthronges had proclaimed himself king, after seizing the town, and was reported to be marching toward Jerusalem to support the forces holding Sabinus and his troops in a state of siege. In dozens of other communities throughout the land—reports said—angry men had risen to destroy the local Roman garrisons and seize their weapons before joining the holy war to retake the temple and oust the Romans from Jerusalem and from Israel.

Simon quickly found himself the cynosure of the group of youths—almost all of them older than he—whom he had joined. Only he among them had been at Jerusalem and had witnessed the beginning of the flame of rebellion now sweeping the land, lit by the very torch that had set fire to the porches of the temple. Excited and proud beyond measure, the boy found it easy to ignore the faint twinges of conscience that sometimes assailed him for failing to go home as his father had planned for him to do.

West of Capernaum, the road ascended rapidly into a range of hills separating the southward-deepening depression of the *ghor* from the fertile Plain of Esdraelon south of Sepphoris. Normally this area was the haunt of robber bands—one of them formerly led by Judas himself—preying upon caravans, and it was said, upon honest Galileans as well. But they, too, had been caught up in the wave of enthusiasm sweeping across Israel, and had already gone to join the forces at Sepphoris, eager for the opportunity to plunder the rich government buildings and palaces constructed when Herod the Great had decided to make that city a district center of administration.

By noon of the day Simon left Capernaum, the leaders of the band he was following reached Nazareth, a small town located among the long, bare hills west of the elevation called Mount Tabor. Groves of olives, clusters of fig trees, and many vineyards covered the lower reaches of the hills, with the lovely and fertile plain stretching southwestward toward the Great Sea.

Until now, the boys following the men from Bethsaida had stayed well behind, so their presence would not be noted. But at Nazareth, several groups had stopped for a council of war in the outskirts of the small town nestled at the foot of a craggy elevation. There they heard news that sent their spirits, already dampened by weariness, plummeting downward.

No one seemed to know exactly what was happening at Sepphoris, now little more than an hour's march across the hills to the northwest. But small groups fleeing eastward had been pouring into Nazareth all morning, each with a different version of the events taking place there. Simon was afraid to press very close to where the council was in progress, for fear of being recognized and sent home because of his age. But from reports relayed back by word of mouth, he learned that a Roman army had appeared before the city the day before, recruited by Varus, the legate or governor of Syria, in response to a desperate plea for aid from the Procurator Sabinus in Jerusalem.

Some reports said the tide of battle was running against Judas and the defenders of Sepphoris; a few claimed it was already lost. Others, however, were equally sure that Judas— since they confidently believed him to be the Messiah—would be strengthened by God's power and the enemy would be destroyed. While the council of war was still in progress, refugees fleeing from the battle front reported that Sepphoris had already fallen to the Romans, but such a thing seemed impossible after Judas's great victory only a short time before. Finally, the men of Bethsaida and Capernaum decided to move nearer to Sepphoris, in the hope of being able to succor their beleaguered brethren there.

Weariness had long since dulled the high pitch of excitement Simon had felt that morning when he had joined the youths from his home city. Like the others, he found it hard to believe what they were hearing from Sepphoris; yet he could not forget that the Romans had set fire to the temple at Jerusalem less than a week before, burning its defenders alive—without any apparent punishment from God. What troubled him most of all, however, was the fact that his father was with the forces of Judas the Galilean and no doubt was in grave peril.

Late in the afternoon, the party Simon was following came over the crest of a low hill and saw the city of Sepphoris, the largest center in Galilee, lying before them. Simon himself had visited Sepphoris only the year before with a merchant of Bethsaida who had brought a load of dried fish to be sold in the market there. He remembered it as a place of beautiful white columns, magnificent buildings and gracious palaces, a city more Roman than Jewish and therefore avoided by pious Jews except when business brought them there.

Much of the beauty that he remembered was now obscured by columns of smoke, mute evidence that the rumors coming to Nazareth had failed to describe fully the debacle which had taken place here only a few days after the victory of Judas the Galilean had been so highly acclaimed throughout the land. Nor could Simon doubt that the defenders of the city had already been captured, for on the slope before its main gate, hundreds of rude crosses had been erected. On each of them a man's arms had been nailed to the outspread crossarm of the *patibulum*—or gallows—and his feet to the upright supporting it.

Crucifixion was a Roman form of execution, a slow and cruel death reserved for rebels and escaped slaves, as reminders of what would happen to others who harbored similar desires. Actually, it was far less humane than stoning, by which Jews condemned to die for breaking the Law had been executed since the days of Abraham. For stoning, however painful and terrible in the few moments before the victim was battered into insensibility, did not prolong the agony. Crucifixion, on the other hand, left the doomed person to hang from the cross, often exposed to the elements for days, until he died of thirst and exposure.

Simon's first reaction was one of horror, followed by an almost irresistible urge to leave the scene of carnage and death as far behind him as he could. He resisted the urge, however, and forced himself to search cross after cross with his eyes, always expecting to recognize the body of his father. But though he did not see Jonas, no one could doubt the identity of at least one of those dying there upon the hill, since the Romans had selected the largest cross of all for the leader of the rebellion. His body slashed by many wounds, Judas of Galilee hung limply from the *patibulum*. And even at that distance, Simon could be sure that the man whom much of Israel, including himself and his father, had hailed as the Messiah, was dead.

VI

The new arrivals were given no time to counsel together and determine whether or not they wished to engage in what was obviously already a lost cause. Even as they stood gaping at the burning city in disbelief, a detail of Roman troops, circling the hill to destroy stragglers, swept down upon them. Un-armed—since they had expected to obtain weapons from the arsenal captured at Sepphoris—the Galileans had no chance against the trained Roman troops. In their frantic haste to escape the spears and swords, the men overran the boys who had been following close behind them, and Simon suddenly found himself facing a soldier in full armor with his spear drawn back to throw.

The boy's only experience in battle had been when he had

stood, frozen with horror under the wall of Jerusalem a few days earlier, while the body of one of the temple's defenders had fallen through the air to strike the stones at his feet. But neither that nor what faced him now were anything like he had imagined battle would be. Paralyzed with fear, he waited mutely for the sudden stab of pain when the weapon thrust him through, and, in that moment of sheer terror could only pray silently that the end would come quickly and that he would not be left to linger like those still dying upon the crosses.

Actually, the very paralysis of fear that had seized him saved Simon's life. As his legs gave way, he pitched forward in a faint at just the moment that the soldier facing him hurled his spear, transfixing the throat of a man who had been standing just behind the boy. And as Simon collapsed, the slain Galilean fell forward, pressing him down against the earth while blood gushed out upon the boy's robe and upon his skin. Simon knew none of this, however, and in the excitement of the battle, the soldier did not realize that the boy was actually unharmed. Jerking his spear from the body, he went on to engage another man, and when Simon finally regained consciousness, the brief whirling melee was over, the Romans had moved on, and darkness was already beginning to fall.

With the body of the dead man pressing upon him so he could hardly breathe and the blood half dry upon his skin, Simon could not help wondering for a moment whether he had not died and was already in *Sheol*—Hades. Then two sounds broke the silence of death that surrounded him, freezing him even closer to the earth; they were the harsh voices of men speaking in the Roman tongue, and the jangle of military harness.

Prostrate upon the already cooling earth, paralyzed once

again by the terrible fear that had drained all strength from his limbs at the sight of the naked spear point, Simon waited for death. His eyes were tightly shut and his heart was pounding in his ears like a Roman drum, but he could still hear the soldiers talking as they moved across the hilltop, calling out to each other in glee when they found a weapon, an ornament or a robe unslashed by a spear, upon one of the dead men. Fortunately, Simon had no weapons or possessions of value, and with his robe and his skin stained by the rush of blood from the slain man whose body still lay across him, the boy did not draw the attention of the soldiers. He lay there, not even daring to breathe during the eternity before they passed on, leaving him upon the hilltop amidst the dead.

It was a half hour later and quite dark before Simon dared to stir. Still dazed from shock and horror, he could think only of the urgent need to escape before other soldiers came searching the hillside for booty. Nor was there any point in searching for his father now—even if he had possessed the courage to do so—since in the darkness he could not have distinguished Jonas's body among those hanging from the forest of uprights erected by the victorious Romans.

Stumbling down the hill, instinctively setting his face toward the faint glow of the rising moon, Simon came upon a brook and lay down to drink deeply. Immediately he was seized by a cramping and retching that left him prostrate and trembling for a long time before he was able to crawl to the brook and drink again. This time, the knot of fear and horror in his stomach seemed to have loosened a little, and after awhile he found strength enough to strip his bloodstained robe from his body and wash himself in a pool where the brook tumbled over a small ledge.

Using a broken branch as a spade, he turned up enough leaves to hide the robe and smoothed over the area by stamping upon it with his sandaled feet. When he moved on again, he was wearing only the loincloth that formed the usual undergarment of the Galileans, but he was rid of the blood-stained robe that would have identified him as a fugitive. Toward dawn he stumbled into the yard of a shepherd's hut where he was given food and the loan of a robe to cover his body so he would not be recognized by any Roman details that might be patrolling the roads.

All that day Simon pushed steadily eastward across the hills of Galilee, avoiding villages and towns and staying away from traveled roads. From an elevation west of Magdala, he looked down upon the Sea of Galilee, lying blue and peaceful in the afternoon sunlight. He could easily see the houses of Capernaum a short distance to the north, but though he knew he would find a welcome in the house of Zebedee, he could not risk going there. Instead, he turned northward, paralleling the Way of the Sea for a time before swinging eastward into the village of Chorazin where his mother had kinsmen. There he spent the night and was saddened by the news that, as far as anyone knew, all of the men who had followed Judas the Galilean in the taking of Sepphoris had either died defending the city or had been executed by the Romans after its capture.

That his father had almost certainly been among those hanging from the forest of crosses before the city, Simon could no longer deny. And knowing his family would need him now more than ever before, he crossed the Jordan the next day and came to his home at Bethsaida. There he found his mother weeping for the loss of Jonas; his brother Andrew, at five, was still too young to understand what had happened.

Simon, too, was sad, for he had loved his father deeply, but during the next several weeks he was caught up in such an avalanche of events that little time was left for mourning. In fact the comfortable and happy world in which he had lived as a child was now gone, it seemed, forever.

VII

During the weeks that followed, the rebellion collapsed almost as quickly as it had begun. The Roman column that had retaken Sepphoris was part of a two-pronged thrust into Galilee; the other half had moved rapidly southward toward Jerusalem, to relieve the garrison besieged there. When the Samaritans in the district between Judea and Galilee obeyed the orders of Varus and furnished troops to put down the rebellion, fighting elsewhere subsided rapidly with the realization that the cause of freedom was now lost.

The inhabitants of Jerusalem had prudently sought to escape punishment by claiming that they had been held prisoners by the Galileans and others who had thronged to the Holy City at the Feast of Pentecost under the leadership of Judas, the shepherd Arthronges, a slave named Simon from Peraea, and other leaders in the short-lived rebellion. And Varus, a wise and experienced governor, had left the situation there.

In Rome, the Emperor Augustus upheld the provisions of Herod's will dividing Israel between his three sons. To Archelaus went the districts of Judea and Samaria. Antipas was given Galilee and Peraea on the east side of the Jordan, except the ten Greek-speaking cities of the Decapolis, which were responsible directly to Rome. And to Philip, mildest of the three sons, went the district east of the Jordan and north of the city of Gergesa, on the eastern side of the Sea of Galilee, including the old city of Dan at the foot of Mount Hermon that traditionally marked the northern limit of Israel.

Of those who had followed Judas the Galilean, only a few had managed to escape the debacle at Sepphoris. One of these was Judas's son Menahem, who became the leader of a band of brigands, as his father had been, in the wild hill country lying west of the Sea of Galilee, preying upon caravans and any others unfortunate enough to come within his grasp. When Archelaus proved himself inept as a ruler, he was removed by Augustus, and the districts of Judea and Samaria, including Jerusalem itself, were placed directly under the rule of a series of Roman procurators responsible directly to the emperor.

The swift ending of the "War of Varus"—as the campaign in which Judas of Galilee had died came to be known—and the destruction of those who had dared to rise against Roman rule, effectively prevented any further rebellion for several decades thereafter. Only once did a near revolt occur when the Procurator Pontius Pilate, newly arrived at his post, made his first official visit to Jerusalem with the eagles of Rome carried before his troops.

Jewish law strictly forbade the presence of any graven image in the most sacred spot of their faith, and Roman governors before Pilate had honored this particular provision. Fortunately, bloodshed was avoided when the leading Jews of Jerusalem followed Pilate to the seaport city of Caesarea, headquarters of Roman rule for the area, and there bared their necks to Roman swords rather than undergo such a desecration again. Impressed by their courage, Pilate—a proud but not always tactful man and a sensible administrator—agreed to relent.

Another wave of resentment had swept Jerusalem and Judea briefly when Pilate had built a magnificent aqueduct to bring a much needed additional water supply to the suburbs of Jerusalem from springs in the nearby hills, dipping into the temple treasury for payment. But the high priest had wisely acquiesced in this intervention into what might have been called strictly priestly affairs, and in the end many of those living in Jerusalem had agreed to the wisdom of the project—though some still refused to drink the water.

For a long time, Simon was not able to think about that terrible day before Sepphoris without experiencing once again the paralysis of utter terror that had seized him at the prospect of death upon the Roman spear point. He dreamed of it almost nightly, sometimes waking the household as he struggled in the grip of the nightmare. And even when he became older, he avoided the drinking houses favored by the fishermen and by travelers along the Way of the Sea, because the sight of violence during the drunken brawls that frequently occurred there could still start the sweat pouring out upon his skin and bring on a fit of trembling. In other situations, however, such as facing the storms that sometimes swept down upon the Sea of Galilee and threatened to sink the fishing boats, Simon never lacked for courage. And through the years he managed to keep his single weakness secret, even from his family.

During the years of his developing maturity following the death of his mother, Simon moved with Andrew to Capernaum, where they became associated with the house of Zebedee in the occupation of fishermen. He took a young wife, who died after only a brief period of marriage, struck down by one of the plagues that sometimes swept through the teeming lake cities like an avenging angel. And, following her death, he lived on with his mother-in-law Naomi, whom he loved very dearly, and with his brother Andrew.

Simon's boyhood had ended abruptly with the death of

his father when the task of supporting his family had suddenly been thrust upon his fortunately broad shoulders. A man who devoted himself wholeheartedly to whatever task faced him, he soon achieved at least local fame as the best fisherman upon the Sea of Galilee, finding his greatest joy in pitting his strength against the gales that often swept the lake, setting the sail of his boat as taut as a drumhead, and driving it through the water faster than a hundred men could have dragged it by tugging upon a rope. Or again, he would rejoice in his own strength as he hauled in the nets filled with the struggling silvery catch that meant money enough for an additional offering when, like every Galilean who could afford the trip, he journeyed to Jerusalem in the spring at the season of the Passover for his annual gift and sacrifice in the temple.

At the death of Aristobulus, Barnabas had left Cyprus and moved to Jerusalem, where he lived with his Aunt Mary and her young son Mark, a student in the School for Scribes at the temple. A merchant whose travels took him to various cities, Barnabas often visited Simon at Capernaum, in addition to their yearly meetings in Jerusalem at the time of the Passover. As a boy, Simon had listened to Barnabas' tales of ships that plied the sea between Cyprus and Israel, and the great copper mines devoted to the production of that metal and of bronze. Now he learned from his friend about such great centers as Alexandria, Ephesus and even far-off Rome, but he was still much too closely occupied with his own work and his own home to think of visiting those faraway places.

In Capernaum, the children knew Simon as a gentle man, always ready to help them with the tiny boats they sailed in the quiet shallows near the shores of the lake. To the boys of Capernaum, the now stocky and broad-shouldered fisherman imparted the lore that made him the best known and most widely respected of the Galilean fishermen; such things as where the fish would school, and the secret of gauging the weather by the clouds massing against the snow-capped peak of Mount Hermon in the north.

More than anything else in the world, Simon loved Galilee and the amethyst-blue lake that was its brightest jewel. He loved his small home near the shore and the warmth of the sun that flooded the land at the end of the brief, mild winter season, bringing out the tender green shoots upon the grape-vines and causing the grain to sprout in the fallow earth. Had he possessed the gift of lyric speech, he might have written of Galilee—as did the Roman poet Virgil in praise of his beloved homeland:

> But fruitful vines and the fat olive's freight,
> And the harvests heavy with their fruitful weight,
> Adorn our fields: and on the cheerful green
> The grazing flocks and lowing herds are seen . . .
> Perpetual spring our climate sees—
> Twice breed the cattle and twice bear the trees.

Even the beauty of Galilee could not hide the fact that misery and want existed there, too. Herod Antipas, though not so strong as his father, had emulated Herod the Great in building magnificent structures for his own comfort and for the purpose of flattering the Roman master by whose favor he held his throne as tetrarch. Over the years, Sepphoris had been rebuilt, following its near destruction during the War of Varus. But not content, Herod had gone on to construct an entirely new city called Tiberias, at a point a little south of Magdala on the western shore of the Sea of Galilee. Though a thoroughly heathen place in the eyes of the Jews of that region—since it stood upon the site of a former cemetery—Tiberias was nevertheless a magnificent and beautiful city.

All of these activities, coupled with Antipas' taste for

luxurious living, placed a heavy burden of taxes upon his subjects and increased their hatred for him. With the Roman troops under his command, he enforced his will and his taxes upon the fiery Galileans, but he could not keep them from hoping and praying for a better and more glorious fate than that of bowing their necks to the rule of an Idumean who was also a toady of Rome.

The Greek term for a leader anointed of God was "the Christ," in Hebrew "the Messiah." To the people of Israel both words meant the same, a king sent by God—as David had been—with divine power to conquer Israel's enemies and form a great independent kingdom. From time to time, claimants to the title of messiah arose, found a following for a while among the credulous, then lapsed into obscurity when their claims proved false. But not since the ill-fated rebellion of Judas the Galilean had one arisen who combined an ability to stir the people to a patriotic fervor, with the qualities of military leadership that could start an actual rebellion—the two characteristics most looked for in the Messiah by the majority of those who devoutly desired his coming.

Meanwhile, as the years passed and the burden of taxation grew heavier, some of the embers left from the fires of rebellion that had once swept the country began to glow again. Bands of angry men joined together, taking once more the name of Zealots or *Kanna'im*, as they had in the days of Judas of Galilee. One group was even rumored to be under the command of Menahem, his son, while others living mainly in the wild and rugged northern section of Judea, only a short distance from Jerusalem itself, were led by a brigand named Barabbas.

Busy with the task of providing for himself and for those he loved, Simon had no time for the plottings and ambitions of the Zealots. But he could hardly escape knowledge of their activities, since John and James, the sons of Zebedee with whom he and Andrew fished every night, were openly sympathetic to the rebel cause, as were large numbers of people in Galilee.

Then something happened that had not occurred in Israel for nearly four hundred years. A prophet—one of the holy men through whose inspired utterances the voice of God himself was brought to his people from time to time—came out of the wild country south of Jericho, overlooking the Dead Sea. A member of the ascetic, almost hermit, sect called the Essenes, whose main center of activity was located in that relatively inaccessible region, the man called John preached the imminent coming of the Kingdom of God, when all would be brought to account for their sins, and the necessity for confession and a symbolic cleansing of the soul from those sins through the typically Essene rite of baptism.

Inevitably, he came to be called "the Baptist"—but many also named him "the Messiah."

Book Two

JOHN THE BAPTIST

". . . I am the voice of one crying in the
wilderness, Make straight the way of the Lord,
as said the prophet Esaias."

JOHN 1:23

I

SIMON could not have described in words just what he had expected from baptism at the hands of the slender, almost gaunt, man in the homespun robe and wooden-soled sandals. On the way back from a visit to Jerusalem for the Passover with a group from Galilee, he had stopped to hear the man called John the Baptist preach at a crossing point of the Jordan called Bethabara, a few miles east of Jericho. Like thousands of others who had come to Bethabara in the weeks that John had been preaching there, Simon, too, had been moved by the fiery eloquence of the Essene prophet and had been filled with the conviction of his own sinfulness and the need for God's forgiveness. As one of a long line of penitents, the broad-shouldered fisherman from Galilee had stood in the water and watched those being baptized before him.

Some waded from the muddy stream with an ecstatic glow in their eyes, signifying a deep and moving experience. Others shouted praise and glory to God, while a few—mostly women, he noticed—were seized with such a convulsion of religious fervor that they had to be carried from the water and laid upon the shore until they recovered. But when finally it came Simon's turn to undergo the strange rite of the Essenes, he only knew that he was disappointed and that for some reason he could not fathom—unless it were his own unworthiness—the new and revitalizing experience he had expected had been denied to him.

It was true that he had felt a moment of high exultation

when he confessed his sin and underwent the symbolic ritual of cleansing. But he had known that feeling before: once when long ago from the Mount of Olives he had first watched the city of Jerusalem and the temple take form out of the morning mists; and again that same day when he had purchased his very first sacrifice, a dove, in the temple market. Years later, he had felt it again when, as a mature man of thirty, he had sat for the first time with the elders of the congregation at Capernaum and taken an active part in the worship service, listening to the sacred words of the Law and the Prophets being read in the synagogue, and hearing the beautiful phrases of the Psalms of David chanted by loving voices.

But even those moments of exalted feeling had differed little, if at all, from the way he often felt when the cords of the nets grew taut with a mighty catch and he pitted his great strength against the task of hauling it in and filling the boat with the struggling fish. Or when the boat grounded in the shallows and he leaped into the water to wade ashore and pull it up on the sand, shouting for all to witness the results of a successful night's work and rejoice with him in it.

It must be, Simon decided, that he had expected too much. But that still did not explain why the crowds of people who had gathered here for months to listen, repent, and undergo the rite of baptism, seemed to have gained so much more from it than he. Both John and James, as well as his own brother Andrew who worked nightly with him in the same boat on the Sea of Galilee, were certain that, under the influence of the Baptist's fiery preaching and the touch of his hand and the water, they had received a revelation from God that John was the Messiah. But no such conviction had come to Simon that morning, and he could not help wondering now, as he watched others being baptized, whether its absence might not be due to some lack within himself, some defect in his own faith that had denied him the revelation granted others.

Standing there upon the riverbank, with the brown flood moving swiftly near his feet, Simon was a striking figure. Broad of shoulder, his hair already showed tints of gray, though he was not yet forty years of age. He was a man of great strength, yet one who possessed the amazing gentleness that so often characterized such men. And more than that, his manner was marked by a humility which could never be mistaken for weakness, the humility of one conscious of his own strength and needing no bluster with which to bolster it, yet willing to acknowledge that, in the eyes of God, he was only a child.

"Simon!" A slender man came scrambling down across the rocky eastern bank of the Jordan. He had an intense, vivid face, and eyes that lit easily, as they did now, with the fires of excitement and enthusiasm. Since boyhood, John the son of Zebedee, and Simon had been close friends, though one seeing them now for the first time would have judged them to be as wide apart as night is from day.

"Simon!" John came to a stop beside his friend, panting a little from the effort of running across the shore. "A delegation has come from Jerusalem to question the Baptist. Now he *must* reveal that he is the Messiah!"

Simon could see the men of whom John had spoken now. They stood out from among the crowd at the fords like the scarlet red bloom of the burnet in a field of weeds. They were standing at the edge of the poplar grove that formed a sylvan amphitheater nearby, with an elevated flat stone jutting from the hillside as a natural pulpit. He recognized them, from his visits to Jerusalem, as several of the most highly respected figures in the councils of the Jewish faith. Their presence here could only mean that the temple authorities were concerned by the size of the crowd that had been thronging to Bethabara for months to hear the fiery Essene prophet.

Two of the visitors were Pharisees, easily identifiable by their dress and their manner. They belonged to the deeply pious sect which had constituted itself the meticulous guardian of both the written Laws of Moses and the mass of oral precepts and traditions handed down from century to century, known simply as The Law. A little to one side, as if unwilling to come any nearer to the rabble at the river crossing, stood two Sadducees, members of the priestly class charged with carrying out the elaborate ritual of worship in the temple at Jerusalem. The robes of both groups were elaborately fringed at the hems, and bound to each man's forehead was one of the small leather boxes, called a *phylactery*, containing a creed from the Hebrew Scriptures.

The men from Jerusalem did not move from their places as the Baptist came out of the water. Without even dropping the hem of his homespun robe, which he had tucked up into his belt to keep it from becoming wet in the water, John approached them, followed by a small knot of his closest disciples.

The Essene's wiry body was bent and worn, and he seemed much older than the roughly thirty years which Simon knew to be John's actual age. He limped a little, too, from having stepped upon a loose rock with his bare feet as he waded into the waters to begin the daily baptism. Simon could not picture him marching at the head of an army such as would be necessary to liberate Israel from Roman rule, yet he knew many of his friends firmly believed that, at the command of the Messiah, even the walls of Jerusalem must fall, as the walls of nearby Jericho had tumbled before the trumpets of Joshua more than a thousand years before.

As he looked over the heads of the crowd from the slight

elevation of the rock upon which he was standing, Simon saw James, the other son of Zebedee, with his own brother Andrew. Beside them were Philip and Bartholomew, friends from the same area in Galilee. Barnabas, too, was with them, and they were all watching the delegation from Jerusalem, eagerly awaiting the outcome of the meeting between the newcomers and John the Baptist.

Simon was sure that all of his friends—except perhaps Barnabas—would have laughed at him if he had told them that he suddenly felt a little homesick for his house beside the lake, his boat with its white sail, and even the pungent smell of the nets hanging on racks near the shore. Those were things Simon loved; the problems arising in their use he could solve easily, something he could not do with such questions as when the glory promised to Israel by the prophets would come again—or how.

A flash of sunlight reflected from the crest of a mountain to the south caught Simon's eye and he shivered a little as, momentarily, an old memory came surging up to attack the walls he had built around it long ago in his mind. He knew the source of that metallic glint; it came from the roof of the palace fortress of Machaerus, the frontier stronghold Herod Antipas had erected on the heights to guard his tetrarchy from an attack by the wild Nabatean tribes dwelling to the east. Herod had good reason to fear the Nabateans, for not long before he had divorced a Nabatean princess to marry the former wife of his brother Philip.

A momentary commotion swirled about John as some of his disciples, gesticulating and arguing heatedly, sought to dissuade the wiry Essene from approaching the spot where the men from Jerusalem stood. Simon understood the disciples' concern, for if the Baptist were indeed the Messiah, even the most exalted among the Sadducees and Pharisees should be upon their knees before him, rather than waiting haughtily for his approach. John, however, waved his followers aside and continued on his way until he stood before the visitors. He welcomed them courteously, but the leader of the delegation, a Sadducee as sleek and well fed—Simon thought—as any of the swine pastured outside the Greek cities of the Decapolis on the eastern shore of the Sea of Galilee, ignored even the ordinary amenities due a prophet who had swayed thousands with his sincerity and his message of repentance.

"Who are you?" the visitor demanded arrogantly.

"I am not the Anointed One," John answered, and a groan of disappointment came from the crowd. Many of them had welcomed the arrival of the commission, for it had seemed that now John must announce his messiahship and begin to rally the dissident forces in Israel for a march upon Jerusalem. Even the Sadducee appeared to be taken a little aback by John's words; obviously he had not expected so easy a victory. But he was clever enough to push his point ruthlessly, once having gained the advantage.

"What, then?" he demanded. "Are you Elijah?"

"I am not."

"Are you the Prophet?" All knew he meant Isaiah, whom

many Jews expected to return in the form of another, bringing God's message once again to the nation, as he had done centuries earlier.

"No."

"Who are you then, so we may give an answer to them that sent us? What do you say of yourself?"

John's eyes kindled again with the fire that had stirred the multitude, and his shoulders straightened proudly. For a moment he was no longer a weary man, knowing that with every word he was building a wall between himself and the crowds who had hailed him during these months at Bethabara.

"I am the voice of one crying in the wilderness," he announced proudly. " '*Make straight the way of the Lord*'— as the Prophet Isaiah has said."

One of the Pharisees stepped from the delegation. "Why do you baptize then, if you are neither the Anointed One, Elijah or a prophet?" he demanded.

"I baptize with water," John answered. "But one stands among you whom you do not know. He it is who, though coming after me, is preferred over me and whose shoe's latchet I am not worthy to unloose."

It was a strange statement, one that Simon, though he was listening intently, could not understand. The Pharisee questioning John was also disconcerted, but before he could ask another question, the Baptist turned and took a path that traversed the rocky hillside to a small clearing where he slept with only a thatch of reeds woven by his disciples to protect him from the night air.

The Pharisee looked after John for a moment, as if he wanted to pursue him and ask more questions, but instead shrugged and joined the others of the delegation. They conferred briefly, then apparently satisfied that they had forced John to disavow completely the role to which so many had elected him, they went down to where the boat which had brought them across the river from the Judean side was drawn up on the shore, and called for the boatman to put them across.

Simon saw John and James and his brother Andrew talking animatedly together, but he did not join them. It had troubled him to see a good man like the Baptist—whether a prophet or not—shamed by the haughty Jerusalem delegation, and he wanted time to think about the whole matter. Leaving the crowd behind, he turned along the bank of the river south of the ford. Few people were camped here, because of the wild and rocky nature of the terrain where the river approached its ending in the Dead Sea, whose waters were so heavy with salt that a man could not sink in them, even if he stood upright. Occasionally the smell of brimstone seeping through crevices in the rocks came to his nostrils, betraying a turbulence far below in the depths of the earth.

Once, long ago, he remembered, in the time of Abraham, the surface of the earth and the region around the Salt Sea had rumbled and torn itself apart while men fled before the anger of the Lord. One of these had been Abraham's nephew Lot, to whom the patriarch had sent God's warning that the area would be destroyed. But the people in the rich and populous cities grouped at the south end of the sea had refused to listen—just as many refused to listen even now when John warned of God's wrath because of Israel's sinfulness— and had been swept into the boiling vortex opened by the cracking of the earth's surface.

A half hour's walk south of the ford, Simon paused to drink from a crystal-clear spring that burst from the rocks to plunge, in a series of small waterfalls, into the river itself. A palm had somehow managed to spring from a crevice in the rocks, turning the area into a shady retreat. And after slaking his thirst, he found a comfortable seat with his back against the trunk and abandoned his thoughts to the music of the water tumbling across the rocky ledges, shortly falling asleep.

The sound of his own name shouted down the rocky gorge woke Simon from a brief doze, and he got to his feet to see Barnabas stepping from rock to rock along the river-bank. The tall Cypriot was panting a little and his face was red from exertion.

"I am leaving at dawn with a party returning to Jerusalem," Barnabus explained when he came up to where Simon was standing. "I didn't want to go without telling you goodbye, and Andrew said he saw you going this way."

"I wanted to think about what happened at the ford just now," Simon admitted.

Barnabas knelt beside the spring and drank deeply, then took a seat on a patch of grass beside an upright slab of rock that supported his back. "One thing is certain," he said, wiping his mouth with the sleeve of his robe, "John will lose much of his following now that he has denied being the Messiah."

"What is he?"

Barnabas shrugged. "A prophet perhaps, sent to warn Israel, as Elijah did in the time of Ahab when the nation went whoring after false gods."

"But we worship only the Most High."

"You and I and many others—yes. But what of the high priest when he sits at Roman feasts where dancing girls posture naked before drunken men? Or Herod Antipas, who pretends to be a pious Jew but cares so little for the Law that he brazenly commits adultery by marrying the wife of his brother Philip?"

"Then perhaps we need someone like John the Baptist to lead us back to God more than we need a messiah to lead us in revolt against the Romans."

"You and I were boys in Jerusalem when my father warned yours against thinking Rome could be defeated," Barnabas reminded him. "When I hear this talk of a messiah who will lead conquering armies, I cannot forget Judas of Galilee. Remember, you believed he was the Anointed One then."

"I know. But what shall we look for?"

Barnabas gave his friend a shrewd look. "Then John did not inspire you, as he did your brothers and the sons of Zebedee?"

"I felt exalted at the moment," Simon admitted. "But no more than I have felt on other occasions."

"And it troubles you that you are not moved to follow anyone who claims to lead—as the others do?"

Simon nodded soberly. "I love God and I love Israel. I would like to see our nation great again, as in the time of David and Solomon. But how can that be when Judeans look upon Galileans with contempt and the priests are more Roman than Jew? My father was crucified for following a false messiah who promised everything. I have no desire to follow in his steps—with a *patibulum* across my shoulders."

"Nor I," Barnabas agreed soberly. "What we need is men like John the Baptist to show us the way back to God, but the people seem to prefer brigands like Barabbas and Menahem." He shrugged. "Fires have always rumbled just beneath the surface of Judea—and Galilee even more. One day they will break through again, as the brimstone breaks through the rocks here beside the Salt Sea, and there will be another War of Varus."

Simon shivered involuntarily and shut the picture that came

with it forcibly from his mind. "When will you be in Galilee again, Barnabas?"

"Who can say? So many brigands infest the land today, calling themselves patriots, that an honest merchant can never be sure his goods will find their way to the buyers. Mark will soon finish his studies at the Scribes' School. I am thinking of taking him and his mother back to Cyprus and making our home there."

"Are you that sure rebellion will break out?"

"Pontius Pilate has learned how to keep the peace in Jerusalem, with the help of the High Priest Caiaphas. Both profit from it, but Pilate has stayed longer as procurator of Judea and Samaria than any Roman before him. He is anxious to return to Rome, and if the procurator who replaces him is stubborn and insists on bringing the eagles of Rome into Jerusalem, as Pilate did when he first came, bloodshed and suffering will follow. I would like to keep Mary and Mark safe from that if I could."

"And I," Simon agreed.

During his visits to Jerusalem for the religious feasts, he had watched John Mark grow into a fine, intelligent stripling, a scholar who was already skilled, not only in writing the Hebrew used in copying religious documents and the Aramaic language spoken by the people generally, but also Greek and Latin. He had come to love the boy as much as he would have loved the son he had never had, and the thought that his friends in Jerusalem might leave there made him sad. Yet he knew Barnabas had spoken the truth in comparing Israel to a volcanic area not quite ready for eruption, but giving alarming signs of the fire beneath the surface.

Barnabas glanced at the sun, which now hung a little above the hills of the wild country lying to the west of the Dead

Sea. "I must go back to the camp and tell the men from Jerusalem I will go with them in the morning," he said, getting to his feet. "Are you coming? Or will you sleep here?"

"I had better go, too," Simon said. "Perhaps I can talk the others into starting back to Galilee in the morning."

"I think not," Barnabas said as they began to pick their way across the rocks, retracing the course by which they had come to the spring. "When I was talking to Andrew and the sons of Zebedee a little while ago, they said they were going to stay on through tomorrow."

"Why?"

"They think John may have denied being the Messiah because he knew the commission from Jerusalem wished to do him harm," Barnabas said. "They still hope he will make the announcement tomorrow."

"But John made it plain that he is only the Forerunner, sent to announce the coming of another."

"When will that be?"

"Who knows? Just as who can tell when the nets will be full or the fish will remain deep in the lake."

"We gain nothing by troubling ourselves with what may not happen," Barnabas agreed. "As the Prophet Isaiah said, *'Let us eat and drink; for tomorrow we shall die.'*"

III

John made no further announcement concerning yesterday's events when he came from his thatch hut the next morning to preach. Depressed and irritated by his inability to help the Baptist, for whom he could only feel pity, Simon prowled restlessly about the camp during the day. When nightfall approached, he bought a haunch of freshly killed goat's meat from a vendor and set it to roasting over a bed of coals. He was sitting beside the fire, morosely watching the coals and turning the goat's flesh upon the improvised spit, when his brother Andrew appeared shortly after dark.

Andrew was as quick and volatile as his older brother was slow and deliberate, but there was a deep bond of affection between the two, and the younger brother worshiped Simon, who had been like a father to him since their parents had died.

"You should have been with me, Simon!" Andrew cried. "We have found the Messiah!"

All the pent-up irritation and sense of futility, all the disappointment—not only with John but with himself—suddenly boiled to the surface within Simon's soul.

"Say no more to me of messiahs!" he snapped. "Would you have us all crucified?"

At another time the look of astonishment upon Andrew's face might have made Simon laugh. But everything else was suddenly submerged in a flood of memory—released by the word "crucified"—surging up to attack his conscious senses.

He had hoped that the paralyzing fear had long since been so deeply shut away in the innermost depths of his mind that it could never be dredged up again. But when it assailed him once more, he found that it still possessed the power to make him break out in the same cold sweat of terror and feel once again an almost uncontrollable impulse to run wildly from the threat and the smell of death.

With a massive effort of will, Simon gained control of his trembling hands and lifted the spit from over the coals. Andrew was staring at him, a look of hurt amazement in his eyes.

"Forgive me, Andrew." The older brother expertly slashed

off a liberal chunk of meat, using his always razor-sharp knife of Damascus steel with which he could expertly dress a fish, removing all the best meat in two quick, slicing cuts. He placed the meat upon a piece of bread cut from a loaf warming on a rock beside the fire, and handed it to Andrew.

"What happened just now, Simon?" Andrew's face was troubled as he took the meat and bread. "You spoke of crucifixion, and for a few moments you looked as if you were possessed by an evil spirit."

"Perhaps I was." Simon cut a slice of meat for himself and placed it upon a piece of bread. "Tell me. Who is this messiah of whom you spoke just now?"

"He is called Jesus of Nazareth. His mother is Mary, a sister to Salome, the mother of James and John. The Baptist himself bore witness that he is the Messiah."

"John?" Simon asked startled.

"Yes."

"How?"

"You heard him tell the delegation this afternoon that there was one among them they did not know, the latchet of whose shoe he was not worthy to unloose?"

"Yes. I heard that."

"John baptized Jesus some time ago. He says that when he did, the Holy Spirit descended from Heaven like a dove and rested upon the Nazarene as he stood in the water."

Simon frowned. "Surely if a dove had landed upon one of those being baptized, there would have been some outcry. Yet I have heard no one speak of it."

"The dove was a message from God intended only for the eyes of Jesus and John," Andrew explained. "I have been with Jesus most of the day, Simon. No one ever taught as he does."

"Is he a soldier to lead us against the Romans?" Simon

asked, a little harshly. "You know James and John seek such a man."

"With the power of God as his sword, no one can stand against the Messiah."

"Then this man called Jesus claims to possess such power?"

"No," Andrew admitted. "But what about the testimony of the Baptist?"

"John is a prophet. They often speak in riddles."

"Surely the dove that landed on Jesus's head when John was baptizing him proved that he is the Anointed of God."

Peter shrugged. "Has no bird ever lit upon you when you were hauling in the net?"

"Of course." Andrew was growing angry at the older brother's grilling. "I could almost believe you want no messiah to lead our people to freedom."

Simon looked toward the river rushing softly southward not far from where they were sitting. The wind had changed and a faint smell of brimstone from the rocky area south of the fords came to his nostrils. It reminded him of what Barnabas had said only that afternoon: that Israel was very much like this region where hell itself seemed to smolder just beneath the surface, waiting for an opportunity to erupt.

Simon himself had witnessed one such eruption, and the memory was a burden of which he could not rid himself, even with the passing of the years. At all costs Andrew must be turned away from following another false messiah, for impetuous always, he would be in the midst of the fighting and sure to die. And the simplest way to save him was to prove that the Nazarene was not what he claimed.

"Where is this messiah of yours?" Simon's voice was curt.

"At the caravansary."

"I will go and see him later. You can be sure I will know if he is an impostor."

Andrew stared at his brother angrily; it was one of the few times they had ever quarreled. Then, clutching his meat and his bread, he turned and plunged into the darkness toward the outskirts of the village.

Simon took his time about wrapping the rest of the meat and bread in a piece of cloth and securing it in the crotch of a small sapling where it would be safe from the scavenging dogs that sometimes came to the camp at night from the nearby village. He did not relish what he had to do, for it gave him no pleasure to hurt any man, but he owed it to Andrew to save him from making a fool of himself.

Every town of any size located upon a traveled road provided upon its outskirts a camping place for wayfarers, called a caravansary. Varying in size and in the comfort afforded by their appurtenances, the camping grounds performed two important functions: they provided places where travelers could sleep, sometimes under cover, and where itinerant merchants could display their wares. Equally, if not more, important, they kept visitors where the elders of the village could watch them.

On the way to the caravansary at Bethabara, Simon paused here and there to exchange greetings with friends and neighbors, for the Baptist had found many followers among the people of Galilee. As a rule, Galileans were a jovial and happy people, much less reserved than their more sophisticated brethren in Jerusalem. But tonight there was little merriment in the camp, for John's failure to proclaim himself the Messiah had exerted a sobering effect upon everyone. Besides, the number of empty reed-walled huts in the best camping area gave mute evidence that a large number of John's own disciples had already deserted him.

At the edge of the caravansary Simon saw the sons of Zebedee sitting with another man, whom he judged to be the Nazarene, around the coals of a campfire. Andrew was beside the stranger, listening intently to what he was saying, but Simon could not hear the words. Compared to Simon's own solid strength, the man from Nazareth seemed almost frail. But when he raised his hands in an expressive gesture— as if painting a picture with them in the air to illustrate his words—Simon saw that they were strong and graceful in their movements, the hands of an artisan who worked in a trade of skill rather than one needing only force and strength.

Remembering the fiery gestures of Judas the Galilean when he had seen him in Jerusalem that day so long ago haranguing the crowd, Simon hesitated a moment. He had long ago come to be suspicious of the flamboyant manner characterizing most rabble rousers, but this man showed none of them. In fact Simon felt a sudden urge to go back to his own campfire, and was turning away when John saw him in the shadows and recognized his bulk.

"Simon!" he called. "Come and join us."

Thus caught, Simon had no choice except to move into the circle of firelight cast by the dying coals.

"This is my brother Simon, Rabbi," Andrew said quickly, as if fearing that Simon would speak first and attack the Nazarene. He gave the other man simply the title of teacher, traditionally reserved for those who spoke in the synagogues during the Sabbath services, and not the title of messiah he had used when speaking of him to Simon.

Jesus of Nazareth wore a beard, as did almost all men of Israel after they became old enough to be regarded as adults in the sight of the Law. But though his hair curled about his shoulders and his soft brown beard, too, showed a tendency to curl, there was nothing effeminate about his appearance. Instead, the clean-cut lines of his face, the rather high cheekbones and the deepset eyes, gave an impression of quiet strength and intelligence.

Simon was somewhat taken aback by the appearance of the Nazarene, for his was not the fevered manner that he had come to associate with those who claimed messiahship. What startled him most when his eyes met those of Jesus was the feeling of having known him before, almost of having somehow yearned for this meeting—though he knew that was impossible, for he had never seen the Nazarene before. Struck with wonder by the answering surge of feeling that rose within his breast at the warmth of welcome in the other man's eyes—in spite of the fact that he had come here with the intention of exposing him as an impostor—Simon was tongue-tied for the moment and could not even acknowledge the introduction.

Strangest of all, for an instant as he looked into the warm brown eyes of the other man, Simon was sure that Jesus of Nazareth fully understood the reason why he had come to the caravansary that night, yet held no resentment against him because of it.

It was an odd feeling, a profoundly disturbing feeling— this sensation of having known before one whom he had never seen and of having even one's deepest thoughts apparent to another. For a moment Simon felt a glimmering of the old fear, an urge to resist the strange force that seemed to be drawing him to the stranger, resist it with every power within him, lest he be drawn into an onrushing current of events over which he would have no control. Unconsciously, he tensed his body to leave the circle of light around the campfire, but the voice of the Nazarene, speaking directly to him, brought him up short.

"You are Simon, the son of Jonas," Jesus said warmly. "I shall call you Cephas."

It was a strange greeting, but no stranger than the other circumstances surrounding their meeting. Feeling his instinctive distrust of the Nazarene ebb away before the obvious pleasure and warmth in the other man's voice, Simon mumbled some words of greeting and settled into a space between John and James. He was not surprised by the name Cephas that Jesus had given him, judging that the others must have been speaking of him before he arrived. For the term meant, literally, a stone, and Simon had always prided himself upon being solid, strong and dependable, qualities that were indeed rocklike.

"I told you he was as strong as a stone," John, always the more ebullient of the brothers, said with a laugh. "You would think him indeed a rock if you saw him anchor a net heavy with the catch."

Jesus had been in the midst of a story when Simon appeared, and as he listened to the quiet but compelling voice Simon could not fail to notice the difference between the teacher of Nazareth and John the Baptist. For where the Essene had warned that the wrath of God would be turned against those who did not obey the Law, hurling it at them almost as a threat, Jesus spoke only of simple things that happened in everyday life, things Simon and the others easily understood.

The talk continued for perhaps an hour, during which Simon listened enthralled. As he and Andrew were about to leave for their own beds beneath a shelter of rushes that Simon had woven on their arrival at Bethabara, John said: "Jesus must leave for Cana early in the morning to attend a wedding feast. The groom is a kinsman, so we are going, too. Come join us, Simon."

John's words broke the spell the Nazarene had woven over Simon, and he felt some of his old misgivings return. "I am not a kinsman," he protested. "Besides, there is work to be done on the boat before we fish again. I will go on and be ready when you get back to Capernaum from Cana."

"Why can't we go with the others to Cana?" Andrew demanded as the two brothers were walking back through the camp to their own sleeping place. "John and James are like brothers to us, and the bridegroom is their kinsman."

"You can go with them," Simon told him.

"But why not you?"

"I have other things to do," Simon said, a little shortly. For now that he was away from the influence of the Nazarene, his old misgivings were flooding up again to torment him.

"Why do you fear Jesus?" Andrew demanded. "I tell you he is the Messiah, Simon. You should hail him."

"Say no more of messiahs!" Simon snapped. "Have you ever felt the blood of another man pouring out upon your body?"

They had reached the coals of their campfire. In the light, Simon saw Andrew's eyes grow wide with horror, for even to be touched by a corpse was a defilement that could only be erased by many washings, or by a special sacrifice of cleansing.

"Surely you don't mean that you . . . ?"

"Yes." Simon stirred the coals and tossed a piece of wood upon them. "Sit down, Andrew, and I will tell you why I fear any man who calls himself the Messiah."

Andrew listened while Simon gave a brief account of that terrible day at Sepphoris when the ill-fated rebellion of Judas of Galilee had collapsed before the might of Rome during the War of Varus. The younger brother shuddered when Simon described how he had looked at the naked metal of the Roman spear point and waited numbly for it to be driven home in his body—and how his legs had collapsed from sheer terror, saving his life.

"Then you saw our father die?"

"No. But I saw Judas the Galilean hanging from a cross. And around him were hundreds of others who believed he was the Messiah, just as you think the Nazarene is now."

"I am a fool, Simon!" Andrew cried contritely. "A fool who listens to anyone and is swayed by the wind."

"The prophets tell us God will one day send a true leader, so we must listen to all," the older brother corrected him gently. "But we must not let our desire to be free blind us to the truth."

"How will we know the Anointed One when he does come?"

"We can only pray for a sign from God that no one can deny." Simon stretched himself out by the fire and pulled over him the heavy cloak most travelers carried. Andrew, too, rolled himself up in his cloak, but after a moment he broke the silence again.

"Was Judas of Galilee the father of Menahem?" he asked.

"Yes. But what do you know of Menahem?"

"John and James sometimes speak of him. They say he leads a band of the *Kanna'im*."

"I have heard that rumor, too."

"I think Simon the Canaanite—the one we see sometimes talking with John and James—is a follower of Menahem," Andrew confided. "And probably the other Judas, too."

"Judas of Kerioth?"

"Yes."

"Why do you say that?"

"Both of them wear the daggers of the *Kanna'im*. I saw them once myself, when they were with John and James."

Simon had never seen Menahem, the almost legendary son of Judas the Galilean, but he knew that the brigand chieftain was said to command a band of rebels against Rome who lived in the wild hill country between the Sea of Galilee and the Great Sea to the west. Simon did know Judas of Kerioth, however, a tall, hawk-faced brooding man, who with the Canaanite called Simon sometimes visited the sons of Zebedee. And if the Nazarene planned to surround himself with such dangerous men, he decided, he would eschew any further relationship with him, in spite of the strange feeling almost of kinship that he had experienced tonight when he had first seen Jesus.

"You are right in not going to Cana, Simon," Andrew said. "We will return to Capernaum tomorrow."

"No," Simon told him. "I want you to go with them. Perhaps you can discover more about the Nazarene for me while you are in Cana."

IV

Simon was mending a net several days later on the pier belonging to Zebedee and his sons when he looked up to see his brother running out on the elevated platform where the boats unloaded their catch.

"Simon!" Andrew cried. "Have you heard the news about Jesus?"

"What news?" Simon had been thinking about the period he'd spent with the Nazarene at Bethabara, and particularly the strange feeling he'd had then of having known the man before, but none of it had done him any good. The memory of Jesus of Nazareth was still as warm as the feeling he'd experienced when his eyes had first met those of the Nazarene, yet he still drew back instinctively from naming him anything except an unusually eloquent teacher.

"Now even you must admit Jesus comes from God," Andrew said triumphantly. "At Cana he turned water into wine."

"Tell me how it happened."

"We were at the wedding feast. The crowd was large, and at the height of the feast there was no more wine. Mary of Nazareth—Jesus's mother—went to tell him of it, since, being a kinsman, it was his shame, too, that the wine had run out. I was standing nearby and I heard Jesus say to her, 'My hour has not yet come'; nevertheless, he ordered the servants to pour water into the mixing vessels and take them to the steward so he could taste the mixture. And at once the steward reprimanded the groom for serving the best wine toward the end of the feast when the guests had already drunk that of lesser quality."

"It could have been a trick," Simon warned. "Surely you have seen the magicians of the East who perform here in Capernaum change water into wine."

"Y-yes," Andrew admitted, a little crestfallen. Then his face brightened. "But they never let anyone else taste the wine afterward, and what Jesus changed was drunk by everyone. I tasted it myself and found it better than the first. How do you explain that?"

"I cannot," Simon admitted.

"Then you must acclaim him."

Simon got to his feet and threw the net over his shoulder. "The only thing I *must* do is set the nets tonight, or all of us will starve. Are you ready for work? Or will you follow this Nazarene because he makes wine for you whenever you want it?"

Andrew flushed angrily, and for a moment Simon thought he was going to turn away. Then, without answering, he took up another net and began to store it in the bow of their boat which was pulled up on the shore at the landward end of the pier. Simon knew Andrew was still resentful, for his movements were jerky and once he kicked the side of the boat in frustration, but he made no move to mollify the younger brother. If the so-called miracle at Cana were really that and not a trick, it did indeed seem that Jesus of Nazareth might be more than merely a man—perhaps even the Messiah who, since he came from God, would possess the power of the Most High himself. But if he were not the Expected One, it was better for Andrew—and for everyone—if they learned the truth early. As it happened, the real truth was even more clouded by news of still another apparent miracle in which Jesus healed a boy in Capernaum—although he was in Cana at the time.

The personal representative, or steward, of Herod Antipas in Capernaum was named Chuza, a pious and respected elder of the largest and most influential congregation in the province. When word came to Simon through the sons of Zebedee—whose mother, Salome, was a sister to Mary, the mother of Jesus—that Chuza's son had been miraculously healed by the Nazarene, Simon went to see the steward. They had been friends for a long time and he did not hesitate to ask Chuza the circumstances surrounding the alleged cure.

"I can tell you little myself," Chuza admitted. "My son was at the point of death, and Herod's own physician could not help him. Then I remembered the story of a Nazarene who had turned water into wine, and went in search of him. He had gone to Cana, I learned when I got to Nazareth, so I followed him there."

"You say you did not know Jesus before?"

"No. But I was desperate, so I begged him to come to Capernaum and heal my son. He only looked at me sadly, however, and said, 'Unless you see signs and wonders, you will not believe.' "

"What did he mean?"

"I don't know, unless he thought I expected him to perform some great miracle there before me to prove his power. But somehow I knew in my heart that he could heal my son, if only he would. 'Sir, come down ere my child dies,' I implored him, and suddenly I felt as if he had taken all my burden upon himself."

Simon remembered the feeling he had experienced on that first meeting with the Nazarene; Chuza had described it almost exactly.

" 'Go your way; your son lives,' Jesus told me then," Chuza continued. "I hurried home as fast as I could, but one of my servants met me on the way with the news that my son had suddenly begun to mend. I asked him the time, but I knew the answer before he gave it to me."

"The hour when the Nazarene had told you he would be healed?"

"At exactly that moment."

"How can you be sure?"

"I looked at the sundial in the garden where I was talking to Jesus in Cana just before I started back to Capernaum," Chuza explained. "But why are you asking this, Simon? Do you know the Nazarene?"

"I saw him once—at Bethabara, when he was talking to John, James and Andrew."

"Then you must have experienced it, too—the feeling of having known him before and of faith that he is more than simply a man?"

Simon evaded answering the question. "Do you believe he is the Messiah—as the others do?"

"He might be the Messiah of whom Isaiah spoke," Chuza said thoughtfully. "But he is certainly not a soldier to lead the people in battle."

"But the purpose of the Messiah is to free us from the burden of being governed by others and to bring back the glories of David and Solomon. Everyone looks for the coming of another military leader like Judas Maccabeus."

"I know," Chuza said. "And Herod is continually watchful, lest such a one rise to prominence in Galilee and Peraea. More than anything else, he fears that his tetrarchy may be taken away from him, as the Emperor took Judea and Samaria away from his brother Archelaus."

As Simon was leaving, Chuza called him back. "I was in Nazareth again yesterday, seeing to the collection of the taxes," he said. "Did you know that Jesus's own people have rejected him?"

"No." This was startling news indeed.

"They told me that last Sabbath he rose in the synagogue at Nazareth as was his custom and read from the scroll of Isaiah. You remember the passage where it says:

"The spirit of the Lord is upon me,
Because he anointed me to preach good tidings to the poor.
He hath sent me to proclaim release to the captives,
And recovering sight to the blind,
To set at liberty them that are bruised,
To proclaim the acceptable year of the Lord."

"Those words apply to the Messiah!" Simon said. "All the scholars agree on it."

"And so do the people of Nazareth," Chuza said. "When Jesus finished the reading, they say he rolled up the scroll and added, 'Today has this Scripture been fulfilled in your ears.' "

"Then he was actually naming himself the Messiah."

"So it would seem," Chuza admitted, "but his own people did not believe him. An angry mob dragged him to the top of the crag above Nazareth and would have cast him down upon the rocks below on a charge of blasphemy. But Jesus

walked right through the crowd, and not one man touched
him to throw him over the cliff."

"Where is he now?" Simon asked, but he already knew the
answer. It was a part of the strange fate that seemed determined to twine together the cords of his own life and those
of the Nazarene, no matter how much he might resist.

"Jesus is already in Capernaum. The elders of the congregation have asked him to speak in the synagogue at the next
Sabbath service."

V

Always when he was disturbed and uncertain—as he was now
over the strange influence the Nazarene seemed to have gained
over his life—Simon found release in his work. John and
James fished with him and Andrew, sailing northeastward
each night from the pier of Zebedee's fishing establishment
upon the shore of Capernaum, for their regular fishing
grounds.

When the Tetrarch Philip—half brother to Herod Antipas,
who ruled in Galilee and Peraea, a district lying east of the
Jordan—had decided to change the former village of Bethsaida, Simon's birthplace, into a beautiful Greek and Roman
city, he had renamed it Bethsaida-Julias, after the wife of the
Roman Emperor Tiberius. The city lay at the extreme northern end of the Sea of Galilee, a little inland and just east of
where the cold, swift current of the Jordan emptied into the
lake.

The water supply for Bethsaida-Julias came from a group
of springs to which Philip had built an aqueduct. But since
this supply had proved to be far more than the demands of

even the rapidly growing city, the excess water poured into the lake before it. And perhaps because a zone was thus created where the temperature of the water changed sharply, fish schooled there almost every night, and at sunset boats from all parts of the lake converged upon the spot.

The boats usually worked in pairs, each manned by two men. First the long nets, weighted at the bottom, were cast out to form an enclosure in which the fish were trapped as the boats drew together to form a slowly tightening noose. Meanwhile the man not engaged in handling the net was busy transferring the struggling catch from the enclosure thus formed into the boat before the fish could escape by leaping over the top or swimming under the bottom edge of the net.

To Simon, the multicolored sails of the boats, materializing out of the mist-covered surface of the lake in the early morning like giant butterflies hovering close to the water, formed a scene of indescribable beauty. Sounds carried for great distances across the water, and the fishermen were in the habit of talking with each other as they sailed or rowed home in the early dawn, trading news of happenings in the various cities around the lake and the world outside.

Simon had never troubled himself very much about the latter. From his talks with Barnabas, he knew a great deal about the world, far more in fact than the average citizen of Galilee. But he had heard little that made even the great cities of the empire—places like Antioch, Ephesus or Alexandria—more attractive to him than his own home at Capernaum, overlooking the beautiful lake that supplied him with a means of livelihood.

After his brother Andrew, Simon loved his mother-in-law, Naomi, most of all. In her house, located upon one of the narrow streets a little back from the shore and at a slightly higher level, he and Andrew had lived since they came from

Bethsaida to Capernaum. When Naomi became gravely ill with one of the terrible fevers that sometimes swept through the land, killing thousands, Simon was able, through Chuza, to have her treated by Herod's own physician, a Jew named Joseph. He had studied medicine in the great school at Alexandria and was therefore very much in demand by the richer people of the area, but still served any to whom he could furnish his services. Joseph, however, proved unable to control the raging fever and gave Simon no hope until Chuza suggested that he ask Jesus of Nazareth to help Naomi.

Simon had learned from Chuza that the Nazarene had moved to Capernaum after his rejection in his home city. But though the logical part of his mind argued that Jesus would cure Naomi if he only asked him, another part held back, instinctively fearing the strange power the man from Nazareth seemed to possess. Only when the Sabbath came and Naomi was obviously not far from death did Simon finally call a neighboring woman to sit with her; then he went to the synagogue where Jesus was to speak that day.

The service had already begun when he reached the synagogue, and the building was so crowded with people, eager to hear the new Teacher who was said to possess powers which not even the holiest men among the elders of the congregation had ever claimed to possess, that Simon was barely able to find a place at the back of the room, near the door.

In Galilee, as in the cities of the Diaspora outside Israel, many in the congregation had only a smattering of the Hebrew tongue, since the Syrian dialect called Aramaic was the most common language. For that reason, an interpreter called the *methurgeman*, or *dragoman*, translated the scrolls—as they were read—from the ancient Hebrew into the popular Aramaic language.

When he came to address the congregation, Jesus spoke of

the same things about which he had talked that night at Bethabara. His words were of seeds sown and falling upon fallow ground, bringing forth returns an hundredfold, while others fell among thorns or along the road and were choked out so they could not grow and were lost. He told of deeds done in the service of others that brought returns many times over, as did the growth of the seed if the doer did not boast abroad of his charity. But most of all he spoke of the concern of the Most High for even the least among his people, likening God to a shepherd who went out in the midst of a storm seeking one lamb which had not come home from the flock.

Simon had never thought of God in that way, as a kind, loving and all-powerful father who was concerned for even the least of his children. Instead, like most Jews, he had been concerned with the Law and obedience to its provisions. And as he listened he could feel a sense of peace and confidence in God's will flooding his soul and a new hope that Naomi would be healed.

The service that morning contained one moment of drama: it came near the end when a man possessed by a demon for many years threw himself down before the platform called the *bima*, upon which stood the desk or *luach*, from which the scrolls of the Law and the Prophets were read.

"What have we to do with you, Jesus of Nazareth?" The spirit which had seized the sick man made him cry out. "Have you come to destroy us? I know who you are: the Holy One of God."

A murmur arose from the congregation at the words of the demoniac, but Jesus spoke quickly and sternly.

"Hold your peace and come out of him," he commanded, and at once the frenzy passed, as if the demon had left the sick man, and his eyes became clear. Getting to his feet, he

ran up the aisle and out the door, passing so close to Simon
that he could have touched him easily.

If he had not come to the synagogue that morning for a
more pressing purpose, Simon would have followed the demoniac and questioned him about what had just happened,
as he had questioned Chuza about the healing of his son. But
the service ended shortly afterward, so he waited outside for
Jesus to emerge with the elders, many of whom always stayed
behind to question a new teacher about his pronouncements
from the pulpit.

As he chatted with friends outside the synagogue, Simon
could not help overhearing people commenting upon the note
of power and authority with which Jesus had commanded the
evil spirit to come out of the sick man. A few openly named
the Nazarene the Expected One because of what they had seen
just now and the miracles of which they had heard. More
thought him to be a prophet, a holy man through whom God
revealed truths which the people could not have otherwise
divined for themselves. But a few insisted that the Nazarene
had cast out the demon with the power of the devil himself.
When finally Jesus emerged from the synagogue with James
and John, Simon stepped forward.

"Master," he said, giving Jesus the title always given to
rabbis who were deeply respected. "My mother-in-law is ill.
I pray you come and heal her."

Jesus left off speaking to one of the elders at once and followed Simon. When they reached the house, a glance at
Naomi told Simon she was much worse even than when he
had left for the synagogue. Turning and twisting constantly
in the delirium of fever, muttering words with neither sense
nor meaning, she picked at the bedclothes as if to remove
vermin which had never been there—for she had always been
a meticulous housekeeper.

Jesus stood for a moment, looking at Naomi; then with a gesture of compassion, he placed his hand upon her forehead. To Simon's amazement, he saw beads of perspiration immediately begin to break out upon her face, as when a fever was brought quickly to its crisis. Naomi's eyes cleared, too, and she looked up at Jesus as if she recognized him, though Simon was sure she had never seen the Nazarene before.

"Master!" she said, seeking to rise. "You are a guest. I must serve you."

Simon put out his hand to keep Naomi upon the sleeping pallet, but let it drop when Jesus took her fingers in his and gently raised her from the bed. All signs of her illness were gone in less time than Simon would have taken to cast one of the small circular nets used for fishing close to the shore. And calling to the woman who had been sitting with her to help, Naomi went into the kitchen and began to prepare food for the guests.

VI

North of Capernaum, near the shore of the lake, lay the Plain of Gennesaret, a particularly fertile region where the warm climate that prevailed in the deep cleft of the Jordan Valley much of the year made the growing of fruit and vegetables for the market at Jerusalem very profitable. Palms, figs, walnuts, olives, vines, citrons, fruit and vegetables of all kinds grew in riotous profusion within sight of the lake, and often several crops of vegetables a year could be harvested. In spring, the aroma from the groves and orchards along the plain and the sloping hillsides nearby almost drowned out the odor of drying fish from the piers, a smell that was as much a part of Capernaum as its reputation for brawling and recurrent eruptions of political unrest against the rule of the Tetrarch Herod Antipas.

A short distance beyond the Plain of Gennesaret, near the caravan road that circled the northern end of the lake, a small natural cove formed roughly the outline of an amphitheater. The bottom of the lake shelved very gradually there, making it a favorite spot for the fishermen who cast their nets in the shallows. Even those who normally went out in the boats often came there to fish with small throw nets at the end of an unsuccessful night, beaching their boats and standing in the shallows, with their robes tucked up to keep them from getting wet, while washing the long nets in the fresh, clear water pouring from a nearby spring, and spreading them upon the rocky outcrop to dry in the bright morning sun.

Simon and his partners spent just such a fruitless night not long after Naomi was healed, and with the coming of morning, brought the boats into the shore. They cast awhile with the small circular nets that sometimes yielded enough fish for the personal use of the fishermen and their families, but this morning not even these yielded a catch. Depressed from the wasting of a night's work, Simon and his partners set about washing the nets and putting them on the rocks to dry. It was while thus engaged that Simon saw Jesus of Nazareth walking along the shore, followed as usual by a crowd of people.

Lifting his hand in a wave of greeting to the fishermen, the Nazarene chose a spot upon the shore where he could be heard by the crowd which scrambled for seats on the rocks making up the shelving sides of the small natural amphitheater. As he taught, Simon and the others continued to wash the nets and spread them upon the rocks. But they had performed these tasks so often that little attention was required and they were able to listen intently to what was being said.

The thriving lake region was an ideal spot for the activities of an itinerant healer and teacher such as Jesus of Nazareth. Not only was the western shore lined with cities, but one could hardly walk for an hour in any direction away from the lake itself without coming upon several towns or villages. Besides, although the Galileans were devout Jews, their somewhat mixed religious ancestry and the large number of Greeks in the area left them less shackled by religious tradition and the burden of the Law—as interpreted by the Pharisees—than those in Jerusalem.

This morning in the little amphitheater upon the shore, Jesus did not speak of the Law, but reduced man's relationship with God to its simplest form, that of father and obedient son. As he listened, Simon continued to pile the now dry nets into the boat but once again found himself strongly drawn to the Nazarene, as he had on previous occasions when they were together.

The sick and afflicted had always flocked in great numbers to the western shore of the Sea of Galilee because many highly mineralized springs burst from the rocks there. For centuries, the region around Magdala in particular had been favored by those whose limbs were crippled and deformed by the ravages of age and rheumatism, and a constant procession of people visited that region. Some had been helped by the warm and highly mineralized waters of the springs, but since Jesus of Nazareth had come to Capernaum the afflicted had begun to follow him, hoping to be healed instantly through a miracle, such as that of Chuza's son.

The crowd in the little amphitheater grew steadily larger that morning while Jesus was teaching. Soon the press of people around him clamoring to be healed made it difficult for him to make himself heard by those sitting upon the rocky hillside. Finally he turned to Simon, whose boat was grounded upon the shore, and asked permission to enter it.

The stocky fisherman steadied the boat so Jesus could stand upon the thwart. Then, holding the prow, he waded a little deeper into the water and held the boat steady there against the gentle thrust of the tiny wavelets rushing toward the shore, keeping it far enough away so the people standing at the water's edge were not able to reach the Nazarene. From this somewhat unusual but very effective pulpit, the teacher finished his discourse.

"Launch out into the deep water and let down your nets," Jesus said to Simon when the sermon was over.

"Master, we have toiled all night and have taken nothing," the fisherman protested, for few fished in the daytime when the warmth of the sun upon the water drove the fish into the depths. "Nevertheless, at your word I will let down the nets," Simon added quickly, realizing that his words might seem ungracious.

With Jesus still in the boat, he and Andrew finished piling the nets upon the thwart and rowed a little farther offshore, followed by John, James and their father Zebedee, in another boat. There, as Jesus directed them, they let down the nets, paying them out gradually while the two boats separated to form a wide semicircle, then approached each other again to close the trap thus formed.

Simon was holding the end of the net when he felt the strain upon the cords against his powerful hands as the fish trapped in the closing circle swam frantically about, seeking to escape. A great excitement began to rise within him and at the same moment, across the narrow isthmus of water separating the ends of the nets, he heard John cry out in wonder at the size of the catch. Fish were boiling to the surface, leaping and plunging as they sought to escape; in fact, never in all the years he had fished upon the lake could Simon remember such a catch as now filled their nets.

Zebedee was already standing upon the thwart of his boat, calling to the shore where some others of his fishing fleet had pulled into the shallows to wash their nets, and ordering them to come to the assistance of the two boats in handling the tremendous catch. To the others, the sudden appearance of a great draught of fish meant only that they had happened to cross the path of one of the schools which often moved about the lake, the silvery bodies breaking the surface and gleaming in the sun before falling back with an audible splashing. Such occurrences always sent a wave of excitement coursing around the lake as the fishermen rushed to their boats in the hope of trapping at least part of the school.

To Simon, however, the pull of the net cords against his hands, requiring all of his strength to hold them; the size of the catch now being drawn into the other boats; the fact that this had happened during daylight when no one expected to find any great number of fish here in the deeper part of the lake—all seemed to have another meaning. Instinctively he sought to shut it from his mind and occupy himself with the task of coping with the unheard of draught of fish struggling within the nets. But deep inside him some remnant of the old fear suddenly made the sweat break out upon his body and caused his hands to tremble so much that John shouted a warning across the lake not to loose his hold upon the net and let the catch escape.

Crouching in the boat, his muscles straining to hold the net, Simon saw in his mind once again, as on that day so long ago, the agonized faces of friends and neighbors hanging from the crosses before Sepphoris, crucified because they had followed a proclaimed messiah who had promised an even greater miracle—that of making Israel free—and had proved to be false. And as on that day, he felt an almost overbearing surge of panic, an urge to flee which he would most certainly have obeyed had he been elsewhere than in a boat well out from the shore. As it was, he had no choice except to go on with the task of saving the phenomenal catch, and the boats that had come out to help were filled before he finally felt the pressure upon the net he was holding lessen and was able to hand the cords to Andrew.

Jesus had been sitting quietly in the boat, and now Simon prostrated himself at the feet of the Nazarene.

"Depart from me for I am a sinful man, O Lord," he begged in his agony of terror and indecision. Then as he crouched there, sweating and trembling, he felt a gentle hand upon his shoulder, and as suddenly as it had come, the panic that had gripped him was gone.

"Fear not," Jesus said quietly. "From henceforth you shall catch men."

Book Three
MARY MAGDALENE

"... the twelve were with him, And certain women, which had been healed of evil spirits and infirmities, Mary called Magdalene, out of whom went seven devils."

LUKE 8:1, 2

I

THE man who stepped into the shallows near the shore to guide the boat into position beside the pier was a different person from the one who had sought to escape the strange pull of Jesus of Nazareth upon him a few minutes before by begging the teacher to leave him alone. The feeling of peace that had come upon Simon when he had felt the other man's hand upon his shoulder and heard the words "Fear not. From henceforth you shall catch men," was more than simply the allaying of his fears. It was rather an intimation, though not yet a revelation—that would come later—of a whole new purpose which had come into his life—it seemed in a single moment.

Looking back upon it later, Simon would have been the first to admit that the change had not been as sudden as it had appeared to be at the time. Perhaps it had actually begun back at Bethabara, weeks before, when he had heard John the Baptist admit he was not the Expected One but merely the Forerunner sent to announce the coming of one far greater than he. Simon had felt sad for John then, particularly when the Baptist's disciples—the very ones who had been so eager to name him the Messiah—had begun to desert him. But it had been almost with a sense of relief that he had turned away from John, for he had never been able wholly to convince himself that the Essene was what his friends, and even his own brother, believed him to be.

Just as strongly, Simon had resisted the conviction that Jesus of Nazareth was the expected messiah, largely because even the word itself was enough to bring back in all its fearful

97

vividness that terrible moment when he had lain beneath the body of the dead Galilean on the hill before Sepphoris and had heard the voices of the Roman soldiers scavenging among the dead. Nor did he accept the identity of the Nazarene unreservedly yet; the bulwarks he had erected in his mind over the years against being disappointed in another, as he had been in Judas of Galilee, were still far too strong for that. But drawn as he was so strongly to Jesus in a bond whose nature he could not yet understand, he no longer hesitated to accept the call to become a disciple. By following in the footsteps— so to speak—of the Nazarene, Simon hoped one day to learn the true identity of the gentle teacher who possessed such an amazing power to move men. And at the same time he was sure that he could learn more of the great truths concerning the relationship between God and man, which Jesus seemed able to express far more clearly than anyone he had ever heard before.

The decision brought a peace to Simon he had not known for many weeks, not in fact since he had first met Jesus of Nazareth at the caravansary outside Bethabara. But there were difficulties, too, and more would follow, he knew, for one did not simply change the whole course of one's life in an instant without them. The first of these involved the tremendous catch that now filled all the boats of Zebedee's fleet, a supply of fish far larger than the capacity of all the drying sheds along the shore at Capernaum. And yet the fish must be sold quickly if they were not to spoil.

Though Simon had decided to forsake the daily life of a fisherman for that of a disciple of Jesus of Nazareth, in obedience to the call he had received there in the boat, he suggested to Zebedee that he first sail southward to Magdala, where a large fishing pier was operated by a woman called Mary, and there sell the catch from his boat. Zebedee quickly agreed to this as a way of saving the valuable catch, and pausing only to cover the fish with a cloth which they wet by splashing water upon it every now and then to combat the drying effect of the sun, Simon and Andrew left the Nazarene at the pier of Zebedee, and followed by another loaded boat, sailed for Magdala, whose Greek name, Tarichaea, came from its greatest industry, the drying and salting of fish.

Simon had seen Mary of Magdala only a few times, though she owned the largest fleet upon the lake, easily distinguishable by its red sails, as well as the most important piers and drying sheds. But he was familiar with the story that she had once been a famous dancer and singer in Alexandria until felled by a mysterious illness which, it was said, often racked her body with spasms. Some people of Magdala claimed that she was possessed by seven demons, but whether possessed or not, she was acknowledged by all to be as shrewd as any man, operating her large enterprise with considerable efficiency.

The sparseness of the catch during the previous night had extended to boats from other cities, and the pier and drying sheds belonging to Mary Magdalene—as she was often called —were almost devoid of fish. At the news that boats from Zebedee's establishment were beside the pier with a large catch for sale, Mary's steward came to make the arrangements for unloading the two boats. Simon said nothing of the part Jesus had played in the seemingly miraculous catch of fish, but Andrew was bubbling over with the story and told it to the men unloading the boats. When the task was finished, Mary's steward came to take Simon to her for payment of the agreed price.

On another occasion Simon might have been curious about the luxurious home of the woman of Magdala, located upon a winding path leading up the hillside from the shore where her pier and sheds stood. But even preoccupied as he was, he could not fail to see that the small Roman villa where she lived could only have been afforded by a person of wealth. When Mary herself came to meet him in the cool atrium where a fountain fed by a spring from the hillside tinkled musically, she showed none of the haughtiness he would have expected a woman of her wealth and position to show toward an ordinary fisherman of Galilee. She paid the price he asked without haggling, but as he was tying the cords of the leather pouch in which the coins were contained to the belt that carried his fishing knife, she asked the same question Simon had been asking himself for the past several hours.

"My steward tells me a strange story of how these fish were caught, Simon," she said. "I know all the fishermen respect you highly. Can you explain why a school would appear at this time of the day?"

"No, noble lady."

"I am not noble but a Jew as you are, Simon of Bethsaida." She smiled wryly. "And few in Magdala, I am afraid, would name me a lady."

Simon did not answer, since no answer seemed called for.

"Was this draught of fish really another miracle performed by the teacher of Nazareth? Like the healing of Chuza's son? And the turning of water into wine?"

"Jesus was with us in the boat," Simon admitted. "But I cannot say whether the fish were caught because of him."

Mary looked at him thoughtfully; he could see that she was quite as intelligent as she was beautiful. "Is it that you cannot say, Simon? Or do you prefer not to say?"

"Who can tell? The will of God is beyond the knowledge of men."

"But not the will of one who comes from God," Mary said cryptically. "Have you seen the Nazarene perform miracles of healing, as the people claim?"

"Only with my mother-in-law when she was suffering from a fever."

"Could it have been that he came to your house at a time when her fever was about to subside?"

"You have asked me a question I cannot answer," Simon replied. Fevers did sometimes break with seemingly miraculous swiftness, he knew, and fish did school in great numbers for no apparent reason. Children became suddenly well, as had Chuza's son. And magicians claimed to be able to transmute water into what at least appeared to be wine. Yet Simon had not been able to convince himself, even though he had tried, that the apparent miracles performed by Jesus of Nazareth were natural occurrences.

"But you have wondered about it?" Mary asked.

"Yes."

"And found no answer?"

Simon shook his head. From anyone else, he might have resented the probing query, for she had put her finger upon the tender spot of his own uncertainty. But he could see that she was troubled about something, and so took no offense.

"Tell me one thing more, Simon, and I will not keep you longer," she said. "Have you seen the Nazarene cure the falling sickness?"

Though he was no physician, Simon understood the term. Like the Greek expression "Sacred Disease," it was used to describe what was actually epilepsy, widely attributed by the people to possession by demons, or conversely, a divine visitation. The purpose behind Mary's question was obvious, too; it was widely rumored around the lake that the woman of Magdala was possessed by seven demons, and some even claimed to have seen her in one of the convulsive seizures.

"In the synagogue at Capernaum, I saw a man healed of possession by demons," Simon told her. "Before it happened he was throwing himself about in the same manner as those who suffer from the falling sickness."

"Did the Nazarene seek him out?" she asked eagerly.

"No. The man prostrated himself before the congregation and the teacher, begging to be healed. The demons left him when Jesus commanded them to loose hold of him."

From the look of despair mirrored in Mary's eyes, Simon sensed that he had failed to give her the answer she sought. And wanting still to help her, because she had treated him with far more courtesy than he would have expected a woman of her wealth and position to show a common fisherman, he said impulsively, "If you are possessed—as the people say— why don't you ask Jesus to help you?"

Mary stiffened, and when the color drained from her face he was afraid he had angered her by his rough and blunt manner of speaking. But the change lasted only a moment, then she was herself again.

"Perhaps you are right," she said. "After all, the Prophet Micah did say that the Lord asks us only to love mercy, to do justice, and to walk humbly."

She had shown him to the door and he was descending the winding path to the shore and the pier where his boat was moored before Simon thought of the words she had failed to speak. For the final phrase in the often quoted saying of the Prophet Micah was actually: "To walk humbly with thy God."

II

Simon had not been the only one called by Jesus to become his disciple—literally pupil—that morning when the boats of

Zebedee brought to his fishing pier the largest catch ever re-
corded on the lake. John and James, Zebedee's sons, not only
were kinsmen of Jesus's family in Nazareth through their
mother, Salome, but they were also close companions, along
with two other friends—Philip and Nathanael, or Bartholomew—of Simon and Andrew. The six were the first formal
disciples to follow the Nazarene teacher, but others joined
them in the succeeding weeks, upon the invitation of Jesus
himself, until finally the number rose to twelve. These quickly
came to form an inner circle, because they had been singled
out by Jesus himself and each had given up his home and his
occupation to accept the call. Of them all, Simon was required
to make the greatest change in his daily life and even more
within his inner self.

That morning upon the lake, Simon had heard in the invitation of Jesus to follow him an opportunity for a close com-
panionship with the Nazarene that might help to settle his
own uncertainties concerning the gentle teacher. Troubled as
he was in his own mind, he had accepted the invitation without stopping to think much about the changes that such a decision would make in his life. But whatever each man's reason
had been to become a disciple, Jesus made it understood to all
of them very early in their association that, in following him,
they had given up their former occupations as well as their
own desires—in fact surrendered their lives to him.

Zebedee and his sons owned the most important fishing
establishment in Capernaum, and as partners, Simon and Andrew had lived comfortably, if not luxuriously, from their
nightly stint upon the lake. Now all this was changed. Jesus
spent the Sabbath days in Capernaum, for the congregation
there was the largest in Galilee, teaching during the regular
services and wherever any gathered to listen. But during the
week he and those who followed him treaded the paths across

the hills of beautiful Galilee or walked along the shore of the lake, visiting villages and hamlets where the Master taught and healed the sick. Always when he taught, Jesus gathered the disciples closely around him; more often than not it was to them as pupils that he directed his discourse against the day when they, too, would be teachers spreading his doctrines even farther abroad.

The change of status was not without its hardships. In Capernaum, Simon had lived in the pleasant house of Naomi and his food had been prepared by her loving hands. He had worked hard at night when the nets were cast, but there had always been a comfortable bed unrolled for him in a room that was cool and airy even in the hot months of summer. He had been required to answer to no one except himself, and as head of the household his decisions had been accepted without question.

Now, however, he found himself—for five days of the week at least—a member of an itinerant band, dependent for food and lodging upon the people in the towns and villages they visited. Often the elders of the congregations in these villages resented them, having heard from Nazareth of Jesus's claims in the synagogue there and his rejection by his own people.

Nor were the days in Capernaum any less wearying than those in the outlying villages. Hours before Jesus arrived each week at Simon's home, where he stayed except while teaching in the synagogue during the Sabbath services, the sick and the afflicted would already be jamming the house and the street outside. Once a group of men, carrying the pallet of one suffering from a palsy, even ascended to the roof of the house and removed some of the tiles in order to let the sick man down into the room where Jesus was trying to teach. Finally the Master was forced to give up teaching altogether for most of the time that he was in Capernaum, and spend it in healing the multitudes clamoring to reach him.

Discomforting though the change in Simon's own life was, with rarely any privacy and rest even in his own home, he quickly perceived as the days passed that the beauty and the truth inherent in the teachings of Jesus of Nazareth were having a considerable effect upon his own inner self, broadening his understanding of others and increasing his inborn qualities of tolerance and fairness. Although he had not yet discarded completely his reservations about the claims of messiahship attributed to Jesus—none of which he had himself heard made —Simon came to love the Nazarene more than he had ever loved anyone, not excepting Andrew and Naomi. And though the privations of the life the band led were sometimes great and he was in a state of relative poverty, when he had formerly lived far more comfortably, he would have been the first to admit that this was a small price indeed to pay for what Jesus was giving him.

In spite of Simon's own hesitancy, the exciting events of the months during that first mission in Galilee were calculated to encourage the rapidly developing belief among many people that Jesus was indeed the Expected One, promised by God through the prophets. During this time, the Nazarene raised from the dead the daughter of Jairus, an influential elder in the synagogue at Capernaum, though denying that she was anything more than asleep, and he healed the servant of a centurion who was widely liked in Galilee.

In a village nearby, Mary of Magdala approached with a group of other penitents, and before Simon had a chance to make her known to the Master, prostrated herself humbly before him and was healed—some observers firmly claimed, of seven devils. Thereafter she traveled much of the time with them, concerning herself with the personal comfort of Jesus, bathing his tired and bruised feet after a day of walking over the rough hill paths, rubbing them with soothing ointments, and often preparing his food with her own hands.

One thing had begun to trouble Simon rather early in his discipleship; it was the fact that the Jerusalem authorities regularly sent representatives to watch and listen to Jesus, obviously fearing that his rising popularity with the Galileans might threaten their own positions. Simon could understand the particular concern of the Jerusalem Pharisees, who prided themselves upon being the "Guardians of the Law." For where they were concerned mainly with physical acts, such as washing the hands to avoid defilement, the amount of work to be done on the Sabbath, or the distance that could be traveled without breaking the Law, Jesus taught obedience to rules of the spirit—principles by which all men might live together in peace and love.

Though untrained in the minute provisions of the Law himself, Simon could not help admiring the skill with which Jesus answered the questions put to him by the lawyers and the Pharisees who sought to undermine his tremendous popularity with the crowds that followed him everywhere. Often, in fact, he was able to turn back the questions upon the questioners and reveal their actual intent, which was to trap him into a statement that could be used as the basis for a charge of blasphemy before the Great Sanhedrin. And being strong himself, Simon was drawn even closer to Jesus by these further evidences of strength in the man who had so changed the course of his own life with the simple invitation: "Come with me and I will make you to catch men."

As a fisherman, Simon had always kept his nets carefully mended, knowing that one break in the cords could start a rent and lose him a large catch. He had daily inspected the cleats securing the sail of his boat to the mast, for in a storm a loose sail could hamper control and let the vessel be swamped by the mountainous waves that rose quickly when storm winds swept down into the cup between the surrounding hills in which the lake lay.

Andrew often accused Simon of wanting things tied up in neat packages, and so the older brother was particularly pleased one day when Jesus spoke to a large crowd from a hilltop overlooking the Sea of Galilee, stating the crux of his teachings clearly when he said—in what the disciples came to call the Sermon from the Mountain:

"Blessed are the poor in spirit:
For theirs is the kingdom of heaven.
Blessed are they that mourn:
For they shall be comforted.
Blessed are the meek:
For they shall inherit the earth.
Blessed are they which do hunger and thirst after righteousness:
For they shall be filled.
Blessed are the merciful:
For they shall obtain mercy.
Blessed are the pure in heart:
For they shall see God.
Blessed are the peacemakers:
For they shall be called the children of God.
Blessed are they which are persecuted for righteousness' sake:
For theirs is the kingdom of heaven.
Blessed are ye when men shall revile you, and persecute you,
And shall say all manner of evil against you falsely, for my sake.
Rejoice, and be exceeding glad:
For great is your reward in heaven:
For so persecuted they the prophets which were before you."

Then had come the final admonition, spoken more directly to the disciples:

"You are the light of the world. A city that is set on a hill cannot be hidden; neither do men light a candle and put it under a basket, but on a candlestick. Then it gives light to all who are in the house. Let your light therefore so shine before men that they may see your good works and glorify your father who is in heaven."

Pleased though he was by the way Jesus managed to turn the arguments and questions of the lawyers and Pharisees against them, Simon could not overlook a still greater threat to the Nazarene's safety. This lay in the presence among the crowds of an increasingly large number of strangers whom he suspected of being spies sent by Herod Antipas. He took this up with his friend Chuza during one of their Sabbath visits to Capernaum, and was not surprised when Herod's steward in that district confirmed that the tetrarch had indeed hired spies to watch Jesus carefully.

"But why?" Simon asked. "The Master does not preach rebellion against Roman rule."

"Not yet."

"Surely you don't think he will."

"I love him as you do, Simon," Chuza said. "And I owe the life of my son to him. But if Jesus is really the kind of messiah that many in the crowds who follow him believe he is, he must one day lead a rebellion against Rome—and Herod Antipas."

"You think that is why the tetrarch is watching him?"

"I know it," Chuza said. "Don't forget that Herod's brother Archelaus lost Judea and Samaria in the ferment stirred up by Judas of Galilee—a self-proclaimed messiah."

"I remember Judas well, but Jesus is not at all like him."

"Can you say as much for the rest of the Twelve?"

"Surely no one would suspect me of treason," Simon protested, shocked. "Nor Andrew, James or John."

"No," Chuza agreed. "The sons of Zebedee are fiery patriots and they talk much, like others, of the day when the Messiah will come. But they would not lead a rebellion."

"You can say the same of Philip and Bartholomew. And of Thomas and James, the son of Alphaeus, with his brother Judas. I have known them since childhood; they love the Master as much as I do."

"True," Chuza said. "And I would vouch for Matthew, even if he was a taxgatherer—being a taxgatherer myself. That leaves only two."

"Simon the Canaanite, and Judas of Kerioth." Simon's face grew sober. "They are the only ones among the Twelve that all of us did not know well, but I have seen nothing to make me think they are traitors."

"Simon the Canaanite is nicknamed the Zealot," Chuza reminded him. "Perhaps not without reason."

"I have thought of that, too," Simon admitted. "And Judas carries the common purse, so in a rebellion he might control the money. It could be a temptation."

Chuza gave him a shrewd look. "Then you have had doubts about them yourself?"

"If it had been left to me, I would not have chosen them to be among the twelve of us who are closest to the Master," Simon admitted. "But Jesus selected all of us himself, so I have no say."

"Still, if *you* suspect that Judas and the Zealot may be in league with men like Menahem and Barabbas—who are known to seek the overthrow of Roman rule in Israel—you can hardly blame Herod for having all of you watched. After all, even a short-lived revolt here in Galilee could easily cost him his throne."

"What can I do?" Simon asked. "You know Jesus obeys no one but himself—and God."

"Nothing—but wait and watch, particularly those two," Chuza answered. "And if you have an opportunity, try to persuade the Master not to speak out against Herod's rule, especially now."

He hesitated momentarily, then continued. "I had word of it only yesterday, from the palace at Tiberias, and was hoping I would not have to be the one to break the news to those who once followed him. Herod has arrested John the Baptist. He is in a dungeon now at the fortress of Machaerus."

"No king of Israel ever arrested a prophet before for speaking out against him!" Simon exclaimed in horror. "Not even David when Nathan condemned him for taking Bathsheba and foretold that their child would die."

"Neither would Herod have dared to risk God's wrath except for that slut Herodias," Chuza said. "She has badgered him night and day, ever since the Baptist publicly condemned them both for adultery because she was once the wife of Antipas' brother Philip."

Remembering John's weary figure when he had trudged out of the water that day at Bethabara to meet his questioners, Simon felt a deep sadness at the thought that the Essene was now shut up in a dungeon of Herod's palace fortress. Neither man voiced the question uppermost in his mind, namely whether a power that could turn water into wine, bring a great draught of fish together in the daytime when fishermen ordinarily did not even trouble to go out upon the lake, and heal Chuza's son of a fatal illness at a distance of several hours' journey, as well as raise the daughter of Jairus from the dead, could not also free John from the prison of Machaerus. But that John himself had asked such a question was proved a few weeks later when Jesus and the disciples returned to Capernaum for the Sabbath and found two of the Baptist's disciples waiting to question the Master.

"John has sent us to ask, 'Are you he that should come, or should we look for another?'" One of the Essenes said brusquely, but Jesus showed no sign of resentment at his manner—or at the question.

"Go your way and tell John what you have seen and heard," he said quietly. "How the blind see, the lame walk, the lepers are cleansed, the deaf hear, the dead are raised, and the Gospel is preached to the poor."

Every word Jesus spoke had been used by the prophets centuries before in describing the Saviour promised to Israel. It was the nearest Simon had ever heard him come to an announcement of messiahship, and he fully expected Jesus to promise the emissary that he would free John from prison. But the words did not come, and finally the Essenes departed, forced to be content only with what had been given them.

III

Simon had been pleased and proud that Jesus elected to stay in his own small home at Capernaum during his Sabbath visits to the city. But following the departure of the emissaries from John, the warm comradeship which had existed between the two men during those first weeks was gradually cooled by Simon's disappointment at the Master's seeming refusal to consider the plight of the Baptist. Simon made no attempt to bring his words to Jesus's attention, for, as far as he knew, John was still in prison and there was always the probability that Jesus would bring about his realease at a time that suited him. Besides, Simon could see as he accompanied the Master from town to town that Jesus also was sad, in spite of the great success which seemed to attend his every effort here in Galilee. And he was sure the Master, too, was troubled over the Baptist.

Someone did notice the change in Simon's manner, however. It was his boyhood friend John, who was more like a brother to him than Andrew, since, being much younger, the latter was like Simon's son. Impulsive, hotheaded, but intensely loyal, John and his brother James—who was only a little less volatile—were affectionately called the "Sons of Thunder" by Jesus and the other disciples. Neither made any secret of his dislike for the tetrarch of Galilee or Herod's Roman master, and his desire to see Israel assume the destiny promised by the prophets under its own king.

"I notice you hanging back lately when the Master is teaching," John challenged Simon as they were eating the evening meal at the house of Zebedee one evening. "As the first of us to be called, you should be in the forefront."

Simon was tired from a day of walking over the hills and helping to cope with the sometimes overzealous crowds that thronged about Jesus. "I think fishing was never this worrisome," he admitted a little morosely.

"Why are you troubled? All of Galilee is following in our train, and we will move on to other districts to rally the people there when our forces are ready."

Simon looked at him sharply. "Ready for what?"

"To turn out the sons of Herod, of course—and Pontius Pilate."

"Philip is a wise ruler. The people in his district have more freedom than they ever knew under his father, or than the Judeans know under Pilate."

"But he is still one of the spawn of Herod, forced upon us by the Romans."

Simon frowned. "You never spoke like that before, John. Where did you learn such words?"

"Others are not so slow as you to seek freedom, my good friend." Though much slenderer than Simon, John was tough, wiry and constantly taut, like a bowstring. "The time is near when Jesus will lead us against Jerusalem."

"You once thought John the Baptist would do that."

"John was only the Forerunner, sent to announce the Messiah's coming to the people."

"And for that he is rotting in prison," Simon reminded him.

"John has to stay in prison—for a little while. His release will be the signal for people everywhere to rise up, the sign that the Messiah has come from God."

"What if Herod executes him?"

"Herod knows if he touches a hair of John's head, the people will rise up against him," John said confidently.

"How much longer must the Baptist stay in prison, then?"

"Since you are not convinced yet that we should rebel against Rome, it is best that you do not know." John had suddenly become secretive. "When the time comes, we will tell you."

"With men like Menahem, Barabbas and Judas Iscariot to lead you?" Simon demanded scathingly. "Why, Judas even steals from the common purse."

John shrugged. "The money is used to buy arms. I only tell you that because I know you will say no more about it."

"Play your games, then," Simon said. "But be sure this time. I have already seen one messiah crucified."

Having fished by night and slept by day for so long, it was difficult for Simon to sleep in the night hours. Nearly every morning found him awake before the rest of the household had stirred; usually he would take a crust of bread and a handful of figs or dates to assuage his hunger while he walked beside the lovely lake, pausing occasionally to quench his thirst at one of the many springs that burst from the rocks.

The thing he liked most about those early morning walks was watching the sails of the fishing fleet materializing out of the fog on their return from the night-long vigil in the northern section of the lake before Bethsaida. He knew most of the fishermen, and as he walked along the shore he could recognize their voices floating with the odd bell-like clarity that sound takes when heard across the water, even though the speakers are invisible from the shore.

Boats from Magdala, Capernaum and the other towns of the western side of the lake, fished nightly with those of Bethsaida and a few from the Greek cities of the Decapolis on the eastern side. In the evening it was always a race to be first where the fish were schooling, and the men in the boats spoke little, lest one betray to another the location of a promising spot. But in the early morning as they returned home, those from different cities exchanged gossip and news freely. And since Magdala was much closer to Herod's new capital of Tiberias than was Capernaum, fishermen of that city often learned of the doings at Herod's court first.

Simon had exchanged gossip with his fellows on many mornings such as this, and as he walked along the shore not long after his talk with John he listened absent-mindedly to the voices from the mist. For the most part what they were saying was only gossip, but suddenly a phrase struck his ears, chilling him to the bone.

"Who would have thought Herod would behead the Baptist?" Simon recognized the voice of a friend from Magdala, fishing with the fleet of Mary Magdalene.

"I had not heard." The second man was from Capernaum.

"It happened three days ago at Machaerus. A servant in the palace at Tiberias told me of it just before I sailed last night."

"But why?" The fisherman from Capernaum asked. "John was only a prophet—and harmless."

The man from Magdala laughed. "Tell that to Herodias. They say she used her daughter Salome's dancing to trick Herod, when he was drunk, into giving her the head of the Baptist upon a platter."

Simon's first reaction was one of deep sorrow for the slender, weary man he had seen limping from the water at Bethabara. But it was quickly replaced by a surge of disappointment in Jesus for letting such a thing happen to John, especially after his call for help through the disciples only a few weeks before. That Jesus could have saved John had he chose, Simon did not doubt for a moment—he'd seen too much evidence of the divine power possessed by the Nazarene for that. It could only be, then, that Jesus had chosen not to help the Baptist, which made Simon's disappointment and his heartbreak even greater. For now there seemed to be a breach of trust involved—both with John, who had stepped back to allow Jesus the center of the stage, and with Simon, who had given up everything else to follow him.

Instinctively seeking to ease his sorely troubled mind through familiar action, Simon started walking along the shore, sometimes stumbling blindly as his steps took him farther and farther away from Capernaum—and Jesus. Just as the sun rose over the eastern side of the deep cup in which the lake lay, he saw the piers and houses of Magdala before him. He and Mary of Magdala had become good friends in the weeks since she had been healed by Jesus, and he realized now that he had instinctively turned to her for help in this, his moment of greatest agony since the day he had returned to Bethsaida after the carnage at Sepphoris.

Mary met Simon on the path leading from her home to the shore and guided him to the small inner court, where the fountain played. Dipping a cloth in the cool, faintly sulphurous water pouring from a nearby spring, she wiped the streaks of tears from his face and gave him a towel upon which to dry it. Then she poured a silver cup of wine and waited until he had drunk it.

"What is it, Simon?" she asked then. "Has anything happened to the Master?"

"I know not!" he burst out. "Nor do I care!"

"I saw you from the house, walking along the shore." Mary knew Simon well enough to realize he would not have been weeping if he were not deeply disturbed. "Did you come from Capernaum this morning?"

"I often walk in the morning before the others leave their beds, and listen to the talk of the men in the boats," he told her. "That was how I heard that Herod has beheaded John the Baptist."

"I thought that might be troubling you," Mary said. "Chuza sent word of it to me last night. He says Herodias tricked Herod into ordering John beheaded by having Salome dance for him. But I didn't know you were so close to John."

"I saw him only a few times," Simon admitted. "Like the others, I was baptized by him—but it meant almost nothing."

"Then why are you so concerned?"

"Jesus could have saved John in the same way he heals lepers and raises the dead. But he let him die instead."

"I was shocked when I heard it," Mary admitted. "I know

Jesus loved John, for I once heard him say that of all those who had come before him, none was greater."

"How could he let him die, then?"

"Suppose Jesus had defied Herod Antipas and released John from prison with a miracle. What do you think would have happened?"

"All Galilee would have risen in revolt against Herod's taxes and acclaimed him the Messiah," Simon said without hesitation.

"But what of Judea and the other districts? Remember, they know little of Jesus. He has spoken only a few times from the Porch of Solomon in the temple at Jerusalem when he went there for the Passover."

"The Judeans might not rise against Rome," Simon admitted, "but the power of the Messiah could free them anyway."

"Are you sure Jesus wants that, Simon?"

Like most of the other disciples, Simon had assumed that Jesus would one day lead Jews everywhere in a great revolution to restore Israel to the glory promised by the prophets. But deep inside himself Simon had not been sure, and that uncertainty had made him hold back from giving himself unreservedly to the Nazarene.

"What else could he want?" he asked.

"I am not sure—yet," Mary admitted. "And neither are you."

The simple statement brought him up short, for it crystallized in a few words his own dilemma. "How did you know?" he asked.

"You are not like the others of the Twelve," Mary said. "I realized that as soon as I was healed by the Master and began to follow him, too. John and James wish to see Jesus king so they may be the chief among his ministers. Simon the Canaanite would lead the army, and Judas of Kerioth seeks to control the purse strings, while others of the Twelve wish for other things. Why do you follow him, Simon?"

"Because he called me."

"And for no other reason?"

"I would like to see Israel restored to glory, as it was in the time of David."

"But you seek none of it for yourself?"

Simon was getting a little irritated by her probing. Besides, too often she was finding the very questions he had not been able to answer himself. "You should know the answer to that," he said brusquely, and saw Mary's face break into a warm smile.

"I do know it," she said. "Most of the others, along with thousands of those who follow the Master, are waiting for his word to take up arms. I have even heard that the release of the Baptist from Machaerus was supposed to be the signal. But Jesus stated a different purpose not long ago, Simon, when some of the Pharisees accused him of casting out demons by the power of Satan. Do you remember when he said 'But if I, with the finger of God, cast out devils, no doubt the Kingdom of God is come upon you'?"

"Yes. But I didn't understand."

"It could mean that the Kingdom is now. That Jesus is the Son of God, sent to earth by the Father."

"How do you know this, when no one else does?"

"I think you know it—in your heart," Mary said. "But you have listened to the others so much, instead of listening to the Master, that you see him only as they do—as another Judas Maccabeus."

"Or Judas the Galilean." Simon had spoken automatically, and when he felt the old chill of terror stirring deep within him he flayed himself into anger at Mary, lest it seize hold of him, as it sometimes still did.

"These are woman's words!" he snapped. "Foolish words."

"I am only echoing the Prophet Isaiah." Mary went to the cabinet at one side of the room and took out a scroll which she unrolled. As she scanned it, Simon saw that the writing was in Greek. "Here it is," she said, "where the prophet says:

"And in that day shall the deaf hear the words of the book.
And the eyes of the blind shall see,
Out of the obscurity and out of the darkness.
The meek also shall increase their joy in the Lord.
And the poor among men shall rejoice in the Holy One of Israel."

Mary raised her eyes from the scroll. "You remember the sermon Jesus gave from the mountain, don't you?"

"Yes."

"Isn't it a fulfillment of this prophecy?"

"Read farther," Simon said. "There is more."

Mary raised the scroll and began to read again:

"For the terrible one is brought to naught,
And the scorner is consumed.
And all that watch for iniquity are cut off."

"There!" he cried triumphantly. "The Prophet plainly says the enemies of Israel will be consumed when the Messiah comes!"

Mary looked at him for a long moment, the scroll still in her hand. "If you really believe that, why are you so angry at Jesus now?"

"Because the Baptist trusted him—and the Master let him die."

"Even John's faith wavered a little," Mary reminded him. "After all, he did send his disciples to ask whether Jesus was the Expected One."

"And the Master answered him in words that all of us took to mean he wanted John to know he is the Messiah. You just read the prophecy from Isaiah yourself."

"That was in the first part of the prophecy, Simon. Not in the last part you had me read."

Simon threw up his hands. "How can an ordinary man be expected to know the truth when even the prophet describes the Messiah differently in the same passage?"

"He must feel it in his heart, Simon—as you will one day." Mary put the scroll upon the cabinet. "You are my friend, so I will tell you something few people know about me, though now that I have confessed it, I am not ashamed. I was once many of the things the people say of me. As a young girl I was the leading dancer and actress in the theaters at Alexandria, but because I sinned in departing from the ways and the faith of my people, the Lord struck me down with the falling sickness." She smiled wryly. "Or I may really have been possessed of seven devils."

"But surely—"

"I was fully as vain and arrogant as people believed me to be, Simon. When I became ill, I crept home like a whipped cur, afraid to be seen in public because I never knew when I would fall to the ground in a spasm and be looked upon with loathing by all who saw me. My heart was filled with a bitterness against the Lord and against people who talked about me —until the day you came here to sell me the fish and told me Jesus only healed those who came to him, begging his help humbly."

Simon's own thoughts went back to that day when he had cast himself at Jesus's feet with the cry: "Depart from me, for I am a sinful man, O Lord." And he seemed to feel again upon his shoulder the soft touch of the Master that had suddenly removed all his fears.

"I had intended to send my steward to Jesus." Mary's voice brought him back to the present again. "It took me a long time to forget myself and come humbly to him with others who were lame and halt and blind. But when I did, my demons were cast out—demons of pride and anger and hate that had been feeding upon my soul and turning me into a shrew. Ever since Jesus touched me, I have known a peace I never knew before."

Simon studied the mirrorlike surface of the pool for a long moment. The face he saw reflected there still showed vestiges of the disappointment, heartbreak and resentment that had brought him here, but much of it was already gone. Finally he looked up to meet again the warm, friendly eyes of the woman he had often heard cursed by the very fishermen who earned their livelihood through her, naming her a harlot and a consorter with heathen.

"Why did you tell me all this, Mary?" he asked.

"Because you, too, were possessed by a demon when you came here this morning. I hope you will soon cast it out, for the time may be short."

"What do you mean?"

Mary picked up the scroll from the top of the cabinet and unrolled it again. "When I heard the news from Machaerus, I was troubled very much, as you were this morning. When I am troubled, I usually go to the Scriptures for help, and last night I read a passage from the prophecies of Isaiah that I had never seen before." She stopped unrolling the scroll. "Listen to this:

> *"He is despised and rejected of men,*
> *A man of sorrows and acquainted with grief.*
> *And we hid, as it were, our faces from him,*
> *He was despised, and we esteemed him not."*

"What does it mean?" Simon asked.

"I am not sure," Mary admitted. "It seems to say that Jesus may soon have need of all who really love him for himself alone. And I am afraid our numbers are few."

Simon got to his feet. "I must go back," he said. "The Master will be sorrowing for John the Baptist; perhaps I can comfort him."

"They do not call you Cephas without reason," Mary said as she bade him farewell. "Having cast out your own demons, I suspect you will be an even stronger anchoring stone for others now than ever—"

Mary's words were drowned out by a shout from the lake, and turning quickly to look in the direction from which it came, Simon saw a boat approaching the pier that extended out into the water. He recognized it as his own, with Andrew at the tiller.

"Simon!" he heard his brother shout across the water. "The Master is gone! Herod must have seized him!"

V

By the time the boat grounded against the pier, Simon was waiting, with Mary beside him, to catch the rope Andrew threw him. The younger brother left the sail flapping loose in the morning breeze, something he would never have done had he not been distraught.

"When did you miss Jesus?" was Simon's first question.

"A little over an hour ago. Naomi was the first to rise after you, and found his sleeping pallet empty."

"He sometimes goes to a spot behind the house to pray."

"We looked there first. John and James are rousing the

other disciples, but I remembered that you often walked along the shore, so I sailed in search of you."

"Did Jesus know about the Baptist?"

"We had word of it last night, after you went to bed. You were asleep, so I waited until morning to tell you."

"Was the Master disturbed by the news?" Mary asked.

"Very much," Andrew told her. "I saw him weeping after he went to his couch."

Simon's anger at Jesus was behind him now. If Herod had indeed sent men during the night to take him by stealth, there was little any of them could do except to arouse the people to the point where, fearing a revolt, Herod might be persuaded not to execute him. But if Jesus had not yet been taken, a boat could easily spirit him across the lake to the cities of the Decapolis which were not ruled by Herod. The important thing now was to find the Master as quickly as possible.

Simon remembered that once or twice Mary had been a guest at Herod's court. "Can you find out for us whether Herod has taken the Master prisoner?" he asked her.

Mary's face brightened at the possibility that she might be able to help. "I will send Hadja, my steward, to Tiberias at once. He often sells fish to the steward of Herod's household; they are good friends."

"If you learn anything, send word of it to us in Capernaum," Simon told her, and turned back to Andrew. "Are you sure no one saw Jesus this morning?"

"A woman was drawing water early at the well. She thinks she saw a man climbing toward the Horns of Hattin, but she could not be sure it was the Master."

"Once before when he was troubled, he went to the Horns." This was Cephas, the stone, a man certain of his every action and a leader who took command as naturally as he had always done when they were fishing and some emergency had presented itself. "Take the boat and go back to Capernaum. Tell John and the others to search upward into the hills from that direction, and I will ascend from here."

"Pray God you find him safe," Mary said. "If he has been hurt, bring him here. I will have everything ready and we can get the physician Joseph from Tiberias if he is needed."

From the shore of the lake, the climb upward was quite steep at first, with the limestone strata forming the lake bottom giving away shortly to black basalt boulders, for this whole area was of volcanic origin, as was much of the deep rift in which the Jordan flowed. Higher up, the slope became somewhat less precipitous, leading to rolling pasturelands where flowers were already in bloom—yellow daisies, blue iris, hyacinths and patches of clover with bright yellow blossoms. The verdant meadows made this area a favorite grazing spot for flocks belonging to wealthy landowners living in the cities below upon the shore of the lake. Here and there huge boulders were tumbled about in masses, as if when He had formed the land God had been angry at first, but had soon yielded to the soothing beauty of the amethyst-blue lake lying like a lovely jewel in its rocky setting.

A road wound up along the face of the hillside almost to the summit, then turned southwest toward Nazareth and the Plain of Esdraelon. Simon did not stop to follow the longer course, however; instead he chose a rough path that led directly upward from the shore below. Occasionally, when he came out upon a lofty crag, he could see Andrew in the boat. It looked like one of the toy craft the children sailed in the shallows near the shore at Capernaum, but he could tell that it was moving steadily northward. Simon wasted little time in watching Andrew, however, concentrating his attention upon where he placed his feet, for a misstep here could result in a painful injury. And every fifty paces or so he paused to sweep the area ahead with his eyes, in search of Jesus.

It was almost an hour after he left Magdala before he saw a solitary figure well ahead of him, standing outlined against the sky upon one of the strange crags that gave the name of Horns of Hattin to this particular region. He was still not close enough to see the other man distinctly, but he was certain that it was Jesus, and a surge of thanksgiving went through him.

Since ancient times, men had avoided the place where Jesus was standing, instinctively feeling that an area showing so starkly the evidence of God's wrath in the jumbled masses of lava, long since cooled into obsidian, must be cursed. Just below the Horns, however, there was a meadow which was almost level; when Simon reached it, he paused to get his breath. Capernaum was plainly visible now, and a large crowd of people could be seen moving up the paths leading toward the elevation where he stood.

Across the lake upon the eastern side, several cities of the Decapolis were easily discernible, with the white columns of Hippos—the most beautiful of the ten—shining in the morning sunlight. Near the water were a number of white marble palaces belonging to rich Roman officials who lived there in winter, some of them with stairways of stone descending to the lake where barges and pleasure boats were moored.

When he turned away from the lake and approached the somewhat higher elevation where Jesus was standing, Simon could see that the Master was a picture of dejection. His shoulders were slumped, as if from bearing a great burden, and his eyes were fixed upon the massive boulders at his feet, not eagerly ahead as they usually were. The realization that the death of John the Baptist had brought an almost intolerable burden of sadness to Jesus drove whatever remained of Simon's own resentment from his mind. And groping for some way to help Jesus in this hour of sorrow—as the Master had helped him that day when he had crouched in the bottom of the boat, stricken with fear in the face of a power he could not understand—Simon did something he had never before dared to do. Reaching out, he touched Jesus's shoulder in an awkward gesture of sympathy that nevertheless came from the depths of his heart.

Never before had Simon felt that Jesus needed help; always he had stood in awe of the power the Master possessed. But having poured out his own sorrow over the death of John to Mary of Magdala, he had felt an instinct to help Jesus, too, find surcease from the suffering that showed in his face and in his eyes. No words passed between them, for none were needed; in that simple, instinctive gesture, Simon told Jesus he understood why the power that could heal across miles of separation had not been used to free a man from prison.

Only for an instant did Simon dare to touch the Master. But when he drew his hand away, Jesus reached out and took it, guiding and supporting himself with Simon's sturdy strength as they descended to the plateau below, where the people were already gathering to hear him speak and to be healed.

Book Four

SIMON CALLED PETER

". . . *thou art Peter, and upon this rock I will build my church* . . ."

MATTHEW 16:18

I

EVEN if he had not felt closer to Jesus now than ever before, Simon could not have failed to notice the change in the Master after the death of John the Baptist. Where previously Jesus and his disciples had traveled leisurely from village to village, spending much of the time in healing the sick, the Master now devoted more of his time to teaching, most of it directed to the disciples. Even here he seemed to be filled with a new urgency, a sense almost as if time was running out, though why, Simon could not see, for the size of the crowds that followed him—particularly the number of those clamoring to be healed—was larger than ever before.

Simon had sensed from the first that Jesus was preparing the Twelve in particular for a larger mission than simply that of pupil. Now the Master announced that they would be sent out in pairs to teach others the things he had taught them and to make new converts to the doctrine he stressed again and again, that the Kingdom of God was at hand, when all should turn away from sin and become once again so filled with the glory and urgency of their ancient faith that nothing else mattered in their lives. In the work and the excitement of preparing for this new mission, Simon quite forgot something of which Mary had spoken when he had talked to her in Magdala on the morning he had learned of John's death—namely that Jesus's preaching of the Kingdom of Heaven might have still another significance, one which none of the Twelve had as yet fully grasped.

In a final charge to the new missionaries, Jesus gave them his promise that none would be forgotten, even though away from him.

"Are not two sparrows sold for a penny?" he said. "Yet not one of them shall fall to the ground without your Father in Heaven knows of it. Fear not! The very hairs of your head are numbered, and you are of more value than many sparrows. Whoever shall confess me before men, him will I confess before my Father who is in Heaven. But whoever shall deny me before men, him shall I deny before my Father who is in Heaven. He that does not take up his cross and follow me is not worthy of me."

Simon could not help shuddering at the final admonition, for when the Romans sent a man to be crucified it was their custom to make him carry upon his back the heavy horizontal beam or *patibulum* to which his hands were nailed or tied before he was hung from the upright. The beam, as everyone knew, was familiarly referred to as "the cross."

Simon had naturally assumed that he and Andrew would be together, since they had always fished as a pair, but the younger brother had other ideas.

"James and I want to travel together when we go out to teach and heal," he blurted out as they were making ready for the several journeys.

"But why, Andrew? We have always fished together."

"On the lake it was different. You are stronger, so you always handled the net. But I want to serve the Master in my own way—and so does James."

Simon could hardly blame Andrew for wanting to stand upon his own feet. He remembered well how disappointed and angry he had been at thirteen when Jonas had sent him out of Jerusalem with Barnabas and Aristobulus at the beginning of the War of Varus.

"Of course you may go with James," he said, and added jokingly, "am I to go alone then?"

"Everybody looks up to you second only to the Master," Andrew protested. "There will be many wanting to go with you."

Simon immediately thought of John and went in search of his friend. He found him in earnest conversation with Judas Iscariot and Simon the Zealot—who had chosen to travel together—but the three broke off talking at his approach.

Since the death of John the Baptist there had been much less talk of political affairs among the Twelve. Jesus's failure to release John and thus cast the gage, so to speak, before Herod Antipas, had disconcerted those who were working actively with forces in the nation intent upon fomenting rebellion. But now it seemed from the guilty looks on the faces of the three men as Simon approached, that such activities might have been resumed.

"What plottings are those two about?" Simon asked when the others had moved away and he was alone with John.

"You will know in time, as I told you months ago," John assured him. "But I can tell you no more now."

"Because Judas and Simon do not trust me?"

John flushed. "They do not understand you as I do, Simon," he said. "After all, we have been friends all our lives."

Simon was glad now that he had come in search of John, for it seemed that Andrew's decision to travel with James might also help him separate his boyhood friend from the influence of the two men he distrusted most among the Twelve.

"Did James tell you that he and Andrew want to travel together?" he asked.

"Yes. I gave him my blessing."

"What about yourself? Have you chosen a partner yet?"

John shook his head. "At first I was angry at James. But then I decided he had a right to follow his own desires."

"Why not travel with me, then?"

"I would like that!" John cried. "It will be like old times when you visited Capernaum as a boy." He hesitated. "But you know my temper."

"And you know how slowly I think," Simon said, smiling.

"At least we will not fight," John said. "You could flatten me like a squash underfoot, with one of those great hands of yours."

"And you can outrun me," Simon added, with a grin. "I think we will do well together."

II

For their journey, Simon and John chose the northern part of Galilee in the neighborhood of Gischala. Only a few hours' walk westward, the upper Jordan flowed swiftly in its narrow, deep-cut bed from the marshy area called Lake Semechonitis at the northeastern corner of Galilee, where it bordered both with Syria and Herod Philip's province of Ulatha. It was a land of mountains, caves, passes and rugged people, but Simon felt at home there immediately, for these people, too, were accustomed to earning their daily bread with their hands. As the two traveled from village to village they announced that they had been sent by Jesus of Nazareth to preach and heal in his name. And so great was the fame now attached to the Nazarene that they were able to attract large audiences everywhere.

Simon was not trained in oratory, or even in the interpretation of the Scriptures, so he felt some doubt at first about his ability to teach. But to his surprise, the words he needed came easily to his lips and the delightful stories Jesus had told the disciples held the inhabitants of the smaller villages spellbound, just as they had the more sophisticated crowds of Capernaum, Magdala and the other cities around the lake. What Simon did not realize was that much of his success as a teacher came from his own deep simplicity and honesty, qualities which anyone could recognize in him and trust instinctively.

The healing of the sick, Simon had left to John, whose natural flair for dramatic action was well suited for that work. But such was not to be the case very long, for as he was speaking to a large body of people one day he was startled by a sudden commotion among the crowd.

The people had been listening intently while he retold one of Jesus's favorite stories concerning a shepherd who went in search of a sheep that was lost. They had accepted the story without question, as well as his explanation that the shepherd was more concerned with the erring member of his flock than with the others, because they were safe while the lost sheep was in danger not only from the wolves and jackals that infested the rough hill country, but also from the elements. Because this was rolling hill country populated to a large degree by shepherds who had faced these decisions many times, the story never failed to find an appreciative audience. But Simon now found them suddenly pushing away to make a path through their midst, as if one of the wolves he had mentioned in the parable were attacking.

As the crowd parted, Simon saw the cause of the commotion. It was a pitiful-looking creature of rags, bones, and skin spotted by the terrible eruption of leprosy. As he stumbled toward where Simon stood, the sick man shouted the "Unclean! Unclean!" which he was required to do by the Law. And the crowd amply took care of another provision, that he must not come closer than six cubits to those contaminated by the disease, when they scattered to make room for him.

"Heal me! Heal me in the name of the Most High God," the leper cried, and cast himself upon the ground before Simon, though still maintaining the required six cubits of distance.

From where he stood, Simon could plainly see the scaly discolorations of the sick man's skin. The odor that came from the festering rags covering the leper's tortured body sent a wave of nausea through him, and he recoiled instinctively from it and from the danger of contamination represented by the open, weeping sores. The crowd had pushed back well beyond the six-cubits mark, leaving Simon and the leper together in an open space. Not knowing what to do, for this was the first time he had faced such a situation, Simon looked hopefully around for John, but his companion was nowhere to be seen.

"They say the Nazarene you claim to serve heals lepers," the sick man cried. "If you truly come from him, heal me with his power."

Simon hesitated no longer. Stepping forward, he knelt beside the leper, and with a tremendous effort of will, touched the man upon the shoulder. "In the name of Jesus of Nazareth, be thou healed," he said, using the familiar ritual he had heard John use when engaged in curing the sick.

The appearance of the scaly, weeping sores upon the sick man's skin underwent no visible change, however, and the filthy rags continued to reek with the familiar odor that was a mark of the disease. In fact, as far as Simon and the crowd could see, nothing happened, and some among the onlookers began to laugh at his obvious disappointment. The laughter quickly spread, encouraged by the uncertainty plainly evident in Simon's face, and as the crowd began to drift away he was assailed by a deep sense of shame, disappointment and failure in this, his first attempt to heal.

But a change *was* taking place in the leper, and no one who remained to watch could fail to see it. Until Simon touched the man's shoulder and spoke the name of Jesus, he had been groveling in the dirt in the manner common to those suffering from this loathsome disease. Now he rose to his feet, his body straight and his face no longer contorted with shame and suffering. Turning, he left the open circle surrounding him and Simon, walking as surely and as firmly as if he had never been sick.

Simon stood for a long moment watching the leper until he disappeared around the corner of a building. He had no idea what had happened, but he could see that the disease had not been healed, and so felt no lessening of the sense of depression and failure that had seized him. That night he talked to John about it, but his friend could give him little help, for John had never healed a leper or even dared to touch a man with the disease. Simon himself was careful to carry out the ritual scrubbing of his hands and his body required of anyone who had touched a leper, but even in the night he woke once or twice and looked at his hands fearfully, half expecting to see them turning white with the familiar bleaching of the skin.

The two travelers had planned to leave the next morning, but Simon was not content to quit the city without making some attempt to learn whether anything else had happened to the man he had touched yesterday. He had no trouble in finding the place where the lepers lived; a small colony of them was located outside almost every Hebrew village. But he did have trouble recognizing the man, for his body was now scrubbed clean and covered with a fresh linen garment, hiding many of the sores which had been apparent the day before.

"I was coming to see you today, Master," he said gratefully to Simon, "to show you that my trouble is fast leaving me."

"Surely you don't claim to be cured!" John was careful not to get close to the leper. "I can still see the marks of leprosy upon your body."

The man held out his hands, and Simon saw that the scaling which had marred them yesterday was considerably lessened. In fact the skin was almost clear in several places and the swelling of his face had subsided considerably.

"When you spoke to me in the name of Jesus of Nazareth," he said, "I felt a sense of peace flood my soul with the assurance that I would be healed. You can see what has happened since then."

"Can you explain it?" Simon asked.

"Yesterday I was healed of a sickness in my soul. The rest followed as surely as night follows day."

"You said nothing about casting out demons from him," John reproved Simon as they took the road to the next village. "Yet he spoke of a sickness of the soul. How did you heal that and his leprosy, too?"

"I don't know," Simon admitted. "Unless the two are bound up in each other."

John stared at him blankly, having no understanding of a truth of which only the faintest glimmering had as yet been revealed to Simon himself. But Simon was not surprised, when they passed through the same village about a week later, to find the former leper completely cured.

III

As Simon and John traveled through northern Galilee, healing and teaching as they went, they heard more and more often the rumor that Herod Antipas was planning some action against Jesus. Whether these reports were based on fact or whether they had been stimulated by the execution of John the Baptist, Simon had no way of knowing. But finally he decided to return to Capernaum and try to discover the truth through Chuza and Mary of Magdala, so that he could take measures to protect the Master in case Herod did seek to arrest him.

Simon had enjoyed the journey through the wildly beautiful mountain region of Galilee, where many of the inhabitants lived in caves. To one proud of his inheritance as a Jew, the area was rife with the glorious history of his people. A thousand years earlier, Joshua had led a lightning-swift invasion into this region when King Jabin of Hazor had come against him, destroying the enemy by the Waters of Merom. And centuries later, King Ahab, one of the leaders of a confederation of twelve kings, had marched north to meet an Assyrian invader in combat in the valley between the Lebanon and Antilebanon ranges. There, the enemy's southward march had been brought to a halt at Karkar, in a climactic battle that had saved Israel from capture for several centuries.

From a high point north of the lake, Simon and John paused to look down upon the beautiful land they loved. Though it was cool on the heights they could be sure that far below, the lovely and fertile Plain of Gennesaret, a little north of Capernaum, was producing its usual crops of vegetables and fruit, many of them tropical in character. Even from the heights, they could see the lilies covering the hillside like a bright carpet, and when they had crossed the Jordan north of the lake the day before, the oleanders lining its banks had been in bloom.

Magdala was also plainly visible in the bright sunlight, as well as the buildings of Tiberias, the new capital a little to the south. Here and there along the shore, where the famous healing springs burst from the rocks, elaborate baths had been erected, many of them with colonnaded shelters where, for a price, those suffering from rheumatic diseases could lie for hours in the warm, sulphurous water.

Seen from the heights, everything was so peaceful that Simon was almost loath to descend to the cities and the controversy that went on there whenever Jesus taught. Scribes and Pharisees from Jerusalem often contended with the Master over the Law and his teachings, seeking to trap him into an admission that would be the grounds for arrest. People by the thousands flocked about him, not so much to hear him teach as to be healed, thinking only of what the strange power he possessed could do for their bodies.

The Zealots and those who sympathized with the cause of rebellion were always in the group, too, waiting for the time when what was still only a somewhat turbulent mission of healing and teaching would erupt into actual rebellion. And of course the spies of Herod Antipas were skulking about, listening for some word of treason which the tetrarch of Galilee could use, not only as an excuse for the arrest of Jesus, but also to salve his conscience over the execution of John— since the Baptist and the Nazarene had been allied, not only by kinship and similarity of doctrine, but also by John's having baptized Jesus at Bethabara.

The other disciples had also returned to Capernaum. And since all were eager to report the success of their missions,

Jesus and the Twelve took boats at the fishing pier of Zebedee and started across the lake toward Bethsaida, hoping to escape from the crowd that followed him everywhere.

As he listened to the jubilant disciples telling of their exploits in healing the sick and casting out demons and the way they had been acclaimed in the villages, Simon realized that the others, too, had yielded to the temptation to gain the acclaim of the people through acts of healing rather than by preaching repentance and the Kingdom of God, as Jesus had instructed them. And looking back on his own experience, he was forced to admit that, following the cure of the leper, he, too, had been as guilty as any. Jesus did not reprove them, but Simon could not help feeling that even though his mission had been outstandingly successful, he had failed in the major charge the Master had given him.

The place chosen for the retreat was a fairly deserted area east of Bethsaida, where the hills rose rather sharply from the lake, separated from the water only by a narrow belt of beach largely covered with grass. From an elevation overlooking the shore, to which they withdrew as soon as the boats grounded there, they could see another fleet of boats, their sails dotting the surface of the lake, moving toward them. And by the time the people in the boats debarked, a multitude from Bethsaida had also approached along the shore. Jesus had only a brief time alone with the disciples before the people began to climb the hill to the place where they were sitting. Finally he gave up any hope of escaping the crowd and descended to the shore to teach and heal as usual.

Philip was the first to call attention to the fact that the sun was sinking and there was not even enough food for the Master and the Twelve. Judas, who carried the common purse, could not help, for all he possessed was two hundred pennies. Besides, there was no longer time enough before dark to go to the market in Bethsaida and purchase even that small amount of bread.

"A boy here has five barley loaves and two small fish," Andrew reported as the disciples were discussing a way out of the dilemma. "But what are they among so many?"

When it seemed that they must all go hungry during the night unless they went to Bethsaida or set sail for Capernaum at once, Simon went to warn the Master that the crowd should be dismissed. Instead, however, Jesus told him to buy the five barley loaves and the two fish from the boy and instruct the people to divide themselves into groups of fifties and hundreds upon the grassy shore. And since Simon had long ago learned to obey Jesus's orders without question, he went at once to carry them out.

When away from home, the peasants and townspeople among the poorer classes in Galilee carried small baskets in which they put anything they picked up along the way— such as fruit fallen from a tree, berries gathered by the wayside and the like. Many in the crowd carried such baskets, and Jesus directed now that they be brought before a flat stone upon which he laid out the fish and the barley loaves purchased from the boy.

The crowd watched in silence as he blessed the food, but when he began to break the loaves and separate the fish into fragments, putting them both into the baskets, some began to laugh. Their merriment quickly turned to wonder, however, for wherever Jesus broke a piece, two additional ones seemed to appear in its place. Basket after basket was filled until not only was the crowd of about five thousand people amply fed, but enough remained to furnish them with food for the morning.

The miracle of feeding five thousand people with only five loaves and two fish was the topic of excited conversation around the campfires that night, but Jesus did not allow his disciples to take part in it. With the coming of nightfall, he instructed them to take to the boats and cross the lake to Capernaum while he went back into the hills to meditate. Though Simon was the best fisherman and boatman of them all, he was so preoccupied with the startling miracle he had witnessed that he did not pay close attention, as they sailed toward Capernaum, to a storm that suddenly swept down upon the lake in the darkness.

Most of the men in the boat were skilled at handling the sturdy craft used by the lake fishermen, and when a sudden gust of wind struck the sail, careening the heavily laden boat, they instinctively scrambled to the upper side to keep it from going over. Water poured in, however, half filling the boat before Simon could let the sail go free, and the trim craft quickly became little more than a waterlogged hulk, placing them all in grave danger of drowning in the storm-lashed sea.

Simon was working desperately to keep the bow into the wind so the boat could ride safely over the giant waves that battered it, while the others were busy bailing out the water. When John shouted something from the bow, Simon paid no attention at first. But when others called Jesus's name, he looked up and saw, still some distance away, what appeared to be the Master himself walking upon the water.

Simon's first thought was that Jesus must have died and that his spirit was coming to them. But then he heard a familiar beloved voice call out "It is I. Do not be afraid."

"Lord, if it is you," he cried, speaking his first thought, "bid me come to you upon the water."

"Come!" Jesus said, and welcoming the chance to prove his own faith after having failed during the mission in Galilee, Simon stepped over the side of the boat upon the water.

It was a strange and exhilarating feeling to take first one

and then another step upon the surface of the raging sea without sinking beneath it. Simon's eyes were fixed upon Jesus, who had stopped a few paces from the boat and was waiting for him with a warm smile upon his face. But suddenly a backwash of the old fears, dredged up from the depths of his childhood memories, assailed Simon, and yielding to them momentarily, he glanced down at his feet to reassure himself that they were indeed treading upon the water. In that instant the thread of strength he had found in Jesus's eyes was broken and the faith which had supported him upon the water suddenly left him.

"Lord! Save me!" he cried in terror as he felt himself sinking, reaching out toward Jesus when the water was about to close over his head. Then a hand seized his and he felt himself being lifted into the boat as easily as if he were only a child—though his weight was half again that of the Master. He lay upon the bottom, panting and retching from the water he had swallowed and from his own shame in failing yet another time. When he finally recovered enough to look about him, he saw that the raging of the storm had been stilled. Jesus was sitting in the boat, while the men at the oars rowed it toward the western shore and Andrew worked to lash the water-soaked sail to the mast.

"Oh you of little faith." Simon's heart contracted with pain at the disappointment in the Master's voice. "Why did you doubt?"

IV

Simon had little time to brood over his shame at failing in the first real test to which his faith in Jesus of Nazareth had been subjected. Even in Galilee, with its abundant fisheries and the remarkably fertile Plain of Gennesaret, the poor rarely had enough to eat, and the news of the Nazarene's miraculous feeding of five thousand struck the area with all the impact of a sudden clap of thunder. When those who had actually eaten the food arrived the next day and testified to its substance and excellence, a great multitude of people besieged Jesus, demanding that he repeat the miracle for them.

"I am the living bread which came down from Heaven," he told those who expected him to furnish food for which they had neither labored nor shown faith in him. "He who comes to me shall never hunger, and he that believes in me shall never thirst."

It was not the answer the crowd desired. In fact the great truth he was telling them was even beyond the comprehension of the disciples, so it was not surprising that the people who had demanded food reacted in a normal, human manner. Angry at being cheated—as they understood it—they began to jeer.

"How can he say 'I came down from heaven' when we know he comes from Nazareth?" one of the listeners shouted scornfully.

"Is this not Jesus the son of Joseph, whose father and mother we know?" a man from Nazareth cried.

Fearing that in their anger the people might harm the Master, Simon called to the Twelve to join him in forming a circle around Jesus. But the fickle populace was no longer interested in one who refused to give them the bread they sought. Shouting and catcalling, they drifted away until only the Twelve and a few others stood beside the Master.

"Will you also go away?" Jesus asked them gravely.

Simon sought for words to comfort the Master. But when they came to his tongue, they were so simple that he did not realize then that he had spoken a great truth.

"Lord, to whom shall we go?" he said. "You have the words of eternal life."

V

The angry reaction of the crowd when Jesus refused to use his miraculous powers to supply them with food marked a sharp turning point in the fortunes of the mission in Galilee. In fact so great was the disaffection of the fickle crowd that Herod was reported ready finally to issue the order for his arrest, secure in the knowledge that the riots which would have inevitably followed such action before the feeding of the five thousand would not now occur.

Simon and John had reported so much interest in the Master's teaching in northern Galilee that Jesus and the Twelve left the lake region and traveled into the more mountainous area, continuing beyond Israel proper into the region around the Phoenician seaport cities of Tyre and Sidon. These had been very closely allied with Israel since the time of David when King Hiram of Tyre had sent skilled workmen to build David's magnificent palace in Jerusalem. The area sometimes known as Syro-Phoenicia, lying between the borders of Syria and Phoenicia, proved to be very fertile ground for the teachings of Jesus. But even though people flocked to hear him and to be healed, Simon could see that the Master was preoccupied much of the time, troubled, he was sure, by the failure of the people of Galilee to understand his purpose.

Leaving Syro-Phoenicia, Jesus and his disciples moved eastward across the upper Jordan into the district ruled by the Tetrarch Philip, and came finally to his capital of Caesarea-

Philippi. There on the slope of Mount Hermon near the several sources of the Jordan, Jesus gathered the Twelve around him for a period of communion and rest together, one of the few occasions when he had been alone with them since the beginning of the mission in Galilee. Beside a camp-fire there one night, with the snow-capped mountain towering over them, he asked a question he had never asked before.

"Who do the multitude say that I am?" he inquired, speaking to the Twelve as a body.

"Some say you are John the Baptist," one of the disciples answered, for it was common knowledge in Galilee that Herod Antipas feared Jesus might be a resurrection in a new form of the prophet he had executed.

"Some say Elijah," another offered.

"Jeremiah or one of the prophets," still another suggested.

"But whom do you say that I am?" Jesus asked them directly.

The disciples looked at one another, each hesitating to answer. Most of them had been sorely disappointed when Jesus had failed to name himself the Messiah at the climax of the Galilean ministry with the miraculous feeding of the five thousand. Simon himself had hoped the Master would resolve the question troubling his soul, the conflict between his desire to see a new leader who would free Israel from bondage and the instinctive understanding—only just beginning to take form in his mind—that Jesus was offering an entirely different freedom to those who trusted and believed in him.

All through the months since he had begun to follow the Master, Simon's deeply instilled fear of a possible repetition of the events which had followed the announcement of another messiah so long ago had made him reluctant to finally name the Nazarene as the Son of God. But now he seemed to hear a voice within his own soul, and without stopping to consider the changes such a declaration might make in his own life, he spoke the words it bade him utter.

"You are the Christ," he said. "The Son of the living God."

The smile upon Jesus's face and the light of pleasure in his eyes filled Simon with a warm glow that swept away all his shame and his sense of failure at having lost faith when he had started to walk upon the water on the night of the storm.

"Blessed are you Simon, son of Jonas," the Master said. "For flesh and blood did not reveal this to you, but my Father who is in Heaven. I say also to you that you are Peter. Upon this rock I will build my church, and the gates of hell shall not prevail against it."

It was not the first time Jesus had referred to the rocklike qualities in Simon, qualities upon which he had come to lean more and more in the months of their association together. At their first meeting, he had jokingly called him Cephas, a word that also meant rock—as did Peter—and some of the disciples called the broad-shouldered fisherman by that name upon occasion. But tonight, Simon sensed, the Master's words had a further meaning beyond the fact that he was a stout bastion to which they all turned in times of trouble and uncertainty. By his simple statement of faith that Jesus was the Christ, the Son of God sent to show men the way to God, Simon, who was now to be called Peter, had also laid the sturdy foundation stone for the future.

For the first time, Jesus had crystallized in words the ultimate truth of his mission upon earth. And though, for the most part, the disciples did not then understand fully the meaning of what he had said, they could see it epitomized in Simon Peter himself. The depth of his faith—not yet unshakable as it was to be in later years, but stronger still than any of the others possessed—had led him to speak the truth.

And with his next words, Jesus left no doubt that he was naming Simon Peter the leader of them all, after himself.

"I will give you the keys to the Kingdom of Heaven," he said, letting his hand rest affectionately upon Peter's broad shoulders. "Whatever you shall bind on earth shall be bound in Heaven. And whatever you shall loose on earth shall be loosed in Heaven."

VI

To Simon Peter, one of the most pleasant parts of his experience as a disciple of Jesus was the annual visit to Jerusalem for the Passover. Coming in the early spring, when the chill winds of winter that swept the hills upon which the Holy City was built had somewhat abated but the hot, dry months of summer had not yet begun, it was a time he loved. All Jews who were able to afford the trip journeyed to Jerusalem for one of the several religious feasts or festivals during the year, but of them all, the Passover was the most loved, since it celebrated an important event in Jewish history. This was the night when the Angel of Death had laid his hand upon the male first born in every house in Egypt—except those of the Israelites, to the lintels of whose doors the blood of a freshly killed lamb had been applied as God had instructed Moses. Appropriately, the beautiful and symbolic ceremony of the Passover culminated in eating the flesh of the paschal lamb and singing the *Hallel*, a hymn of praise.

On his Passover visits to Jerusalem, Jesus had always taught from the Porch of Solomon, as did many visiting rabbis, and each year an increasingly large number of people gathered to hear him. Simon had expected the Master to go to Jerusalem as usual in the spring following his visit to Syro-Phoenicia, but, to his surprise, Jesus announced shortly after their return to Galilee that he would attend the Feast of Tabernacles also.

Second only to the Passover in popularity among the several religious holidays, the Festival of Tabernacles or Booths celebrated the gathering of the rich harvest from the vineyards. During the week of celebration, people everywhere spent much of the time outdoors in open booths or tabernacles woven from freshly green branches in the form of shaded arbors. It was a time of joy and celebration in thankfulness for the harvest. And because the fruit of the vine in particular was usually freely sampled, it was also a time when political passions frequently ran high, with rioting an occasional occurrence. For that reason, the temple authorities kept a close watch upon all who spoke there during the festivals, as well as elsewhere in the city.

As usual when he was visiting Jerusalem, Jesus spent the nights at the home of two devout women, Mary and Martha, who, with their brother Lazarus, lived at the village of Bethany on the eastern slope of the Mount of Olives, just out of sight of Jerusalem itself. The home at Bethany was comfortable, and Mary, Martha and Lazarus were fairly prosperous, so it was a convenient place for him to remain safely away from the crowds that often made the city quite turbulent at that time, but still allowed him to visit the temple daily.

Simon Peter usually stayed at the home of Barnabas, Mary and John Mark during these visits, not only because he was very fond of them, but because from their home in the Lower City he was able to keep a close watch on what was going on in Jerusalem, particularly as it affected the man he served. Since Jesus had named him the leader of all who followed him, Peter stood beside the Master when he spoke from the Porch of Solomon, once again putting into a few simple words the great truth of God's relationship to man. He could see that the chief priests and the leaders among the Pharisees were disturbed by the large number of people who flocked to hear Jesus, and he fully expected that some attempt would be made to harm the Master while he was in Jerusalem. But for the time being at least their attacks were limited to questions by some of the Pharisees, which Jesus answered with the great truth to which Simon Peter had testified on Mount Hermon, though couched in terms they could not legally turn against him.

The first news that the High Priest Caiaphas had finally determined to destroy what he termed the "rabble rouser from Galilee" was brought by John Mark. During his studies in the School for Scribes, Mark heard most of the temple gossip. And when he learned that Caiaphas and the Pharisees had secretly determined to destroy Jesus on a charge of blasphemy, he hurried to bring the news to Peter.

The plan, as Mark described it, was simple. At the beginning of Jesus's teaching the following day, a team of authorities on the Law would question him, as they had done for several days before. This time, however, they would skillfully seek to lure him into a statement which might be made the basis for a charge of blasphemy. The plan did not include bringing the Master before the Great Sanhedrin, Israel's highest court, where a controversy among the rabbis over doctrine might defeat the plotters. Instead, they would stir up the temple rabble—made up of beggars, merchants and petty thieves, all of whom owed their living in one way or another to the tolerance of the chief priests and the temple guards—with the charge of blasphemy. And once aroused, the rabble could be counted on to rush the accused outside the walls without trial and there stone him to death, much as

Jesus's own fellow townsmen of Nazareth had once tried to hurl him from a cliff on a similar charge.

It was a clever plan, one that had worked before when the authorities wished to get rid of what they considered a troublemaker without running the risk of involving the Romans and jeopardizing the nominal amount of independence Pontius Pilate had granted them. To Peter's surprise, the Master did not oppose his urgent plea that they leave Jerusalem at once, and early the next morning they turned northward into the hill country of Judea. There they remained during the cool, pleasant weeks of autumn, and once again people in great numbers flocked to hear Jesus preach and to be healed of their diseases, as they had during those first exciting months of the Galilee campaign.

Only with the approach of the Feast of Dedication, the religious holiday celebrating the beginning of winter, did Jesus and the disciples return to the Jerusalem area. No attempt had been made to interfere with their activities in the hilly northern part of Judea, but Peter would have preferred that they stay away. Jesus, however, insisted upon the visit.

The Feast of Dedication was held in celebration of the time when the temple had been rededicated by Judas Maccabeus, after he had wrested control of the Holy City from the Seleucid emperors of Syria several centuries before. It lasted for a week, as did most of the festivals, and large crowds usually gathered for it. Continually alert for the Master's safety, Simon was fully expecting trouble when they came back to Jerusalem. The temple authorities, he was sure, knew of their sojourn in northern Judea, since they had been followed there by spies of the High Priest Caiaphas, as they were now followed everywhere they went.

Simon did not doubt that Jesus's enemies would connect his being in northern Judea with the presence in that region of several bands of rebels—or common brigands—notably one led by a robber called Barabbas. Although the band of Menahem, the son of Judas the Galilean, had its haunts farther to the north in southern Galilee, it was known that the two groups were not far apart and worked together at times. In addition, Barabbas had so stirred up the admiration of the people in that area by his brazen challenge to the forces of Rome controlling the district, that he had come to hold in the affections of the people much the same position Judas of Galilee had occupied some thirty years before.

Jesus had had no contact with these potential rebels during his stay in the Judean hill country that fall, but Simon was not sure that others of the Twelve had not. In fact he was reasonably certain that Judas Iscariot and Simon the Canaanite, at least, were in league with them, and he was not at all sure that John and James did not look to Barabbas as a potential military leader when Jesus publicly announced himself the Messiah and claimed all power in Israel—as all of them now expected him to do before very much longer.

Just as Simon had expected, Jesus was challenged at his first appearance on the Porch of Solomon during the Feast of the Dedication. The challenge came in the form of a question hurled at him by a member of the rigidly narrow Pharisaic sect which, in conjunction with the High Priest Caiaphas, opposed him.

"How long will you make us doubt?" the Pharisee demanded. "If you are the Christ, tell us plainly."

The intent of the question was obvious; if Jesus claimed to be the Messiah, the rabble waiting for just such a declaration could immediately charge him with blasphemy and stone him from the city. If, on the other hand, he denied his messiahship, inevitably he would lose much of his following, just as John had lost it at Bethabara when he had been forced to admit he was not the Messiah, and as Jesus had lost many of his Galilean adherents in Capernaum when he had refused to create bread for them.

"If I do not do the works of my Father, do not believe me," Jesus answered. "But if I do, though you do not believe me, believe the works, that you may know and believe the Father is in me and I in Him."

Jesus had attacked the questioner at the weakest point of his argument, an interpretation of the Scripture about which the Pharisees themselves often argued. A controversy arose at once within the crowd, some taking one side and some another. During it, Jesus and his disciples were able to leave the temple, for it was obvious that he could not teach there without harassment. To Peter's considerable satisfaction, the Master did not insist upon remaining in the Jerusalem area any longer. Stopping only to say farewell to Mary, Martha and Lazarus at their home in Bethany, he and the disciples took the road eastward toward Jericho and the fords of the Jordan. Early the next morning they crossed over into Peraea at Bethabara.

As he looked about him at the familiar poplar grove and the rocky bank where he had watched John baptize a long line of penitents in the muddy waters of the Jordan below, Simon Peter could not escape a feeling of deep frustration. Here his connection with the Nazarene had begun, and now it appeared that he had come a full circle. For, having lost favor with the people of Galilee and having been forced to flee from Jerusalem in order to escape death at the hands of the rabble, it seemed that Jesus had gotten nowhere.

Book Five
JUDAS ISCARIOT

". . . That thou doest, do quickly."

JOHN 13:27

I

PROOF that Peter had been wise in persuading Jesus to leave Jerusalem came almost within hours after they crossed the Jordan. Travelers from the Holy City brought news of a brief but violent and bloody incident within the temple itself during the latter days of the same Feast of Dedication for which they had made the brief visit to the Holy City. A band of Galileans and other malcontents, under the leadership of the brigand chieftain Barabbas, had begun the affair. But whether they had intended to seize control of the temple or merely to cause a commotion during which they could rob and pillage unhindered never became known.

Pontius Pilate, always watchful for trouble, was in Jerusalem at the time and had sent the tough, merciless legionnaires of the Antonia garrison across the bridge from the fortress to the temple court to attack the rebels. In the brief battle, Barabbas had been seized and many of his followers cut down in the temple court, a desecration that brought outcries of indignation from the devout. These accused Pilate literally of mixing the blood of the Galileans concerned with their sacrifices, but their protests had no effect on the governor, the travelers reported, and the life of the city had quickly resumed its tenor.

With Barabbas—the only rebel leader to achieve anything like the following once possessed by Judas of Galilee—now in prison, the revolutionary movement was set back sharply. In fact the few among the disciples who had espoused the desperate cause were left with no hope except that Jesus would now be forced to name himself the Messiah and over-turn Israel's present rulers by divine power.

Without such considerations to trouble him, Simon Peter would have found much to enjoy during this late winter and early spring sojourn in the district of Peraea. Almost per-petual summer reigned there, because the deep, natural rift in the earth called the *ghor* trapped the rays of the sun and held them prisoner. The Jordan Valley rarely saw frost, and vegetables for the markets of Jerusalem were grown practi-cally throughout the year. In addition, the hills to the east, covered by thick copses of pine, cedar, terebinth and other trees and broad expanses of rolling velvet meadows, formed an excellent grazing ground for flocks and herds.

Through this land Jacob had driven his own flocks after separating them from those of his father-in-law Laban, more than fifteen centuries before. On the banks of a brook that during the rainy season, which was now slowly building to-ward its peak, became a raging torrent, Jacob had wrestled with the angel and in victory had conquered his own fears. Here, too, David had fled from Absalom, seeking time to build up the army with which he put down the rebellion— at the price of losing his beloved, though wayward, eldest son and breaking his own heart.

Peter could see a change in Jesus during these months, a change that troubled him and made him wary concerning the future. The look in Jesus' eyes sometimes seemed to be one of resignation, but again there was a strange urgency in the Master's manner and he was almost militant in his criticism of the Pharisees and others who opposed him, lashing out at them for their hypocrisy and their pretensions.

As the weeks passed, those among the disciples who listened to Judas Iscariot and Simon the Zealot when they talked about the glorious future that could be Israel's, recovered some of the confidence and hope they had lost with news of the arrest of Barabbas and the failure of the short-lived revolt. And since Simon Peter shared in that hope—though not as certain as they concerning how it could be accomplished—he, too, found Jesus's new militancy heartening.

Then something happened that filled them all with sorrow: the news brought by a servant of Mary and Martha from Bethany that their beloved brother Lazarus was gravely ill.

"Master, the people recently sought to stone you there," Peter protested when Jesus announced that he would go to Bethany. "Why would you go again?"

"Our friend Lazarus is asleep, but I go that I may awake him," Jesus answered, and as soon as the other disciples could be called in from the surrounding villages, they set out again for Bethany. There they found that Lazarus had died four days before and was resting in his tomb, but Jesus ordered the stone closing the opening rolled away. And when he called "Lazarus come forth," the young man emerged from the tomb, still wrapped in grave clothes and with a napkin covering his face.

The startling miracle of raising a well-known man from the dead practically upon the doorstep of the temple was a flaunting of power which could not be ignored by Jesus's bitter enemies in Jerusalem. To Simon Peter, resting with the others at Bethany and celebrating the raising of their friend, Barnabas sent word that the small but powerful group of the Great Sanhedrin—known generally as the Priestly Council —had already met and condemned Jesus of blasphemy, charging that the power he possessed to raise the dead had come directly from the devil himself.

At Peter's insistence, the party left early the next morning and moved into the region of Ephraim, a hilly area lying north of Jerusalem, which they had not yet visited. Peter could take little satisfaction in having spirited Jesus out of Jerusalem, however, for the Master announced that he planned to return to the Holy City for the Passover, now only a few months away. And since he was not able to dissuade Jesus from this decision, Peter determined upon another method of protecting him.

The plan was simple in concept but required much work in the brief time remaining before the Passover. It was to arrange for the largest possible number of loyal followers from Galilee, people who had great reason to love Jesus because they had been healed of diseases or otherwise helped by him, to accompany them to the Holy City for the religious festival. To accomplish this, Peter sent word to the cities around the lake—and particularly to Mary Magdalene, who had remained in Galilee—that all who loved the Master should come to Jerusalem for the Passover.

It was a large and joyful crowd that finally took the road from Galilee to Jerusalem; they were joined by Jesus and the disciples near where the River Jabbok entered the Jordan. Mary of Magdala had gathered a large number of women to accompany the party, including Jesus's mother Mary and her sister Salome, the wife of Zebedee and mother of John and James, as well as Joanna, the wife of Chuza. It was Peter's hope that should trouble occur, both the Roman and Jewish authorities would hesitate to attack a delegation that included a large number of women.

People from every walk of life made up the procession. Some, Peter was sure, still hoped to carry off a swift rebellion and put Jesus at the head of the nation. But their number had shrunken considerably in the past several months, discouraged by the Master's failure to use the power he had demonstrated in raising the dead and feeding the five thousand. And, watching the throng passing along the road, he dared to let himself hope that Judas Iscariot and some of the others might still be right and that the freeing of Israel would be accomplished by divine power—against which not even Rome could stand. Jesus himself largely shattered even that small hope, however, as he sat with the disciples around a campfire one night not far from Jericho.

"Behold, we go up to Jerusalem," he said, "and all the things that are written by the prophets shall be accomplished concerning the Son of Man. He shall be delivered to the Gentiles and shall be mocked and spitefully treated and spit upon. They shall scourge him and put him to death, and the third day he shall rise again."

II

Troubled by Jesus's words and the thought that he might be leading his Galilean friends into a trap at Jerusalem, Peter left the camp and went to walk along the bank of the stream. The sound of moving water, whether flowing in a stream or washing in wavelets upon the shore, usually calmed him in a time of trouble. But he found no peace tonight in the murmur of the brown flood sweeping southward to meet the heavily salt water of the Dead Sea, and after awhile started back to the camp. Near the outskirts he heard a familiar voice call his name and saw Mary Magdalene standing beside a tree at the edge of the camping area, with a cloth thrown over her hair against the dampness beside the river.

"I saw you leave the others just now, Simon," she said, "and realized that you were troubled. Is it because you fear that our own people may be cut down trying to defend Jesus when Caiaphas arrests him?"

It was not the first time Peter had been startled by her almost uncanny ability to understand his thoughts, but the two were close friends and he did not ordinarily resent it. Tonight, however, his own troubles made him irritable.

"Caiaphas would hardly risk a riot during the Passover," he said curtly. "That would only give Pontius Pilate another opportunity to mingle the blood of more Galileans with their sacrifices."

Mary took no offense at his tone. "What do you think the Master meant by what he said just now?"

"He has been teaching all evening."

"You know what I mean, Simon: when he said 'Behold we go up to Jerusalem and all the things that are written by the prophets concerning the Son of Man shall be accomplished'?"

"That he will be named the Messiah. What else could it mean?"

"But Jesus said he would be delivered to the Gentiles— which must mean the Romans. And that he will be scourged and put to death."

"He was speaking as prophets do," Peter said harshly. "Don't repeat such foolish talk."

"Are you sure you do not call it foolish because you don't want to believe it, Simon?"

"The Master was speaking in parables. How could ordinary men kill the Son of God?" Peter realized he had almost shouted the question that was troubling him, and lowered his voice. "He was telling us that Caiaphas and the others will reject him at first, as they have always done, but that in the end he must triumph over his enemies."

"Do you really believe that?"

"How can I believe anything else? Would you have me

lose faith in God himself?" Turning, Peter stumbled away into the darkness, leaving his own question unanswered.

Others, too, were troubled by the same uncertainty, Peter discovered after they reached Bethany and the Master took up his usual residence at the home of Mary, Martha and Lazarus. The Galileans who were not of Jesus's own party continued across the Mount of Olives to seek camping places upon the slope facing the city. And since the home of Mary, Martha and Lazarus was not large enough for the Twelve and the women who had come with them, some of the disciples unrolled their sleeping pallets on the floors of the outbuildings. As Peter was passing one of these on the way to his own couch after a conference with John concerning preparations for Jesus's triumphal entry into Jerusalem tomorrow, he heard the voices of Judas and Simon the Zealot, and paused to listen.

"What do you think the Master meant by saying he will be taken prisoner in Jerusalem and put to death?" the Canaanite asked.

"He was talking in parables," Judas said impatiently. "Here of late, he speaks of nothing else."

"Do you really expect Caiaphas and the Romans to accept him as the Messiah?"

"Of course not. But the Master will triumph over them." The floor creaked as one of the men turned over on his pallet, and Peter took advantage of the sound to move a little nearer.

"Everything we hope to gain is built upon that," the Zealot agreed. "But can you be sure, Judas?"

"Of course I am sure." Judas spoke with a similar note of anger, Peter thought, to that he had used to bolster his own waning conviction when he had talked to Mary of

Magdala on the road to Bethabara only two nights before.
"You saw how anxious the Master is to get to Jerusalem.
Would he go so eagerly to his own death?"

"I suppose not—"

"Jesus must proclaim himself Messiah when he enters
Jerusalem," Judas said confidently. "With so great a crowd
around him, Caiaphas will not dare to take him."

Peter was about to pass on when Judas spoke again, on a
more thoughtful note. "But if he delays this time—"

"What then?"

"Why ask, when you know the answer as well as I? If
Jesus does not use his power now, Caiaphas will arrange some
secret way to take him prisoner and all of us with him. We
cannot let the Master leave Jerusalem again without proclaim-
ing himself the Messiah. Our very lives depend upon it."

"But if Jesus still does not—"

Judas did not let the other man finish. "In that case it would
be better for one to die than for many."

III

Looking back upon that Passover week from the perspective
of the years, Simon Peter could see a remarkable parallel between the rapid succession of events during the few climactic
days, extending through the sixth when Jesus and the disciples
ate the Passover supper together, and that other brief period
so long ago during which he had watched Jerusalem literally
burst into flames when the Procurator Sabinus sent his troops
to capture the temple and its treasures. The tension had started
to build up rapidly when Jesus entered the city in triumph,
with the Galileans who accompanied him shouting: "Blessed

is the King who comes in the name of the Lord! Peace in heaven and glory in the highest!"

At the temple, Jesus went at once to the market area where, as a boy, Simon had purchased his first dove. But no longer was the Master the meek and lowly teacher of Nazareth whom Simon had first come to know and love in Galilee. Instead, he suddenly became a militant, dramatic figure, shocking the entire city when he began to cleanse the market, tossing aside the coops of the sellers of doves and other animals, and overturning the cabinets of the moneychangers before turning to the crowd to shout: "It is written, *'My house is a house of prayer.'* But you have made it a den of thieves."

Even the temple rabble recognized the challenge in Jesus's forthright action. And when he went on to teach from the Porch of Solomon, as was his custom, Caiaphas sent learned men again and again to question him, hoping to trap him into a statement which could be used to raise the cry of "Blasphemy" and loose the rabble upon him. But this time Jesus not only parried the questions expertly but denounced the Pharisees as whited sepulchers, hypocrites and self-appointed blind guides of the people, straining at gnats and swallowing camels.

Watching the people listen eagerly to this denunciation of the religious authorities who sought to control their every action through interpreting the Law, Peter was reminded of the tension he had seen in the faces of the crowd when he had come out of the temple on that morning so long ago, after making his first sacrifice, to find the whole city waiting for the next act of the Procurator Sabinus and the inexorable chain of events that had followed. And remembering the turn those events had taken, Simon Peter could not help feeling a sense of dread.

More than once during those days when Jesus flayed the

temple authorities from the Porch of Solomon, yet made no
public declaration that he was the Messiah, Peter had noticed
Judas Iscariot watching with a puzzled frown. And once he
was awakened in the night at Bethany by the voices of Judas
and Simon the Zealot raised in a quarrel—though he was not
able to make out what they were saying. That Judas was
under a considerable strain Peter could easily see, but, there
was only one moment during the week that could have been
called a clash of wills between Jesus and the man of Kerioth.
It came during a banquet at Bethany given in honor of the
Master by Simon, a leper whom he had cured.

While the feast was in progress, a woman entered the room
bearing a box of alabaster such as was used to contain very
expensive perfumes and ointments. When she broke the box
to let the precious oil soak into Jesus's hair while its fragrance
filled the room with the aroma of spikenard—one of the most
costly of unguents—Judas's face was suddenly suffused with
anger.

"Why was this waste of ointment made?" he demanded.
"It might have been sold for more than three hundred pence
—and given to the poor."

"Let her alone," Jesus said. "Why trouble her when she
has wrought a good work upon me?"

It was the sharpest rebuke Peter had ever heard the Master
make to any of the disciples. He saw Judas flush deeply, but
before the tall disciple could retort, Jesus continued, "The
poor you have with you always, and whenever you will you
may do them good. But you do not have me always, and she
has done what she could, by coming beforehand to anoint
my body for burial."

It was the fourth time in Peter's own memory that Jesus
had spoken as if his death were imminent—the second in as

many days. Watching Judas, he saw the flush of anger replaced by a look of decision, as if a question troubling him had finally been answered. When the feast broke up, Peter started to follow Judas, troubled by what he had seen in the other man's face. But just then John called him about preparations for eating the paschal meal next day, and he had no more chance to think of Judas.

Peter had naturally assumed that they would celebrate the Passover—as on other occasions—at the home of Mary, Martha and Lazarus at Bethany. Jesus, however, chose to join the disciples in the symbolic meal at the home of Mary, the mother of John Mark, in Jerusalem. And since Peter was sure that Caiaphas would not dare to disturb the Passover in the city by choosing such a time to seize the Master, he did not object. Besides, Mary's house was particularly suited for the occasion, since its upper chamber was large enough to hold Jesus and the Twelve, along with those who served.

As was customary in preparing the Paschal meal, Peter and John purchased a lamb in the temple that morning and let it be sacrificed, the entrails and other unusable parts being burned upon the altar, while the flesh was brought to Mary's house and prepared with savory herbs before being roasted over live coals during the afternoon. Thin cakes of bread without leaven were prepared to be served with the meat, as well as wine diluted with water and the traditional bitter herbs eaten at the Passover season to symbolize the persecution in Egypt from which the Children of Israel had been led by Moses.

When Jesus and the disciples gathered in the upper room a little after sunset, a benediction was pronounced and the ritual cup of wine with which the meal always began was drunk. Basins of water and fresh cloths had been brought in by the women for the ceremonial washing preceding the meal itself. Jesus now removed his robe, and taking a basin and one of the cloths, started to wash the feet of the disciples.

"Lord, do you wash my feet?" Peter protested.

"What I do you do not know now, but you shall know hereafter," Jesus said enigmatically.

"You shall never wash my feet." Peter's conscience would not let him accept without further protest this act of servitude by the man he had named the Son of God.

"If I do not wash them," Jesus answered sternly, "you shall have no part with me."

"Lord, do not wash only my feet then, but also my hands and my head," Peter said humbly, and made no further objection as the Master washed away the dirt that always stained the skin through the open leatherwork of a man's sandals, even in the city. Drying them with a towel, he went on to do the same for each of the Twelve.

The ritual meal was almost over when Jesus took a piece of the unleavened bread, broke it into fragments, and passed the dish to Peter, who sat at the end of the row of cushions arranged around the table.

"Take; eat. This is my body," he said. And though Peter did not entirely understand the meaning of the act, he nevertheless put a piece of bread into his mouth and passed the dish on to the next disciple. Jesus, meanwhile, poured a silver cup of wine and passed it to Peter.

"This is my blood of the new covenant, which is shed for many," he said. "Truly I say to you, I will drink no more of the fruit of the vine until I drink it new in the Kingdom of God."

"Say not so, Lord," Peter started to protest.

"Simon, Simon!" Jesus said sadly, "Satan has desired to have you that he may sift you as wheat. But I have prayed for

you, that your faith shall not fail. And when you are converted, strengthen your brethren."

"Lord, I am ready to go with you both into prison and
into death," Peter protested, but he realized that Jesus had
long ago searched his innermost thoughts and had seen there
the doubts which has assailed him more than once during the
early months of their association together. Peter had tried to
tell himself these doubts had been removed on Mount Hermon when he had named Jesus the Christ, but he knew now
that some shreds of uncertainty still remained, brought about
by the Master's prediction of his own death—for it was hard
to understand how the Messiah could be killed by ordinary
men.

"I tell you, Peter," Jesus said sadly, "the cock shall not
crow this day before you shall deny three times that you
know me."

Peter started to protest again, but Jesus's next words forestalled him. "Behold, the hand of him that betrays me is with
me on the table," he said, and Peter saw now that his eyes
were upon Judas Iscariot, who was sitting across the table
from him. "Truly the Son of Man goes as it was determined,
but woe to that man by whom he is betrayed."

"Lord, who is it?" John asked.

"It is he to whom I shall give a sop when I have dipped it."
Meat was such an expensive and precious item that it was
customary to dip up the remaining juices from the plate with
a crust of bread called the sop, which was then given to
another as a tidbit. When Jesus had finished the portion of
meat on his plate, Peter saw him dip a fragment of bread into
the gravy and hand it to Judas Iscariot.

The man of Kerioth stiffened, and for a moment Peter
thought he would refuse the sop. Finally he took it with

shaking fingers and put it into his mouth, but it still almost seemed to choke him. Only those closest to Judas heard Jesus say to him in a low voice, "What you do, do quickly."

With a strangled cry, Judas rose and lurched from the room.

IV

Troubled by the look of desperation he had seen in Judas's face, as well as the strange words he had heard the Master speak to the man of Kerioth, Peter left the room and descended the steps from the upper chamber. He went a little way up the street, hoping to be able to tell in which direction Judas had gone, but the other man was already out of sight. As Peter was returning to the house he saw those who had been with Jesus in the upper room descending the stairway to the street outside. Talking together, they moved toward another street which, Peter knew, would take them to one of the city gates and the road leading to Bethany.

Peter did not follow the others. Instead, obeying an impulse that seized him suddenly, he ran up the steps to the room where Mary and another woman were gathering up the remains of the feast and the dishes and cups that had been used.

Mary looked up in surprise when she saw him. "The others have gone, Simon," she said. "I thought you were—"

"Where is Barnabas?" Peter demanded hoarsely.

"He went with them."

"Was he armed?"

"No, Simon." Mary's eyes widened. "He is not one of the *sicarii*."

"Is there a weapon in the house?"

"Barnabas has a sword. He carries it on his travels, to defend himself against rob—"

"Get it for me," Peter demanded peremptorily.

"Why are you so concerned?" Mary asked as she gave him the sword. His awkwardness as he buckled on the weapon and hid it beneath the folds of his robe betrayed his unfamiliarity with its use, but he didn't stop to answer. Instead, he plunged into the darkness in the direction the others had gone.

Peter wasted no time in searching for Jesus and the disciples; he knew the Master always took the same route to Bethany at the end of the day and would no doubt do the same tonight. Hurrying on, he overtook the others just outside the city wall. Part way up the slope beyond the stone bridge across Kidron was a beautiful garden called Gethsemane, lying just off the regular road between Jerusalem and Bethany. Jesus usually stopped there for a period of quiet prayer and meditation when he was going to Bethany in the afternoon, and Peter was not surprised that he did so tonight, although it was past midnight. Just inside the gate, the Master left the other disciples, and beckoning to Peter, James and John—the three who had always been closest to him—went on into the center of the garden. Where the shadows cast by the gnarled olive trees growing there formed a dark retreat, he left the three to watch, and went a little farther away beneath a towering tree to pray.

Peter and John had gone into the city early that morning to arrange for the sacrificial slaying of the Passover lamb in the temple and to supervise the preparation of the feast. Now that they had gotten safely out of the city without being troubled by the authorities, Peter felt a tremendous sense of relief, and as he sat with the others watching, his eyelids began to droop and finally he fell asleep. Once, as if in a dream, he thought he heard the voice of the Master, but he came wide awake only when he heard Jesus say, "Behold, the hour has come and the Son of Man is betrayed into the hands of sinners."

Peter scrambled to his feet, stiffening as a sound entirely alien to this peaceful place cut through the stillness of the night from the direction of the Brook Kidron below them. It was the rhythmic tramp of marching men wearing the Roman half boots called the *caligae*—plus the rattle of weapons and military gear.

"Rise up and let us go," Jesus said calmly as he moved toward the gate. "He who betrays me is at hand."

On another night long ago, Simon Peter had heard the thud of Roman boots and the rattle of weapons. Hearing it again now, he felt the cold sweat of fear break out upon his body and his limbs begin to tremble with the old remembered terror. At the bottom of the slope a line of torches was already moving across the bridge spanning the brook. It turned into the entrance to the garden where the gnarled silhouettes of the olive trees loomed like macabre sentinels in the darkness, and seconds later there came the challenge of an officer demanding to know the identity of those who waited there.

Peter instinctively put out a hand to restrain Jesus. But the Master shook it off. And though it took all the strength he possessed to control the surge of remembered terror, Peter followed close behind Jesus to where a group of men bearing flaming torches had just entered the garden. A quick glance told him that both the temple police and legionnaires from the Antonia garrison were represented in the party of soldiers waiting there. Among them was the steward of the High Priest Caiaphas, no doubt representing his master upon this mission, and beside him was the tall form of Judas Iscariot.

Most of the other disciples had fled from the garden, warned by the torches, the tread of the *caligae* and the clank of military harness. When Jesus moved toward where the Roman officer in charge was questioning those who had remained, Judas stepped forward and greeted him warmly with a kiss, as if they had been separated for a long time. The kiss was obviously a signal previously agreed upon, for two of the Romans seized Jesus immediately.

Again and again in the months since Jesus had first predicted his own death, Peter had assured himself that the Christ could not be taken prisoner and executed by ordinary men. Now the moment of crisis had come, when in order to prove beyond question that he was indeed the Messiah, the Master must use his divine power to strike down those who opposed him in establishing a true Kingdom of God in Israel. But Jesus made no move to oppose the rough hands that had seized him, and in desperation Peter did the only thing he could think of that might force the Master at last to announce himself. Drawing the sword from beneath his robe, he slashed at the servant of the high priest, the agent of the man who was the Master's greatest enemy, not doubting that the power he knew Jesus possessed over life and death would protect him.

Peter's lack of skill with weapons betrayed him, and the sword only slashed the ear of Caiaphas' steward. In desperation he turned to Jesus, but saw only reproach and what seemed to be disappointment in the eyes of the Master. And as the steward staggered back with blood spurting from his face, one of the soldiers raised his spear, ready to throw.

When for the second time in his life Simon Peter found himself facing death upon the point of a spear, an overwhelming surge of terror washed against the bulwarks of courage and faith that had made him risk his own life in an attempt to force Jesus at last to act. Sweeping away his defenses, it left him helpless, and throwing away the sword with a cry of anguish, he plunged into the darkness, seeking the protection of some large boulders guarding the entrances to several rock tombs hewn from the side of the slope a little distance away.

Stumbling blindly down the hillside, ignoring the pain lashing his body as the thorns of the burnet bushes tore his skin, Peter expected momentarily to feel the sharp agony of a spearpoint in his back. At the foot of the hill he crouched numbly in the bed of the Brook Kidron, from which still rose the thick-sweet odor of blood washed from the temple altars. From this hiding place he watched the torchlit procession recross the bridge on the way back to the city, with Jesus now a prisoner between two Roman guards. Of the other disciples, only John was among the stragglers following the arresting party.

Scurrying from shadow to shadow, flattening himself behind trees or against the fronts of houses whenever anyone in the column ahead looked back, Peter followed not far behind. Pausing only for a brief period at the palace of the old High Priest Annas—father-in-law of Caiaphas and titular head of the Sadducees who made up the priesthood—the arresting party continued on to a building with a walled court, which Peter recognized as the ornate and luxurious palace of the high priest. When Jesus was taken inside the building, he slipped into the court with the crowd, now numbering several hundred people, and waited in the shadows to see what fate the Sanhedrin would decree for the prisoner.

It was now several hours after midnight, and the damp cold that characterized the nights in Jerusalem—except in summer—had already descended upon the heights where the palace stood. The soldiers on guard in the courtyard had built several fires for themselves and the bystanders, and, finally, shivering from cold and fear and still half dazed by the sudden collapse of his whole world, Peter approached one of them to warm himself. Almost immediately, though, a girl serving refreshments to the soldiers noticed him there.

"Are you not one of this man's disciples?" she asked.

"I am not!" he cried, and lurched away from the circle of the firelight. Soon he began to shiver again, however, and somehow found enough courage to approach another fire where a few of the Roman soldiers were standing, hoping they would not recognize him.

"Are you not one of his disciples?" a soldier demanded, his hand dropping to his sword.

"No, I am not!" Simon shouted, and started to move away, but a servant in the high priest's household seized him by the shoulder and spun him half around.

"Did I not see you in the garden with him?" he demanded.

"No!" Peter shouted hoarsely, and driven now by the blind terror which had assailed him in the garden, twisted out of the man's grasp and ran through the gate of the courtyard. Crouching in the darkness outside, he saw two of the guards bring Jesus out of the door to the palace. And though he had been sure he was safely hidden from sight, Peter seemed to feel Jesus's eyes search him out while at the same moment he heard a sound that stabbed his heart with a pain fully as severe, he was sure, as would have been the spear point of the soldier in the garden. It was the crowing of a cock, and with it he heard once again the reproachful words Jesus had spoken to him that very night in the upper room: "Truly the cock shall not crow until you have denied me thrice."

Overcome by the enormity of his guilt in denying the man he had named the Son of God, solely to save his own miserable life, Simon Peter gave a great cry of pain and rushed into the darkness. Stumbling, sometimes falling upon the stone pavement but always getting up to move on, he found his way to the home of Mary, Barnabas and Mark, and without disturbing those who were sleeping, he climbed the outside stairway to the same upper room where only a few hours before Jesus had washed the feet of the disciples. There he threw himself, sobbing, to the floor.

V

All through the night Peter wrestled with his conscience as Jacob had wrestled with the angel on the banks of the River Jabbok east of the Jordan. And as the hours passed he finally came to recognize his true adversary, the foe he must conquer if he were to regain his own self-respect and be worthy to lead those whom Jesus had called.

The enemy was his own reluctance to follow without question the way Jesus had plainly marked for all of them, but for none more clearly than for Peter himself. It was the way of faith and certainty in God's purpose, even if that purpose should take him to the very thing that had hung over him, like a sword suspended by a thread, all the years since that terrible day before Sepphoris. At last he knew what Jesus had meant the night before when he had said "But I have prayed for you that your faith shall not fail. And when you are converted, strengthen your brethren." With this realization, Peter's battle with himself and with his fears was finally won and he descended the stairs to where Mary was working in the kitchen.

She was alone, for Peter had seen Barnabas and John Mark go out shortly after dawn. And though they had been close friends for many years, she did not speak in greeting, but silently poured out water for him to wash and put food before him. He knew what was in her mind—that the disciple Jesus had trusted most should have stayed with the Master and not hidden like a child fearful of his shadow.

"Is—is there any news of the Master?" he asked when he had finished eating.

"Barnabas and Mark have gone to the temple," Mary told him. "It is said in the streets that Jesus was arrested last night in the garden and taken before the high priest."

"I was there," Peter said. "And I ran away."

At the pain and shame revealed in his voice, Mary's accusing eyes softened a little. "The others, except John, fled, too," she said. "Barnabas has gone to find them and tell them to come here. The upper room is large enough to hide all of you until you can leave Jerusalem."

Peter finished eating and got to his feet. "If any of them do come here," he told Mary, "tell them to stay until I return."

"You will only be arrested if you leave," she protested.

"If I go to Jesus now," Peter said simply, "some of what I did last night will be undone."

Before Peter could leave the house, however, Mark burst in, panting from having run across the city. "The Master has been condemned by Pontius Pilate!" he cried. "The Romans are taking him to the Place of the Skull, to crucify him!"

Peter was not really surprised to learn that the final act of the tragic drama that had begun last night in Gethsemane was about to be played out. Like the others, he had not wanted to accept the Master's prediction of his own death and had gone on hoping that at the last moment Jesus would invoke the divine power with which he had fed the five thousand and performed other miracles, putting his enemies to flight. Peter himself had risked death in attacking the servant of the high priest, hoping finally to force the Master to act. But when he had seen Jesus emerge from the palace last night after his third denial and had heard the crowing of the cock, he'd known that the Master's prediction would be fulfilled.

"They say the high priest paid Judas thirty pieces of silver to betray Jesus," Mark added. "But it did him no good. Some people coming to Jerusalem from Bethany this morning found him hanging from a tree beside the road—dead by his own hand."

"It is no more than he deserved as a traitor!" Mary cried.

"Judas loved money, and he was angry when Jesus reprimanded him at the house of Simon the leper," Peter said. "But when he betrayed the Master last night, I think it was not really for the thirty pieces of silver, or because he was angry."

"Why would he do such a thing, then?" Mark asked.

"Many expected Jesus to become another David—including me, I suppose. We never really understood that he wanted only to show the way to eternal life through following his teachings. I think Judas betrayed Jesus in an act of desperation, hoping the Master would strike down his enemies rather than let himself be put to death."

"You still think Jesus will save himself, don't you?" Mark asked.

Simon shook his head. "The Master foretold his own death, exactly as it is happening. I will go to Golgotha, so he will at least know I did not deny him a fourth time."

A strange silence and emptiness gripped the city as Peter made his way along the narrow, curving streets of the Tyropean Valley, separating the eminence upon which the temple stood to the east from the richer suburbs to the west. Golgotha —called the Place of the Skull because the rock formation there resembled the shape of the bony skull case, or *calvarium* —lay north of the suburbs. As he looked across the valley, Peter could see the temple, but its golden dome was almost obscured by a strange and ominous-looking cloud that hung over the eastern part of Jerusalem like a pall. From the cloud came the occasional mutter of thunder, as if a storm were in the making. And as Peter moved northward it spread rapidly until soon almost the entire older part of the city was shrouded in a cloak of semidarkness.

Peter recoiled when a bolt of lightning appeared to strike the temple itself, hidden now by the cloud; the clap of thunder that followed was so intense that it almost knocked him to the ground. As he moved on, a strange, high-pitched wailing sound rose from the depths of the Tyropean Valley—the voices of thousands crying out in fear. And along the streets people were pouring from their houses, their eyes turned fearfully toward the strange cloud that still hovered like a black omen of destruction above the temple.

Even Mark's words had not quite prepared Peter for what he saw when he came over a rise and faced the elevation of Golgotha. Three wooden crosses were starkly outlined against the afternoon sky, and even from that distance he recognized the figure upon the center cross and could tell by the way the body sagged against the upright that Jesus was either unconscious or already dead. He did not hold back at the knowledge that the Master was already beyond help, however, but moved on toward the foot of the hill. There he stood near the crosses, looking up at them. And as upon another occasion on the shore of the Sea of Galilee, tears rolled down his cheeks without his knowing they were there, tears of sorrow for the man who had died upon the cross—and for another who had failed him.

VI

The sound of voices raised in laughter startled Peter. When he looked for the source, he saw a group of soldiers sprawled out on the grass near the foot of the center cross. One of the heavy cloaks the Romans used both as wearing apparel and to wrap themselves in when sleeping was spread out in the midst of the group, and they were throwing dice, apparently for a garment which lay in the middle of the cloak. When Peter recognized it, a sudden anger filled him and he started toward them, intending to wrest the Master's robe from heathen hands.

He had taken only a few steps when a brawny forearm was thrust in front of his chest, stopping him. His eyes traveled up the arm to the face of its owner, a handsome man wearing the helmet and crest of a centurion in the Italian Band, one of the elite corps of the Roman army. Strangely enough, he saw no threat in the man's eyes, but rather pity and understanding.

"It is only a piece of cloth," the Roman said. "Not worth being killed for."

"But it was his."

"He does not need it now. The merchant, Joseph of Arimathea, has gone to ask Pilate's permission to place his body in the tomb before the sun goes down and your Sabbath begins. They will surely bring winding cloths when they come to take him down."

"Who are you?" Peter asked.

"My name is Cornelius, from Caesarea. My command has been here ever since the affair of Barabbas, reinforcing the regular garrison of the Antonia."

"Then you helped to crucify him?"

The centurion shook his head. "I came on duty just now. The Nazarene was already dead when I arrived, but the men say he asked your God to forgive those who executed him. It was a strange thing for a dying man to say."

"Not if you knew him as I did. Jesus could ask the Most High to do that—because he was God's own Son."

The Centurion studied him for a brief moment, as if debating whether or not to believe what he said. "We will talk of this another time," he said then. "Now you had better go and join those who wait at the foot of the hill, before someone points you out as one of his disciples."

"Did you say Joseph is making preparations for the Master to be buried?" Peter asked.

"He and the lawyer Nicodemus, with one called Barnabas."

"It should be soon." The sun was not far beyond the western hills, and unless they could bring the body down from the cross before the beginning of the Sabbath day at sunset, it must hang another full day at the mercy of the elements and the vultures that often turned the hill of Golgotha into a place of horror after a crucifixion.

Mary of Magdala was among the women who waited at the foot of the hill. She came to meet Peter when he descended the slope from where he had been talking to the centurion.

"They say you hid in the upper room after you denied the Master last night, Simon," she said. "Why were you so afraid, when they took only him?"

Except for Andrew, to whom he had told the story at Bethabara, Peter had not spoken of that terrible day before Sepphoris to anyone else—not even, he remembered now, to the Master himself, though he was sure Jesus had known of it and understood.

"When Judas of Galilee and his followers were crucified, I was saved from death by the body of a dead man that fell upon me and hid me," he explained. "Last night, when the soldiers came to take him in the garden and one of them was about to thrust me through with a spear, I was seized by a panic and ran away."

Mary looked up at the cross and the lonely figure hanging there, then back at Peter. "But you came here just now nevertheless."

"If the Son of God could let himself be slain for us," Peter said simply, "how could anything that might happen to a fisherman of Galilee be important now?"

"What do you mean, Simon?" Mary asked.

A new voice spoke, and they turned to see the lawyer Nicodemus, who had become a follower of Jesus on one of his earlier visits to Jerusalem. Joseph of Arimathea was with him and four servants who carried an improvised litter.

"The Master himself gave me the answer to Mary's question during one of the religious feasts when I came to where he was camped on the Mount of Olives," Nicodemus said. "I remember his very words: 'God so loved the world that he gave his only begotten Son, that whosoever believes in him should not perish, but have everlasting life.' "

The estate of Joseph of Arimathea was not far from the hill of Golgotha. After the body of Jesus had been gently released from the cross, willing hands carried it tenderly to the garden and placed it in the merchant's own tomb. There was not time enough to anoint the body with spices and carry out the other customary practices of burial before sunset and the beginning of the Sabbath, so the Master's body was only wrapped in cloths soaked in myrrh and laid upon a stone shelf inside the large, empty tomb hewn from a rocky outcrop in the garden. This done, the stone that closed the opening was rolled into place and sealed, on the order of Pontius Pilate, and soldiers were set to watch at the tomb.

In the nearby part of Joseph's estate an area of rough crags and shallow caves provided a safe shelter for Peter and the others among the disciples whom Barnabas was able to gather together. There they kept a lonely vigil over the Sabbath, but early on the morning of the third day Peter was awakened by Mary of Magdala, who came running into the camping place, her eyes afire with indignation.

"They have taken him from the tomb, Simon!" she cried. "We went to prepare the Master for burial, but now we know not where they have taken him."

Peter and John accompanied Mary back to the garden. They found the stone rolled away from the tomb, as she had said, but the guards who had been stationed there were gone. And when Peter entered the tomb and searched it carefully, he found only the print of Jesus's body upon the cloths in which it had been wrapped, though the odor of myrrh permeating the tomb indicated that it had only recently been opened.

While Peter went to see whether Joseph of Arimathea knew anything about the desecration of the tomb, Mary waited in the garden. The merchant could tell him nothing, however, so—still puzzled as to why Caiaphas or anyone else would have ordered the Master's body removed—Peter returned to the garden to watch. Before he reached it, Mary Magdalene came running to meet him, her eyes shining and her face glowing with happiness.

"I have seen the Lord, Simon!" she cried. "He has risen—as he foretold."

"B-but how?"

"Jesus has risen from the dead! He spoke to me here in the garden."

Peter's first thought was for Jesus's safety. "Where is he? The guards may be searching for him now."

"I saw him only for a moment, then he disappeared," Mary said. "But an angel who was with him said to me: 'Go quickly and tell his disciples that he is risen from the dead. He goes before you into Galilee and there you shall see him'!"

Another—and lesser—person might have been filled with envy because the Master had chosen to reveal himself first to Mary instead of to the man Jesus himself had named the rock upon which he would build his Church. But the thought never occurred to Peter.

"Go quickly and gather the women," he directed Mary. "I will find the men, and we will all meet on the road to Jericho, beyond the Mount of Olives. When the Roman authorities learn that the tomb is empty, they will try to seize us, but if we hurry across the Jordan into Peraea, Pilate cannot arrest us there."

Book Six
RABBAN GAMALIEL

"Then stood there up one in the council, a Pharisee named Gamaliel, a doctor of the law . . ."

THE ACTS 5:34

I

THOUGH it had still been chilly and damp on the hilltops of Jerusalem when Peter left the Holy City, spring
was already at the zenith in the upper *ghor* where the
Sea of Galilee lay. Along the lower slopes of the hills daffodils
were in bloom and clumps of sea leek had already appeared,
along with the star-shaped blossoms of purest white known as
the "Flower of Sharon." Patches of "cuckoo flowers" showed
mellow hues of lilac against the white, contrasting with the
bright green of the carob bean, the foliage of vine and grove.

Around Jerusalem the burnet bushes rarely showed their
scarlet blossoms before the Passover, but here in Galilee most
of the blooms were already gone and the sharp thorns were
performing their useful function of guarding the lush green
vineyards and olive groves from both animal and human
marauders. As he trudged into Capernaum at the head of the
Galileans, who had gone to Jerusalem for the Passover only
two weeks before, Peter could not repress a shudder at the
sight of the burnet thorns.

The Romans had fashioned a crown from them and pressed
it upon Jesus's head before they led him out to be crucified,
and the thorns themselves were a reminder that the same fate
might still come to those who followed the now risen Lord.
But Peter was glad to be home again and particularly pleased
that he had been able to lead those whom the Jerusalem authorities would have recognized as close associates of Jesus
safely across the Jordan at Bethabara into the district governed
by Herod Antipas.

The Master's last words to Mary, when she had seen him

that morning in the garden by the open tomb, had been: "Go to my brethren and say to them, 'I ascend to my Father and your Father and to my God and your God.' " During the almost week-long journey to Galilee, Peter had found time to ponder on the meaning of the miracle in Joseph's garden and its significance to those whom Jesus had left behind to carry on his work. And though he could not yet fully understand why the Master had let himself be tortured and subjected to the most cruel and ignominious of executions, he did realize that, through his Resurrection, Jesus had assured the gift of eternal life to all who followed him.

After the weeks of intensive effort preceding the gathering of the Galilean party that had accompanied Jesus to Jerusalem for the Passover, and the flight following the Crucifixion and Resurrection, Simon Peter had every right to look forward to a period of rest in Capernaum. He did not choose to do so, however, for everywhere around him were reminders that Jesus had not rested in his effort to bring a message of hope and salvation during the all too short period of his ministry on earth.

When he walked in his own garden, Peter could plainly see the still partially displaced tiles in the roof of his house where a paralytic had been let down through the roof by his friends and had been healed by Jesus. In the great synagogue at Capernaum—largest in all the lake area—Peter himself spoke from the same platform where Jesus had delivered some of his most effective sermons. And drawn up on the sand beside Zebedee's pier was Peter's and Andrew's own boat, from which the Master himself had first called them to be his disciples.

Many of the close followers of Jesus had been scattered abroad after the Crucifixion. From them, in the days following Peter's return to Galilee, came a number of reports that Jesus had been seen in the flesh. Relying upon the angel's promise to Mary that the Master would come to them in Galilee, however, Peter did not trouble himself about those appearances. Instead, he was busy telling the story of the wondrous thing that had happened in Jerusalem during the season of the Passover and its meaning for all.

Busy as he was, Peter could not put off the feeling that he was somehow failing in the charge Jesus had given him and that some further effort on his own part was needed. When one week passed and still another, with still no revelation from the Master, he was seized by a strange restlessness he had never before experienced in this beautiful land he loved so well. Hoping to throw it off, he persuaded Thomas, Andrew, the sons of Zebedee, Nathanael and Philip—including the six who had been the earliest disciples of the Master—to embark with him for a night of fishing upon the lake.

It was hard work casting the nets, especially when the fishermen had been so long away from their former occupation. All of them were thoroughly tired—and discouraged—when they sailed homeward in the hour just before dawn, for the night's work had not even yielded enough fish for the needs of themselves and their families. As they sailed along, they spoke of their experiences with Jesus, the lessons he had taught them, and the great days of the Galilean ministry, but even these memories had already begun to grow somewhat faint in the absence of the Master himself.

It was almost dawn and a faint glow already showed above the hills to the east and the cities of the Decapolis when they came to an area on the northwest shore of the lake between Capernaum and the Plain of Gennesaret, not far from the natural amphitheater where Jesus had preached on the morning when he had called Peter and the others to follow him. Known as the Seven Springs, it was the site of a beautiful garden marked by towering palms, cypresses growing at the water's edge, and wide-branching eucalyptus trees.

The cold water of the springs flowing into the lake often caused fish to school in that area, but tonight they could make no catch, even with the small nets used in shallow water. Finally they piled the nets into the bottom of the boats and started rowing toward Capernaum, but they had gone only a short distance when a man's voice hailed them from the shore.

"Do you have any meat?" the shadowy figure on the shore asked in a somewhat muffled tone.

"No," John answered somewhat shortly.

"Cast the net on the right side of the boat and you shall find fish," the stranger said.

The man was still only a vaguely outlined figure in the darkness, and Peter hesitated to cast the nets again, just as upon another occasion he had hesitated when Jesus had told him to go out upon the lake and lower the nets in daylight. But something about this occasion reminded him of the other, so he obeyed the stranger on the shore. And no sooner were the nets thrown out than he felt the surge of life trapped within them, and with a sudden rush of joy, realized who it was that had called to them from the shore. His first impulse was to clamber over the side of the boat, but the instinct of a fisherman, ingrained through the years, would not let him loose the net and free the catch.

In the other boat John, too, had felt the tug of the catch against the cords of the net, and shouted for Peter to hold fast. The two worked together, bringing the ends near so the fish were trapped. But once that was accomplished, Peter leaped from the boat into the shallow water and began to wade ashore, dragging the heavy net loaded with fish behind him, as if it had no substance at all.

"It is the Lord!" he heard John cry, and the others followed quickly, hauling the heavy nets ashore until the silvery catch lay everywhere upon the sand and between the rocks.

Peter would have knelt before Jesus, but the Master raised him to his feet and gave him a fragment of fish he had been roasting over some coals and a piece of bread. He did the same for the others when they followed Peter ashore, but only when all were eating did he speak directly to Peter.

"Simon, son of Jonas," he said then. "Do you love me more than these?"

It was a strange question, but in the years he had known Jesus, Peter had learned that the Master often said things of which he understood the full meaning only much later.

"Yes, Lord, you know I love you," he answered.

"Feed my lambs," Jesus told him.

Peter was nonplused for a moment, but before he could ask for an explanation, Jesus repeated the question: "Simon, son of Jonas, do you love me?"

"Lord, you know I love you." This time Peter could not keep the hurt from his voice.

"Feed my sheep," Jesus said.

Peter suddenly remembered the three times he had denied the Master on that terrible night in Jerusalem, and was not surprised when Jesus said to him once again, "Simon, son of Jonas, do you love me?"

"Lord, you know all things," Peter answered humbly. "You know that I love you."

"Feed my sheep," Jesus said for the third time. But now his voice was warm, like a mantle wrapping Peter in its protecting folds as he continued: "When you were young, you girded yourself and walked wherever you would. But when you shall be old, you shall stretch forth your hand and others shall gird you and carry you where you would not go."

Peter did not fully understand the meaning of Jesus's latter words—that would only come many years later. But he felt no more doubt, restlessness or uncertainty, now that the Master had shown him where his duty lay, and he turned to tell Jesus that at last he understood. But the place where the familiar and beloved slender figure had sat was empty.

"Jesus is gone!" John cried. "Will we ever see him again?"

"We will always see him," Peter said confidently. "We will see him in our hearts and in our minds—if not with our eyes —and we will know he is always with us."

"But he did not tell us what he wants us to do."

"We must return to Jerusalem."

Startled faces stared at him in the firelight, and he saw fear reflected in their eyes, the same fear he had once experienced —but which was now behind him.

"Why must we go back and be crucified as the Master was?" John demanded.

"You heard just now when he told me to feed his sheep," Peter said. "Jesus once told us that he is the bread of eternal life. In Jerusalem we can give that bread to all who come there, so it will multiply as the fish and the bread multiplied on the shore beyond Bethsaida when he fed the five thousand."

"But we will all be killed!"

"If it is the Lord's will, yes—for we can do no other." Peter spoke from the depths of the new understanding he had achieved since the night when he had denied the Master in the courtyard of the high priest's palace. "Jesus loved us enough to die for us and to rise from the dead, and for myself I am willing to go where he sends me, even to the ends of the earth."

For a moment no one spoke, and Peter wondered whether John would challenge his decision—and the authority behind it. For John, too, had been very close to the Master and was also, through his mother Salome and Mary of Nazareth, a kinsman of Jesus's family. It was the nearest the two friends had come to an open break since the days when John had been swayed toward the faction represented by Judas Iscariot and Simon Zelotes. But when the eldest son of Zebedee spoke again, Peter knew that those days, too, were behind them.

"It is only a few weeks until the Feast of Pentecost," John said. "Many among the Dispersion come to Jerusalem then and we can tell them the story of the Lord's death and Resurrection."

II

Though Peter himself had no doubts concerning the direction in which his own duty lay, he did not take the group of disciples and close followers of Jesus, who accompanied him on the return journey from Galilee, into Jerusalem without first evaluating what they might face there. Leaving the others at the home of Mary, Martha and Lazarus in Bethany, he and John entered the city and went to the house of Mary, the mother of Mark, where Barnabas also lived. The tall Cypriot embraced them joyfully, but when Peter asked about the followers of Jesus in Jerusalem, Barnabas' face became grave.

"Only a few of us dare to meet together and talk about the Master," he said.

"Surely the news that Jesus rose from the dead after the Romans had put him to death stirred the city," Peter protested.

"It would—if the people knew of it."

"What of the guards who left the tomb? They must have told Caiaphas what happened there."

"I am sure they did," Barnabas agreed. "But the high priest

bribed them to say the Master's disciples attacked them in the night and stole his body from the tomb, so they could claim that he rose from the dead. Caiaphas has spread the story abroad, and I think even Pontius Pilate believes it."

This was bad news indeed, for Peter had been counting on the startling miracle of a crucified man rising from the dead to convince everyone that Jesus was the Son of God. Now, it seemed, Caiaphas had forestalled him by anticipating the claim and denying it in advance.

"Have any of you been persecuted?" Peter asked.

Barnabas shook his head. "The high priest chooses to ignore us. Whenever we try to tell the story of what happened at the Passover, beggars from the temple rabble follow us and laugh us to scorn."

"Then the cause is lost," John said. "We might as well return to Galilee, Peter. At least people will listen to us there."

"Jesus sent me back to Jerusalem to tell his story," Peter said firmly. "I shall tell it here—until he sends me away."

"But where can you begin—if the people will not listen?"

"We will start here, where Jesus ate the last meal with us. If others will not listen, then we will tell the story over and over again to each other, so none of us can forget it. The Greeks, the Alexandrians, the Cypriots and many others have their own synagogues, so we will organize a synagogue of the Nazarenes in this very room that is so sacred to the Master's memory. Caiaphas cannot ignore us very long then."

"It may mean persecution," Barnabas warned. "Mark tells me it is commonly known in the temple that Caiaphas has sworn to stamp out even the memory of Jesus in those who knew him."

"We can endure that, too—as Jesus did," Peter said calmly. "Nowhere else in the world will we reach so many people as here, so we must stay in Jerusalem as long as its walls shall stand."

Depressed and discouraged though they were, the others could not help being heartened by Peter's faith and his quiet determination that the work begun by Jesus in the Holy City must go on at all costs. The rest of the day was spent in visiting those who could be counted on to work unstintingly in furthering the new synagogue of the Nazarenes and in laying plans for selecting the ten elders whose presence was required for the organization of a congregation of worshipers within the Jewish faith. Barnabas was charged with the task of sending word abroad through the city that Simon Peter, the man designated by Jesus himself as the leader of the flock, was taking up his residence in Jerusalem and that all who loved the Lord should rally to him.

While plans were being completed for the entire party who had come from Galilee to move into the city, Peter and the others traveled daily between Bethany and Jerusalem, as Jesus had done upon his visits during the religious festivals. The Master had loved the Mount of Olives, and Peter was not surprised when, late one afternoon as he and the other disciples were returning to Bethany, Jesus appeared to them once again where the road crossed its summit. He spoke only briefly, however, as if in farewell, ending with the words:

"Thus it behooved Christ to suffer and to rise from the dead the third day, and that repentance and remission of sins should be preached to all nations, beginning at Jerusalem. You are witnesses of these things, and I send the promise of my Father upon you. But tarry in the city of Jerusalem until you are endued with power from on high."

This time Jesus's words seemed to promise a long absence before he returned in glory to establish his kingdom on earth

—as all of them fully expected him to do. But Peter did not allow himself to be discouraged by the fact that the kingdom might not be established soon. The man he served had set him a task—that of feeding the sheep, wherever they might be, with the bread of life identified by Peter himself on the slope of Mount Hermon when he had said: "You are the Christ, the Son of the living God." Busy with that task, he put everything else from his mind.

The organization of the new synagogue or congregation of the Nazarenes was accomplished on the first Sabbath following the return of Peter and the disciples to Jerusalem. In form, the new organization was like hundreds of others within the city, governed by its elders, most of whom had been Jesus's disciples, or as in the case of Barnabas, members of the Seventy, a somewhat larger group which the Master had sent out to teach.

As a meeting place for the small group that gathered on the first Sabbath, no better location could have been selected than the upper room in the house of Mary. For not only had Jesus shared with them there the mystical Sacrament of the bread and the wine—which from the beginning they made a part of the worship service—but its location in the teeming Lower City enabled the Nazarenes, as they were called from that very first meeting, to reach large numbers of the poorer classes to whom Jesus's teachings had always had a great appeal.

One task faced the synagogue of the Nazarenes as soon as it was officially established—the selection of a twelfth member to replace Judas Iscariot among the inner circle of the disciples. Peter preferred Barnabas, upon whom he knew he could always depend. Others, however, opposed Barnabas because he was originally from Cyprus and therefore of the Dispersion or Diaspora—Jews living outside Israel who, however pious, were considered by the Pharisees to be less than ritually pure. In the end, a devout man named Matthias was chosen, but his election marked the beginning of a cleavage between a conservative group of former Pharisees within the congregation and those with more liberal views concerning the Law. This cleavage was to trouble the new congregation—and in fact the entire church—more and more as the years passed.

Even though he had favored Barnabas, Peter was not displeased by the choice of Matthias. In time he came to see that things had actually happened for the best, since Barnabas was left to become his entrusted aide, with an experience of the world outside Israel that would prove to be of great value when they began to obey Jesus's instructions to "preach to all nations."

Even though the synagogue of the Nazarenes was officially organized and holding services of its own, the nucleus of those who dared to tell the story of Jesus in the very spot where he had been crucified was still very small. Many who had listened while the Master taught here in Jerusalem were afraid to ally themselves openly with the Nazarenes lest they be caught up in the persecution which everyone expected the high priest to launch at any moment.

Peter himself experienced none of this fear; all that was behind him. But deep inside him he had always felt an instinctive distrust for Jerusalem itself, compounded from the natural aversion of one whose life had been spent in the open for the crowded streets, the smells, the petty jealousies and sharp dealings, the easily aroused fury of the mob, and his own sense of responsibility for the safety of those he had led back to the Holy City.

Like John, Peter had seen in the coming Feast of Pentecost, when approaching summer brought an end to the winter storms and Jews of the Diaspora particularly flocked to Jerusalem, a chance to tell large numbers of people the thrilling story of Jesus's death and Resurrection. But the number of those willing to tell that story and risk the anger of the high priest remained distressingly small, and when the fifty days between the Passover and Pentecost had run their course and the eve of the festival approached, Peter could hardly be blamed for being discouraged. When the day of Pentecost dawned, he rose from the couch where he had tossed sleeplessly most of the night, asking himself what he might do that he had not done, and left the city to seek help in the only place he knew to look for it—the spot where he had last seen Jesus.

Following the same road by which he had escaped from Jerusalem with Barnabas and Aristobulus long ago during the war of Varus, Peter crossed the aqueduct built by Pontius Pilate to bring water from springs in the hills south of the Hinnom Valley. Turning eastward, he passed the Field of Aceldama, purchased with the thirty pieces of silver given to Judas by the high priest for betraying Jesus's whereabouts that night in the Garden of Gethsemane and allowing him to be taken without stirring up an outcry.

Judas, Peter knew, had been buried in that field. And remembering vividly his own grievous sin that night, he paused to speak a prayer for Jesus's betrayer who had been driven to his terrible act, Peter himself was convinced, by the same desire to force the Master into naming himself the temporal Messiah and true King of the Jews that had made Peter slash at the servant of the high priest with Barnabas' sword.

Only a few people were stirring this early. A party of thorngatherers on the way to pull up dead burnet bushes—favored by potters to fire their ovens because the tough, dry wood burned with a hot flame and almost no ash—looked at him curiously. A weaver from Hebron, whose looms produced some of the finest wool cloth in the region, responded to Peter's courteous greeting with a grunt as he tugged on the

lead rope of a line of mules upon whose backs the bales were
piled high, urging them toward the city so he could be first in
line when the markets opened and the haggling over prices
began.

At the gate of the Garden of Gethsemane, Peter paused
for a moment at the spot where he had experienced the second
greatest fear of his life. No vestige remained of that fear now,
and he knew that what had happened there was part of a fore-
ordained plan revealed on several occasions by Jesus himself,
though the disciples had been unable to understand his meaning at the time. Peter did not go into the inner part of the
garden where Jesus had prayed that night, but not because he
was afraid of the dark, tortured shadows cast by the gnarled
olive trees or the looming boulders marking the nearby tombs.
Rather it was humility that held him back, humility and a conviction of his own unworthiness that made him reluctant to
violate with his presence a place sacred to the memory of the
Master.

Nor did Peter pray for himself when he reached the spot
where he had waited with James and John that night and had
fallen asleep. Instead, he asked only that the Master's will
concerning those left in his care be revealed to him, so he
might not fail in his task. But though he remained for a long
time in prayer, hoping to see a familiar figure emerge from
the shadows in the depths of the garden, he did not feel the
warm assurance of Jesus's answering—but unseen—presence
in his heart. Finally, he left the garden and climbed to the top
of the hill where they had last seen the Master.

The sun had not yet begun to show itself above the eastern
range of mountains marking the high tableland of the desert
beyond the *ghor*, though the hills of Moab, even in the half
darkness before dawn, were already beginning to take on the
pinkish haze that marked them during the day. Peter had

never been beyond that line of heights to the east, but he had often heard caravan drivers and travelers along the Way of the Sea describe the riches of Babylon and other cities in the Tigris-Euphrates Valley and the broad alluvial plains which were said to be as fertile even as the Nile Valley of Egypt.

Many Jews lived in Babylon, he knew, for less than half of those taken there at the time of the Assyrian conquest had chosen to return when the Persian rulers, Cyrus and Darius, offered them the right to colonize their homeland once again and restore the glory of Jerusalem laid waste by the brutal Assyrian kings. Peter could not help feeling a rising sense of excitement at the thought that Jesus's charge to preach in his name among all nations might one day take him to the fabled lands of the East. But he had no inkling then that the same charge would one day lead him to preach to Gentiles in the far-flung cities of the empire and even in its very heart— Rome.

III

By the time Peter returned to Mary's house, the congregation had already begun to gather in the upper room for the celebration of Pentecost. He did not let them see the depression of spirit that had gripped him. Instead, he rose to lead them in prayer but had barely begun when he became conscious of a mighty roar, as if a storm were rushing down upon the city— although the weather outside was sunny and bright. He had only time to wonder whether it might be another such storm as had assailed Jerusalem upon the day Jesus was crucified and the lightning had rent the veil of the temple, before the roar of wind filled the house, drowning out his words as he prayed.

Afterward, those who were watching swore that tongues of fire filled the upper room, touching each of the Twelve, and that at the same time the whole company was seized by a frenzy in which they shouted aloud in tongues none of them had ever used before. Most remarkable of all, listeners declared afterward that no matter from what part of the world they had come, each heard words spoken in his own language—though most of the Twelve were relatively unlettered fishermen from Galilee.

Simon Peter was not concerned with what was happening to others, however. With a surge of joy, he recognized that the very spirit of Jesus, nonetheless tangible though unseen, was there with them in the room. And with that conviction he experienced a sense of unlimited power filling every part of his being and sweeping away all doubt and uncertainty, all depression and discouragement.

The roar of the wind, the ecstatic shouts of those in the upper room, and the excited stories of the onlookers created a sensation in the narrow streets of the Lower City. And as word of the miraculous events taking place in the congregation of the Nazarenes raced through Jerusalem, people from all sides poured into the area, eager to see the men responsible for such strange and mysterious occurrences.

Some of the onlookers said Jesus of Nazareth had returned and was in the upper room with his followers; others that the Galileans had been seized by an unseen presence, perhaps even by the very spirit of God. A few laughed derisively and accused them of being drunk with the new wine that was traditionally the favorite beverage during the Feast of Pentecost. But of them all, only Simon Peter fully understood what was actually happening. Jesus himself had promised upon his last appearance to Peter and the others that they would be "endued with the power from on high." And now at last the

Master had given them his final legacy, the Holy Spirit through whose presence they were endowed with power from God himself.

The sight of Barnabas' worried face at the door leading to the stairway finally brought Peter back to a consciousness of the world outside. Something must be badly wrong, he knew, to make Barnabas break in upon him during this hour of highest exaltation. Getting to his feet, he went to the doorway where the tall Cypriot was standing.

"They are saying outside that all of you are drunk," Barnabas said anxiously. "If that report spreads abroad, it will do all of us harm."

Peter knew what was troubling Barnabas—the certainty that those responsible for the Crucifixion of Jesus would quickly seize upon any excuse to discredit the men who followed the Nazarene. Even more important, it might be a long time before Peter himself would have an opportunity to speak to so large a crowd as had gathered outside the house. Nodding to Barnabas to follow, he stepped out upon the small balcony, or landing, at the top of the outside stairway, and lifted his hands for silence. As far as he could see in either direction, a sea of faces looked up at him, and as he waited, calm and certain, the hooting and catcalling gradually died away.

"Men of Judea and all you that dwell at Jerusalem, let this be known to you and listen to my words." Peter's voice, ringing with an assurance and authority none of them had ever heard in it before, stilled the last derisive cries of the crowd. Every eye was upon the sturdy, broad-shouldered figure standing there upon the balcony, well above their heads, and every ear was attentive to his words.

"These men are not drunk as you suppose," Peter assured the crowd. "But this is that which was spoken by the prophet Joel who said: *'It shall come to pass in the last days, saith God,*

I will pour out of my spirit upon all flesh, and your sons and daughters shall prophesy, your young men shall see visions, and your old men shall dream dreams. On my servants and on my handmaidens you shall pour out in those days of my spirit, that they shall prophesy. And I will show wonders in heaven above and signs in the earth beneath, blood and fire and vapor of smoke. The sun shall be turned into darkness and the moon into blood before that great and notable day of the Lord. And it shall come to pass, that whoever shall call on the name of the Lord shall be saved.'"

Peter held the rapt attention of the crowd now, for the scrolls of the prophets from which he was quoting were read each Sabbath in the synagogues and were highly respected by all—particularly where they concerned the coming of the Messiah.

"Men of Israel hear these words," he continued. "Jesus of Nazareth was a man approved of God among you by miracles and wonders and signs which God did through him in your midst, as you yourselves know. He was delivered by the determined counsel and foreknowledge of God, but you have taken and crucified him. You have slain by wicked hands this man whom God raised up, having loosed the pains of death because it was not possible that he should be held by it."

A murmur rose from the crowd at this bold assertion that Jesus of Nazareth had actually risen from the dead and that his body had not been spirited away—as the high priest had bribed the guards at the tomb to testify. It was also a forthright claim that the Nazarene was truly the Messiah, since no one else could triumph over death. In fact, none listening could fail to realize that with his words the stocky Galilean fisherman was casting a challenge into the very faces of the chief priests and the Pharisees who had conspired to have the Nazarene crucified under Roman law.

"Let me freely speak to you of David." Peter had not yet finished excoriating those who had crucified the man he served. "For being a prophet and knowing God had sworn an oath to him that from the fruit of his loins he would raise up Christ, the Messiah, to sit upon the throne, David spoke of the Resurrection of Christ that his soul was not left in hell, and neither did his flesh see corruption. We are witnesses that God raised up Jesus and therefore, being exalted by the right hand of God and having received from the Father the promise of the Holy Spirit, he has caused the things that you have just seen and heard. Therefore let all the house of Israel know assuredly that God has made that same Jesus whom you crucified both Lord and Christ."

"What shall we do?" A man begged from the back of the crowd, and others took up the cry, pressing forward to the foot of the stairway.

"Save yourselves from this untoward generation by believing upon the name of the Lord Jesus Christ," Peter told them. "For God so loved the world that he gave his only begotten Son, that whoever believes in him shall not die but receive eternal life."

Calling to the rest of the Twelve to follow him, Peter descended the steps to the street. There they fanned out through the crowd, telling over and over again the story of the Christ who had been sent to free men, not only from sin but from the burden of death itself.

All that day as word of what was happening at the synagogue of the Nazarenes spread through the city, people flocked to hear Peter and the others who fearlessly gave testimony to the death and Resurrection of Jesus of Nazareth without regard for what might happen to them because of their boldness. And when this first great day of the new mission in Jerusalem ended, more than three thousand people had been added to their number.

IV

The startling events of the day of Pentecost changed the congregation of the Nazarenes as nothing else could have done—except perhaps the return of Jesus himself. From a small and struggling group, constantly fearful lest they be arrested by the authorities for following a man who had been executed under Roman law on the charge of treason, the group was transformed almost overnight into a large body of worshipers whose very size made it necessary to find another meeting place. This in itself did not prove difficult, however, and a large building nearby was rented, the upper room in Mary's house being retained as a meeting place for the disciples themselves and the elders of the congregation.

All of this sudden activity in what had been almost a dying group posed many problems for Simon Peter, its acknowledged leader. The matter of authority he solved by delegating to others of the Twelve in Jerusalem as much responsibility as possible for guiding sections of the church. And since the mere size of the group made the designation of "synagogue" rather inappropriate, they chose for themselves the Greek term *ecclesia*, meaning a church or a congregation.

Barnabas, too, was of great help to Peter in the day-to-day administration of the church's affairs. Being one of the Seventy, he was accepted by the disciples as next only to themselves in authority. And having come from the Diaspora, he was also acceptable to the Greek-speaking Jews who were drawn to the teachings of the new faith by the broader concepts of love and tolerance for one another which the Master had preached—concepts that Peter, even with his limited education, recognized as very similar to the teachings of great Greek philosophers such as Socrates and Plato.

From the beginning, a considerable part of the congregation chose to live as Jesus and his disciples had always lived, sharing all their possessions and their wages, and providing for their needs from a common purse. Though this, too, increased the day-to-day details of administration and the burdens upon Simon Peter, he was glad to see the new followers of Jesus take up the old custom, for it brought them close together in body and inevitably, he hoped, in spirit.

From the cross with his dying words, Jesus had committed the care of his mother, Mary of Nazareth, to her kinsman John, the son of Zebedee. One of Peter's first acts as leader of the Nazarene congregation in Jerusalem was to send John to Nazareth, asking Jesus's own family to join the group in Jerusalem. His reasons for this action were twofold. First he hoped their presence in Jerusalem would serve as a living symbol of the Master himself, encouraging his followers in whatever vicissitudes they might encounter because of their faith. But most of all he felt sure that James, the eldest kinsman of the Lord, could fill an important position in the young church.

"Do not think that I came to destroy the Law or the Prophets," Jesus had said. "I came not to destroy but to fulfill." And mindful of these words, Peter had insisted from the first that those who followed the Master in the new church at Jerusalem should not relax their customary obedience to the Laws of Moses.

James, in particular, was deeply versed in the intricacies of the Law as interpreted by the Pharisees. And by placing this aspect of the young church in his hands, Peter threw the weight of the natural reverence felt by most of the congregation for the family of Jesus on the side of the Law. This in turn, he hoped, would assuage some of the resentment developing in the other synagogues in Jerusalem over the loss of many from their membership to the congregation of the Nazarenes.

It did not occur to Peter then—or would he have been influenced by the consideration if it had—that by thrusting James into a position of prominence, he might lessen his own role in the church. A man with strong ties to both the earth and the water, Peter had seen in his own role of "the rock" only that of a foundation upon which the more elaborate structure of the church could be built. And as the foundation —after Jesus himself—he saw in his role an opportunity to hold together the varying materials of the structure, rather than to dominate others and make them do his will.

Jesus himself had outlined that role in Galilee when he had given the Twelve in a parable the lesson that a house built upon an unstable foundation of sand could not survive the onslaught of the storm, while one built upon a rock would withstand any attack. And Peter was instinctively carrying out this teaching of the Master when he worked to strengthen the congregation of the Nazarenes at Jerusalem and make it become the keystone upon which could be fashioned a larger structure.

Under Peter's inspired guidance, it was a joyous group indeed who lived together in Jerusalem during the early months after the outpouring of the Holy Spirit at Pentecost. The congregation grew daily as more and more people heard and accepted the good news—characterized best perhaps by the Greek word *evangelion*, meaning glad tidings or gospel—that the promised Messiah had come to Israel, and though condemned to die a cruel death upon a Roman cross, had risen from the dead in final proof that all who believed in him and followed his way could find eternal life.

Those able to work performed their tasks gladly, giving their hire to the common fund from which all in this household of Christ were fed and clothed. And those who contributed all their possessions and their earnings to the common purse—as did Peter, the other disciples, Barnabas and many others—were naturally looked up to by the rest, as more and more joined the *ecclesia* of the Nazarenes and shared with one another.

With the church thriving as it had not thrived even during Jesus's life on earth—save perhaps in those first exciting months of the early Galilean ministry, following the Master's rejection at Nazareth and the calling of the Twelve—Peter had every right to be satisfied with his accomplishments. But though he would hardly have named it such or even have realized what had happened, Peter had been infected with the divine discontent which Jesus instilled into the hearts of all those who served him. And being infected, Peter could not long be content even with the magnificent reality of the growing church of which he was the head.

If the command of Jesus to preach the glad tidings to all nations were to be carried out, Peter had sensed from the first that a larger platform by far would be needed than was afforded by the congregation and the building where it held its services. In fact, only the largest rostrum in Jerusalem—and later an even wider sphere—would suffice, which meant beginning with the Porch of Solomon in the temple itself. There in a single day, particularly during the great religious festivals, more people would hear about Jesus, his mission, death and Resurrection than the apostles—as the disciples had renamed themselves—could reach in a month of preaching on the streets of Jerusalem. When Peter broached the subject of this new venture to the elders, however, he met immediate opposition.

"Why bait Caiaphas when he has not set his curs among the rabble upon us?" Barnabas demanded. "The congregation grows daily, and soon ours will be the largest in the city."

"What Barnabas says is true, Peter," James, the kinsman of the Lord, added. "If we stir Caiaphas into action now by appearing on the Porch of Solomon, all we have gained may be lost."

"Jesus could have held the multitude, after he fed the five thousand, by giving them bread for which they had not labored," Peter pointed out. "But he chose to remind them that the real bread of life was found in him."

"And they deserted him for it," one of the Twelve reminded him. "So we had to flee into Syro-Phoenicia to escape from Herod Antipas."

"Yet it was in Syro-Phoenicia that the Lord first brought his message to others than Jews," Peter said. "Have you forgotten that he told us to go and preach to all nations?"

"Surely he meant for us to stay here in Jerusalem where Jews from all parts of the world come for the feast days," James protested. "Already we have sent many of them back to establish congregations in their own cities. Is that not enough, Simon?"

It was true, as James had said, that many from the Diaspora had already heard the good news in Jerusalem and had gone out to tell it again in other lands. Already, letters were beginning to come from these congregations, telling of progress almost as rapid as that made here in Jerusalem. But deep inside himself Peter could not escape the feeling that even this was not enough, a feeling he'd experienced often enough now to recognize it as the will of the Master revealed in his own soul.

"Other teachers speak freely from the Porch of Solomon," he said. "If we do not take what is our right, then we can claim no rights when we are challenged by the high priest. As an established congregation, the Sanhedrin will protect us, for Nicodemus and some others among our number are members of the court. But only if we claim the same rights as any other synagogue, can we demand protection."

None could argue against his logic, but as he looked around the group Peter could see fear and apprehension concerning the result of the action he proposed in almost all their faces. Nor could he find it in his heart to censure them, for he knew the picture that was foremost in their minds. It was the rounded, rocky crest of Golgotha or Calvary at the northern edge of the city, where more than once, all of them had seen Roman crosses outlined against the sky, and where, if Caiaphas launched an attack against them as he had against Jesus, each of them might hang.

"I shall go to the temple because I know it is what Jesus would have me do," Peter said firmly. "But I will order no man to accompany me."

For a moment there was silence, then John stepped from among the group. "Two will be enough," he said. "I will go with you to the temple, Peter."

"Pray for us, all of you," Peter told the group. "Tomorrow we two will speak from the Porch of Solomon."

V

It was about the eighth hour when Peter and John approached the temple the next morning. In the market beneath the Royal Porch, the moneychangers were already sitting before their cabinets with the coins arranged in orderly stacks before them. The cries of the vendors filled the area with a babble of sound, just as they had on the day Jesus had cleansed the market so dramatically, but Peter had no desire to embroil himself with the temple authorities by a similar action today. His purpose was simply to establish the right of the apostles —as leaders of the congregation of the Nazarenes—to teach from the Porch of Solomon. Once that was done, he planned to send one or more of their number there daily.

As Peter and John were crossing the outer court to the Beautiful Gate, through which they planned to enter the sacred area, they saw a crippled beggar being carried by two others and deposited beside the gate. John would have passed the beggar by as they had passed others in the Sanctuary— since it was a favorite spot for mendicants—but Peter looked down and saw that the man's legs were shriveled and useless, either from some wasting disease or from birth, and was filled with a deep sense of compassion.

"Silver and gold have I none," he said quietly to the cripple," but such as I have, I give you. In the name of Jesus Christ of Nazareth, rise up and walk."

For a moment the man stared up at Peter uncomprehendingly. But when the apostle reached out and took his hand, tears of joy began to roll down his cheeks as he felt strength coursing through paralyzed limbs.

"God be praised! I am healed!" he cried, and with Peter

210 § UPON THIS ROCK

supporting him, rose to his feet. He tottered unsteadily at first, for he had never walked before. But encouraged by Peter, he took a tentative step, followed by another and still another, each time stronger and more sure of himself. Finally, filled with joy over his deliverance, he broke away and ran ahead of the two apostles, shouting to all he passed that he had been healed by the leaders of the Nazarenes.

News of the miracle spread through the temple rapidly for thousands had seen the helpless paralytic lying beside the Beautiful Gate day after day, begging for alms, and recognized him when he came running across the court. By the time Peter and John reached the Porch of Solomon, a considerable crowd had gathered, with the healed man in their midst, still babbling the news of his miraculous cure and fairly skipping with joy because his wasted limbs had been made whole.

No one sought to interfere when Peter mounted one of the platforms used by the teachers. But as he waited for the excited babble of the crowd to subside he could hear the rhythmic tramp of the soldiers in the Roman garrison walking their post upon the wall of the nearby fortress of Antonia. And he could plainly see the walkway from the Roman prison to the courts of the temple by which they could reach the Sanctuary quickly in case of a riot.

Many of the students who customarily sat before the rabbis had already left their teachers and joined the crowd around Peter and John. As the paralytic who had been made whole continued to tell the news of his healing to all who would listen, questions were asked from every side, but Peter did not choose to answer them. Instead, he took a more direct approach.

"Men of Israel, why do you marvel at this?" he demanded. "And why do you look so earnestly upon us, as though we had made this man walk by our own power or holiness? The God of Abraham, Isaac and Jacob, the God of our fathers has glorified his Son Jesus, whom you delivered up and denied in the presence of Pilate—although Pilate was determined to let him go. You denied the Holy One and desired that Barabbas, a murderer, be granted to you instead. You killed the Prince of life whom God raised from the dead, and we are witnesses of it." Turning, he pointed to the former paralytic. "This man whom you see and know has been made strong through faith in Jesus's name, and indeed by faith he has been given perfect soundness in the presence of all of you."

Every eye was fixed now upon Peter. Though his robe was cut from the rough homespun cloth woven by the women of Galilee and he showed none of the pretensions with which the rabbis were wont to announce their great learning, no man listening failed to realize that he spoke with an authority and conviction greater than even the most learned of the teachers.

"Brethren, I know you did it through ignorance, as also did your rulers," Peter continued. "But what God had already spoken by the mouth of his prophets, namely that Christ should suffer, he has now fulfilled. Therefore, repent and be converted in order that your sins may be blotted out when the time of refreshing shall come from the Lord. Then he shall send Jesus Christ who was preached to you before, and whom the heaven must receive until the time for restitution of all things which God spoke by the mouth of his holy prophet since the world began."

Upon the occasion of his first great address, when the Holy Spirit had descended upon the Twelve and many others at Pentecost, Peter had referred frequently to the writings of the prophets foretelling the coming of the Messiah. Now he once again chose this method of bringing home to his listeners the divinity of Jesus by adding: "Moses truly said to the fathers: '*A prophet shall the Lord your God raise up to you of your brethren, like to me. You shall hear him in all things that he shall say to you, and it shall come to pass that every soul who will not hear that prophet shall be destroyed.*' "

From the second level of the temple came the tread of marching feet, and the crowd around Peter and John began to drift away, fearing that the high priest had called the Romans to seize these bold followers of a man they had crucified on a charge of treason against Rome itself. Peter and John could have escaped in the crowd but remained in their places, even when a detail of troops appeared upon the stairway leading down from the level above.

They were not Romans but temple guards, easily identified by their dark skins and colorful uniforms. Several priests in rich vestments accompanied them, and at the foot of the stairway the detail of soldiers wheeled and crossed the portico to where Peter and John still stood, deserted now by everyone except the paralytic who had been healed. At the command of the captain, the two apostles were quickly surrounded, hiding them from observation by the sentries on the walls of the Antonia nearby, in case there was resistance. And before Peter and John could protest the injustice of their arrest for doing no more than any teacher had always been free to do, they were hustled away to a secluded room in the temple and locked inside.

Only a few months before, Peter would have been seized by fear at the prospect of the painful death that remained as such a vivid memory from his childhood—the agony of hanging from a cross while he slowly went mad from exposure and pain as his father no doubt had done. But there was no fear in his heart now, or in that of his slighter companion John, though they were in much the same danger Jesus had been in on the night of his arrest in Gethsemane. Instead, the two spoke once again the prayer the Master himself had taught them and which they had all come to love, asking only that the will of God should be done.

VI

The Great Sanhedrin, highest court of Hebrew authority, met twice a week in a building of its own on the west side of the hill upon which the temple stood. Peter had expected that they would be brought before the great court and charged there. But, to his surprise, when the guards came for them shortly after the Levitical trumpet announced the beginning of the following day, the two were taken to a smaller room where about a dozen men were gathered behind a table. The paralytic they had healed was also in the room, sitting upon a bench in the corner, presumably as a witness.

Caiaphas, the high priest and bitter enemy of Jesus, was in the group, with his father-in-law, the old High Priest Annas, whom he had succeeded in office. The rest were prominent Pharisees and Sadducees, with a few lawyers. This, Peter realized, must be the so-called Priestly Council which the lawyer Nicodemus had told him was largely responsible for the bargain with Judas and the subsequent condemnation of Jesus.

Caiaphas sat at the center of the table, staring angrily at the two who had dared to preach the Nazarene heresy in the very temple itself. But when he spoke, his voice was guarded, and Peter realized with a start that the high priest was afraid. Nor did he need to look far for the cause.

It had been Caiaphas, Peter remembered now, who had requested of Pilate that the tomb in which Jesus's body was placed be sealed and guards posted before it. On the morning when Mary of Magdala had gone to the tomb to prepare the body for burial, she had found it open and the guards gone. And from Barnabas, Peter had learned upon his return to Jerusalem that, finding the tomb empty and the stone rolled away by unseen hands, the guards had fled to the high priest in terror.

Caiaphas, however, could not accept the truth of Jesus's Resurrection, even when testified to by the guards, since to do so was to condemn himself for treacherously arranging to have the Romans crucify the Son of God. He had therefore bribed the soldiers to swear that the followers of Jesus had stolen the body from the tomb during the night, and had published that story abroad in Jerusalem. But Caiaphas' gold could not purge his own soul of the fear that Jesus had truly risen from the dead, and Peter realized now that the high priest must be slowly undergoing destruction by the knowledge of his own guilt.

Peter had felt no personal fear, even when he and John had been shut up in the hold—as the small prison was called. Now, with the realization that the man responsible for Jesus's death was afraid, he was filled with a new sense of assurance and power. Drawing himself up proudly, he waited for his accusers to speak.

"This man you healed yesterday by the Beautiful Gate," Caiaphas said, "by what power and in what name did you do it?"

Peter saw Nicodemus, his face anxious, enter the chamber as the high priest finished speaking. The lawyer started toward the two apostles, but when Peter began to speak, he stopped and moved back to take a seat among some clerks and other minor officials who occupied one side of the chamber.

"Rulers of the people and elders of Israel." It was not a

rough and unlettered fisherman of Galilee who spoke, but a leader of men—strong, resolute and sure of himself as the designated earthly lieutenant of the Son of God. "If we are being examined concerning the good deed done to an impotent man and by what means he is made whole, then let it be known to all of you and to all the people of Israel that this man stands here before you, healed by the name of Jesus Christ of Nazareth, whom you crucified and whom God raised from the dead. This same Jesus, the stone that was set at naught by you builders, has now become the head of the corner, and there is no salvation in any other, for no other name in Heaven is given to men whereby we must be saved."

The cripple was next called to testify. He stated that he was more than forty years old and had been paralyzed from birth; yet, as he lay by the gate asking for alms, the two men standing before the council had healed him. No one questioned him, for all knew him and could plainly see that the limbs which had been paralyzed were now filled with strength and that he was able to walk and even run and leap.

When the testimony was completed, Peter and John were ushered outside the chamber and left under guard in the corridor. Through the closed door they could hear voices raised in anger, and Peter was sure Caiaphas was demanding their deaths on the grounds that it was blasphemy to attribute divine power to the followers of a Nazarene heretic. But when they were brought back into the chamber, it was Annas who addressed them, proving, he judged, that a conservative faction of the council must have overridden the high priest in this particular controversy.

"We command you not to speak or teach at all in the name of Jesus," Annas told them, but Peter refused to abide by the old priest's decree.

"Judge yourself whether it is right in the sight of God to

hearken to you more than to God," he said boldly. "For we can only speak the things we have seen and heard."

Annas blustered and threatened awhile, but in the end the two apostles were released, since even so biased a court could find neither sin nor blasphemy in healing a man who had been paralyzed from birth. As Peter and John were leaving the temple, Nicodemus caught up with them.

"I came to the chamber of the Sanhedrin as soon as I heard you were to be brought before the Priestly Council, hoping to help you," the lawyer said. "But I could see that you needed no help."

"Most of the men on the council are godly men," Peter said. "When I pointed out the truth, they could not deny it."

"Those same godly men sent our Lord to be crucified," Nicodemus reminded him. "What stopped them today was your boldness, Simon. They expected anything but that, and were not prepared to combat it."

"I spoke only the truth. It was that they could not withstand."

Nicodemus looked at him for a long moment, then he smiled. "Perhaps we are both right," he conceded. "After all, the psalmist says: 'His truth shall be thy shield and buckler. Thou shall not be afraid of the terror by night, the arrow that flies by day, the pestilence that walks in darkness, nor the destruction that wastes at noonday.'"

VII

As leader of the congregation of the Nazarenes, it was Peter's custom to receive each morning the gifts of those who had chosen to devote their lives to the work of furthering the spread of Jesus's teachings. When they had numbered only Twelve besides the Master, the keeping of the common purse had been simple enough—though even then Judas had managed to dip from it for his own use. Now, with hundreds of people sharing, the task of handling the funds and purchasing needed supplies quickly became time-consuming and arduous. Besides, since those who gave everything were highly regarded in the church, a few sought to gain that respect by claiming all their worldly goods had been given, while in fact holding back some for themselves.

Before Peter one day came a man named Ananias, laying a purse of money upon the pile of gifts to be presented that morning. Peter knew Ananias was a rich man, and the size of the purse did not seem in keeping with his wealth—though he claimed, like the others, to have sold his possessions and brought them to the common fund.

"Ananias!" Peter called.

The other man was about to pass on after making his gift, and quickly averted his eyes, but not before Peter saw the guilt written there. And angered that anyone should be so covetous as to give to the Lord less than was rightfully due him, the apostle's eyes blazed with a sudden wrath.

"Why has Satan filled your heart to lie to the Holy Ghost and keep back part of the purse of the Lord?" he demanded.

The culprit tried to bluster but could only quail before Peter's wrath.

"While it remained, was it not your land; and after it was sold, was the money not under your control?" Peter demanded.

"I—I." Ananias sought to speak but managed only a hollow croak of fear.

"You have not lied to men, Ananias, but to God!" Peter thundered.

Guilt was written in the sickly fear in Ananias' eyes, in the drops of sweat upon his forehead, and in the trembling of his hands, as if he had been suddenly afflicted with a palsy. He swallowed convulsively and opened his mouth as if to answer, but again only a harsh croak emerged. Then convulsively his hands reached up to tear at the collar of his robe, as if he were being choked by unseen fingers. And still without answering a word in his own defense, Ananias' eyes glazed over and he toppled heavily to the floor.

Barnabas had been standing near Peter, while the young scribe Mark was sitting at a little table nearby with pen, ink and parchment before him, keeping a record of all that was being given. Barnabas knelt beside the stricken Ananias for a moment; when he looked up, his face was grave.

"He is dead," he announced in a tone of awe.

"The Lord struck him down for his perfidy," Peter said harshly, still angry that anyone in the congregation had sought to deny God a part of his possessions. "Take him away and prepare him for burial."

When he looked at the people waiting in line to place their gifts before him, however, Peter saw only fear and horror written in most of them, as well as in the eyes of John Mark who was looking up at him as if he were unable to believe the evidence of his own eyes. And seeing himself—as it were —reflected in a mirror through the gaze of Mark, Peter was suddenly overcome with a sense of guilt at the enormity of what he had done in loosing a power stronger than any yet given to the other apostles, stronger even than the ability to raise from the dead—the power to kill.

Always deeply honest and fair in everything, Peter realized that it was too late for any action he might take to help Ananias, whose body was already being carried away by some of the younger men. But there was one way to learn the truth—and perhaps relieve his own conscience.

"Does Ananias have a wife?" he asked Barnabas when the tally of the gifts had been completed.

"Yes. Her name is Sapphira."

"Send for her, so I can question her."

"Why trouble yourself about the woman? Or about Ananias? The man was lying; it showed in his face. If you had allowed him to hold back part of what he owned, others would have followed his example—as Judas did."

"He had no opportunity to speak in his own defense," Peter explained. "Or to repent."

"Who could speak against the will of God?" Having given everything he possessed unreservedly, Barnabas obviously felt little sympathy for one who had tried to cheat. But when he saw the troubled look still in Peter's eyes, he added, "Nevertheless, I will send her to you as soon as I can find her."

Sapphira had gone into the city that morning to put the rest of the price she and her husband had received from the land into the hands of moneylenders, where it would earn usury at a rate and under conditions strictly governed by Mosaic Law. When she returned, Barnabas brought her to Peter immediately, giving her no chance to learn what had happened and make up a story in advance. Peter received the woman courteously, but he could hardly fail to see the guarded look in her eyes or notice the way she twisted an expensive ring nervously on one of her fingers.

"For what price did you sell the land?" he asked, and Sapphira named the amount in the purse her husband had given to the common fund that morning.

"Are you sure you sold it for that sum?" Peter insisted.

"Yes." In her agitation, the woman reminded him of an animal cornered by hunters, but he knew he must show no mercy until he had obtained positive proof of her guilt—or innocence. For only in that way could he combat the fear he had seen in the eyes of those who had watched Ananias die a few hours earlier and—even more important—ease the pangs of his own conscience.

"Why did you and Ananias conspire to tempt the spirit of the Lord?" he demanded, hoping to shock the woman into an admission of guilt by a direct accusation. "Behold, the feet of those who buried your husband are at the door to carry you out."

It was a brutal thrust, and when the color suddenly drained from Sapphira's cheeks and she cried out in horror, Peter realized that she had not yet been told of her husband's death. But it was already too late to remedy that oversight. The same glazed look showed in her eyes that Peter had seen in those of Ananias a few hours before. Like a sack of grain split with a knife, she collapsed at his feet. And even as he shouted for Barnabas with a sense of horror that clutched at his throat and threatened to strangle him, Peter knew the woman was dead.

"Sapphira was struck down by the knowledge of her own guilt—as was her husband." Barnabas tried to comfort Peter while the woman was being carried away. "When Ananias held back the money, I suspected she might have gone to place the rest of it at usury for her own gain, so I sent someone to follow her. She even told the moneylender that the purse she gave him came from the sale of the land, so both of them were equally guilty. It was God's hand that struck them down, not yours."

"I am going to the garden," Peter said, as if he had not

heard Barnabas at all. "See that they are buried properly and their money given to the poor and the widows."

VIII

It was cool and pleasant in the shade of the gnarled olive trees growing deep within the beautiful Garden of Gethsemane where Jesus had often sought strength and comfort through prayer. Weary and deeply troubled, Peter felt a strong impulse to stretch himself upon the soft grass, but did not yield, for he had come there to think and pray, hoping for a revelation from Jesus telling him just how he had erred in the case of the two who had lost their lives that morning. What troubled him most was the realization that he did not know whether to pray for forgiveness, guidance or for strength to contain his wrath so nothing like this might ever happen again.

His first sin had been in letting himself become angry with Ananias that morning, Peter decided when he had retraced the events of the morning step by step in his mind. Instead, he should have pointed out the man's sin in such a way that Ananias would have been brought to see it and repent, undoing the evil that he and his wife had committed.

"Whoever shall be great among you, let him be your minister," Jesus had said on the road between Galilee and Jerusalem as they had journeyed to the Holy City for the final Passover. "And whoever will be chief among you, let him be your servant, even as the Son of Man came not to be ministered unto, but to minister and to give his life as ransom for many."

He had indeed sinned grievously, Peter admitted; he had

sinned in being so proud of his own position of authority that he had let himself become angry when someone had dared not to yield completely to it. Moreover, in his anger he had used a power which he promised himself now would never be used again in such a cause. And with that decision he at last knew what it was for which he should pray most.

It was for humility, the humility not to become puffed up because Jesus had made him leader of the flock; the faith to move mountains, should that be necessary to protect those left in his care; and the self-control never again to use the power of death, when through the power of life instead, he might enable sinners like Ananias and Sapphira to save their souls for eternity.

These were the things Peter prayed for as the sun sank toward the range of hills to the west and the shadows of the heights crowned by the glory of the temple began to creep across the Kidron Valley toward the mount and the garden. And, in answer to his prayer, he seemed to hear a familiar beloved voice saying once again:

"Come to me all you that labor and are heavy laden; and I will give you rest. Take my yoke upon you and learn of me, for I am meek and lowly in heart, and you shall find rest for your souls."

Comforted now and sure of his future course, Simon Peter stretched out upon a patch of soft grass and slept until the sound of a familiar voice calling his name awakened him. He sat up, very much refreshed, and when the call came again, saw a slender figure ascending the slope toward the gate leading to the garden.

"I am up here, Mark," he called to the boy. "Beneath the olive trees in the depths of the garden."

"Barnabas and I were worried." The relief Mark felt at finding Peter showed in his face when he ran panting through the gate of the garden and stopped beside Peter. "We were afraid—"

"That I was troubled by guilt for what happened to Ananias and Sapphira?"

"Y—yes."

"I saw the doubt in your eyes when Ananias fell dead. You were right to question my causing his death, Mark."

"It was his own guilty secret that killed Ananias," the youth protested loyally. "I talked to Barnabas and I know that now."

"No, Mark," Peter told him. "I was guilty of using a power whose strength I did not know—a power that killed two people when they might have been saved."

"Wh— What are you going to do?"

"Jesus showed me the way and forgave me my sin. I hope I shall not prove so weak again."

"The Master spoke to you? Here?"

"Not in the flesh, but in the same way he speaks to all who believe in him—through prayer. He reminded me of some words he once spoke on the road between Scythopolis and Jericho when we were making the last journey with him to Jerusalem."

"You remember every word of the Master's, don't you?" the youth asked in a tone of awe.

"Not everything. Besides, not all of us were with him every day, so some heard him say one thing and some another. Why do you ask?"

"I was thinking that the sayings of Jesus should be written down somewhere so they can be preserved."

"It is a good suggestion," Peter agreed. "Before long the Twelve must journey abroad and bring the good news to others. Some of us may not come back."

"I will soon finish my studies in the Scribes' School at the temple," Mark said eagerly. "Let me go with you then, and as you tell the story of Jesus and his teachings I will write them down."

Peter had become very fond of Mark since he had been living in the upper room of Mary's home. The youth would be a pleasant companion, he knew, and it would help him rekindle the memory of Jesus and his teachings if he were required to make the effort of recalling them so they could be written down. Afterward, too, many copies of the account could be made by one of the establishments of scribes who prepared scrolls of the Law and the Prophets for sale. Then, carried to all parts of the world by Jews from the Diaspora returning to their homes from the festivals in Jerusalem, the good news of the Messiah's coming and his teachings could be spread abroad—as Jesus had instructed them.

"You will be a joy to me, I am sure," Peter said, putting his hand upon Mark's shoulder. "And who knows? The words you write may one day be read by people everywhere."

IX

The deaths of Ananias and Sapphira caused some depletion in the ranks of the Nazarene congregation when those whose faith was not great enough to let them part with their possessions fell aside. But it also strengthened the position of Simon Peter considerably, for no one could doubt now that he was indeed acting as the agent of the Lord himself in guiding the group. And with Peter, John or some of the other apostles preaching boldly every day from the Porch of Solomon, the truth of Jesus's coming, his shameful death and triumph over the hated Roman cross, new converts continued to swell the group. Even more important to Peter's purpose—for he was already looking to the day when the ministry of those who had been closest to Jesus would expand to a much wider sphere—was the large number of people from the Diaspora who heard and believed, returning home to sow seed in the fallow ground provided by their own synagogues.

For centuries, Jews of the Dispersion had been drifting slowly away from the rigid tenets of Mosaic Law, though they still looked to Jerusalem as the Holy City of their faith and paid the temple tribute. Surrounded largely by Gentiles—though holding themselves apart when they could, as in the Jewish quarter of Alexandria, whose population was larger than that of Jerusalem itself—they were constantly exposed to different ways of thought, particularly the broader philosophies of the Greeks.

To these Jews of the Diaspora, the teachings of Jesus that men should govern their relationships with each other by what he had called his new commandment: "That you love one another, as I have loved you," had a special appeal. And when Caiaphas saw more and more of them taking what he considered the Nazarene heresy to their own synagogues, inevitably lessening the hold of the temple authorities over the most prosperous group of Jews within the faith, he was forced to an action he might not otherwise have taken. His strategy was simply the same he had sought to use in destroying Jesus—that of naming the Nazarenes as blasphemers before the Sanhedrin and having them condemned to death by the Jewish court, trusting that Pontius Pilate would approve the decision, as he had done in the case of Jesus.

While they were preaching within the city, Peter and John were arrested like common malefactors and thrown into prison with thieves, murderers and felons of every sort awaiting trial. For several days nothing happened, and though

Peter felt no fear, he was very much concerned about the fate of the congregation for which he was responsible. Caiaphas, he knew, would like nothing better than to have him and John condemned and executed as blasphemers, for then he could use the decision of the court as grounds upon which to harry all those who followed Jesus of Nazareth, putting them to death by stoning wherever he found them.

On the other hand, Peter himself had much to gain from a hearing before the full court. For if the Sanhedrin refused to name the leaders of the congregation of the Nazarenes as malefactors under the Law, the stage would be set for the widening sphere of activities he contemplated. To gain this, Peter was willing to risk imprisonment and possible death at the hands of the same man who had brought about the Crucifixion of Jesus, though he would have been better pleased if John had not been in the same grave danger of death.

Under the Roman procurators, the Jewish high court had been given considerably more freedom than it had possessed during the reign of Herod the Great. It was now empowered to arrest and condemn criminals—though the capital offense required approval by the governor. Pontius Pilate, however, was said to have become very moody since the death of the Nazarene, spending much of his time studying the writings of the Greek philosophers, searching for an answer to the question he had asked Jesus as he stood before the governor for sentencing—"What is truth?"

Mindful of Pilate's temper, Caiaphas had decided that nothing must go wrong in this trial, so an impressive group gathered in the palace of the Sanhedrin on the morning when Peter and John were finally brought before it. Even the old and feeble, who ordinarily did not come to the meetings—since its deliberations could be carried out with only twenty-three members—were present. When he had determined that the full membership was seated, Caiaphas ordered Peter and John brought before it.

The members of the Great Sanhedrin were arranged in a long curve behind tables extending from one corner of the room to another. Most of them were richly dressed, Peter saw, as befitted the leading Sadducees and Pharisees in the province of Judea and elsewhere, from which the membership of the court was largely drawn. But a few artisans were among them and a number of teachers or rabbis, men who exerted great influence upon the thinking of the people through their students and their utterances from the Porch of Solomon.

Generally speaking, the teachers of Israel were divided into two schools: those who followed the pious and saintly Rabbi Hillel, who had died some years before; and a smaller group who were adherents of the much more sternly minded Shammai. Hillel had taught the virtues of charity, humility, patience and true piety, and the principles of his school were still carried on by his grandson Gamaliel.

First in Israel to be known by the title of rabban, or master teacher, Gamaliel occupied a prominent place on the Sanhedrin. Though formulated more than two decades before the birth of Jesus, the teachings of Hillel bore a striking resemblance to those of the Master, except where Jesus had named himself the long-expected Christ. Hillel had been lamented after his death as "the humble, the pious, the disciple of Israel," and his followers were among the most influential men in Jerusalem and throughout Israel. In fact, the school of his grandson Gamaliel was one of the most popular and respected of all the various institutions training young men to be rabbis.

The followers of Shammai, on the other hand, were far narrower in interpreting the letter of the Laws of Moses. If any one thing could be said to characterize them, it was their intolerance of change in any form. As a result, debates which were often vitriolic and even violent took place between Pharisees of both persuasions over such things as the distance that might be covered in a Sabbath day's journey without sin, how many times the hands must be washed to cleanse them after accidental defilement—as with blood, pork or flesh sacrificed to idols—whether or not a physician could treat a person for an illness upon the Sabbath day without doing work, and similar absurdities.

As he waited for the proceedings to begin, Peter's gaze swept the chamber casually, then suddenly was riveted upon one man whose eyes stared back at him with a burning look that seemed almost one of hatred—though Peter was sure he had never seen the other man before.

"Who is that?" he whispered to Nicodemus, who sat beside him and John.

"Where?"

"At the end of the court, beside the scribe."

It took Nicodemus a moment to locate the man Peter had indicated in the crowd filling every available space in the chamber of the Sanhedrin. Peter studied him meanwhile, puzzled that his own attention had been so drawn to the other man. It was true that the other's head was majestic and almost godlike in appearance, but otherwise he was short and broad-shouldered, giving him a curious bandy-legged appearance. His mouth was wide and mobile, the cheekbones broad, and his eyes did not waver when they met Peter's, but continued to burn with the zeal of a fanatic.

"That is Saul of Tarsus," Nicodemus whispered to Peter. "Until a few months ago, he was Gamaliel's most brilliant pupil, but lately he has become an agent of the high priest."

The trial began just then, and Peter had no chance to speak

to Nicodemus further about the man called Saul. But all during the hearing he was conscious that Saul's eyes hardly ever left him and that the burning enmity in the other's gaze never seemed to waver—though for what reason, Peter could not surmise.

As he had at the former hearing before the Priestly Council, Caiaphas launched the attack. But he was no longer uncertain, as on that other occasion; instead, his manner was assured, as if he had somehow managed to convince himself that the story he had bribed the guards at the tomb to tell concerning the theft of Jesus's body were true. None of which really surprised Peter, for he had learned by now that people often convinced themselves they were right rather than face the truth that they were wrong.

"We commanded you not to teach in the name of Jesus of Nazareth," Caiaphas accused Peter and John. "Yet you have filled Jerusalem with your doctrine and intend to bring the blood of the Nazarene upon us."

Peter rose at once to defend himself. As his eyes swept the court, he was cheered somewhat by the fact that not all of those facing him appeared to be hostile, though there was no lessening of the antagonism in the eyes of Saul of Tarsus.

"We ought to obey God rather than men," Peter began his argument. "The God of our fathers raised up Jesus, whom you slew and hung upon a cross. Him, God has exalted with his right hand to be a Prince and a Saviour, to give repentance to Israel and forgiveness of sin. We are the witnesses of these things, and so also is the Holy Spirit, whom God has given to them that obey him."

"Blasphemer!" Caiaphas shouted, and a babble of supporting voices rose in the council and from among the onlookers.

Question after question was thrown at Peter and John, but they answered quietly, repeating again and again the simple truth that Jesus of Nazareth was the expected Messiah and Son of God, that he had come to earth to assume the burden of sin for those who believed in him, and to bring to them forgiveness and the assurance of everlasting life.

In the same quiet manner, the two apostles told again how Jesus had been seized by the minions of the high priest and unjustly brought before Pontius Pilate for sentencing, even though the kingdom of which he had spoken was that of God and not of men. Finally, they restated the simple truth of the Resurrection, testifying that Jesus had appeared on a number of occasions to a host of people, that many had seen the nail wounds in his hands, and that one of their number had actually touched the wound made in the side of the dying Messiah by the spear of a Roman soldier.

They described, too, how they had watched upon the crest of the Mount of Olives a short time before the day of Pentecost when Jesus was taken up into Heaven. And, as final proof of their Master's divinity, they told how his followers had prayed together on that day and how the Holy Spirit had come upon them, giving them the power to heal— of which some of the court already knew—and perform the other miracles many of the court had seen in the temple and elsewhere.

As the two accused men answered without hesitation the barrage of questions hurled at them by unfriendly members of the court, Peter was heartened to see that a few at least appeared to be impressed by their defense. One of these was Gamaliel, who, as the grandson of Hillel and the most influential teacher in Jerusalem, could no doubt influence the court strongly—if he were to intervene in their behalf.

Gamaliel remained silent, however, listening carefully to what was said and studying the two thoughtfully as they stood before the court, bearing without flinching the tongue-lashings of the priests and the Pharisees who in their anger accused them of all manner of crimes. Only when the questioning had died away and Caiaphas was preparing to call for a verdict of death did Gamaliel rise to his feet.

"I would speak, noble Caiaphas," he said quietly.

"The Rabban Gamaliel may speak in any council of Israel," Caiaphas said grudgingly. "We wait to hear the words of wisdom from his lips."

"In the days of the taxing there rose up Judas of Galilee," Gamaliel reminded the court. "He drew away much people after him, but he also perished, and all, even as many as obeyed him, were dispersed."

The court was silent, but Caiaphas gnawed at his beard. Obviously he would have silenced the speaker if he could have done so. But not even the high priest could deny to the most respected teacher in Israel—the only one ever granted the title of rabban—the right to speak.

"Now I say to you let these men alone," Gamaliel continued. "For if this council or this work be of men, it will come to naught. But if it should be of God, you cannot overthrow it, lest you are found to fight even against God."

It was a potent and telling argument. Listening to the discussion that followed among the members of the court, Peter saw how much the majority were impressed by Gamaliel's logic that the Sanhedrin should leave the final decision concerning the accused men to divine will. Even Caiaphas' arguments against such a defense were only half-hearted, and in the end the verdict was handed down that they should not be prosecuted further.

The high priest did achieve at least a modicum of the revenge he wished against the two, however. Upon his order, Peter and John were beaten severely with staves by the captain of the temple guard before they were released. They were also cautioned once more against speaking in the name of Jesus, but this admonition they chose to ignore, happy that they had been counted worthy to suffer shame and the physical pain of the beating in the name of Jesus so the work in Jerusalem could go on.

One thing about the trial, however, Peter found hard to put out of his mind. It was the burning intentness with which the man called Saul of Tarsus had regarded him, and the strange conviction—for which he could think of no reasonable explanation—that their paths, those of the sturdy fisherman of Galilee and the brilliant scholar of Jewish Law from Tarsus, would somehow cross again.

Book Seven
SAUL OF TARSUS

"As for Saul, he made havoc of the church, entering into every house, and hailing men and women committed them to prison."

THE ACTS 8:3

THE refusal of the Great Sanhedrin to vote the death sentence for Peter and John was widely regarded in Jerusalem as a victory for the congregation of the Nazarenes, bringing further converts into the church. But since many of these came from synagogues to which Greek-speaking Jews who had formerly lived in the cities of the Diaspora belonged, the very success of the fledgling church only added fuel to the fires of resentment against it already burning in Jerusalem.

Nor was the church itself without its own controversies. Jesus had lashed out against the often senseless distortions of the Law preached by many of the Jerusalem Pharisees, particularly the adherents of the Rabbi Shammai. But though much of the resentment against Jesus by high-ranking Pharisees had come from this cause, many earnest and pious members of the same group had found in his teachings a peace and assurance far greater than that which came strictly from obeying the Law. On the other hand, many of those who joined the congregation were of the far more liberal persuasion represented mainly by the Greek-speaking Jews of the Diaspora who wished to replace the narrowness of cant and creed with a broader understanding of man's relationship to his fellows and to God.

The foremost advocate of a strict observance of law and ritual in the Nazarene congregation was James. Because he was the eldest among the close kinsmen of the Lord, he spoke for the entire family, and gradually the church tended to become divided into two factions. One wished it to be only a sect within the Jewish faith, like the Essenes, the Therapeutae of Alexandria and a number of other small groups. The other side conceived of Christ's purpose as that of creating a new religion entirely, one open to all who believed Jesus to be the Son of God and who looked to him for the supreme gift of a life after death. Meanwhile Peter was torn between two loyalties and unable to give himself unreservedly to either.

"Feed my sheep," Jesus had ordered Peter on the shores of the Sea of Galilee. And when they had last seen the Master on the Mount of Olives, he had counseled them to "preach to all nations." Deep within his heart, where the voice of the Lord counseled him, Peter was sure that the latter injunction particularly meant carrying the good news to men everywhere, regardless of whether they were Jew or Gentile, but he had grown up in the strict observance of the Law and the ritual of worship, things that were not put aside in a day. And besides, he was busily occupied with the supervision of the church, a task that grew more and more burdensome daily as time passed and the congregation increased in size.

Continuing the tradition Jesus had established at the Last Supper in the upper room, Peter and the other apostles at first waited upon the tables, where all shared the food bought from the common purse, fulfilling the Master's teaching that they who would be the greatest among those who followed him should become servants of all. But even though the apostles themselves served, some of the congregation still complained that they received less than others—not only of food but also from the outlay for other expenses—creating bickering and discord in what had been at first a happy company of believers.

Peter could have silenced the complainers with a command

to cease their squabbling or be punished severely, but since the death of Ananias and Sapphira he had been careful to use judiciously the power that had been given to him. He therefore called the apostles and the leaders of the congregation—including the Greek faction—together, so they might discuss what was best to do concerning the complaints that were causing so much discord.

"It is not reasonable that we apostles should leave off preaching the word of God and serve tables," he told the company. "Therefore, select seven men of honest report who are filled with the Holy Spirit and with wisdom, so we may appoint them over this business. Then we can devote ourselves continually to prayer and to the ministry of the word."

Since Greek-speaking Jews in the congregation now outnumbered the Aramaic-speaking from Galilee and Judea, Peter was not surprised when those elected proved to be largely from the former faction. But the new deacons—as they were called, from the Greek term *diakonos*, meaning servant—were all men of good character with a deep faith, and he had no fear that the temporal affairs of the church would not be well handled by them.

First to be chosen was Stephen, an educated and highly literate man who was well liked in the community. After Stephen, six others were selected: Philip, Prochorus, Nicanor, Timon, Parmenas and Nicolas, a Gentile convert from Antioch, the capital of Syria. Finally, in the now traditional ceremony of prayer and the laying on of hands begun by Jesus, the deacons were inducted into their new offices.

Relieved largely now from the everyday cares of ministering to the congregation, Peter and the other apostles began to visit the towns around Jerusalem, preaching the same glad tidings that had found such fertile soil in the Holy City itself. Nor did the seven deacons let their purely administrative duties occupy them entirely, but actively continued to tell the wondrous story of the coming of Christ, his Crucifixion and his Resurrection. Of them, none was more eloquent or faithful than Stephen, and because he could speak fluently in Greek, he shortly began to make many converts among those who had formerly belonged to other synagogues in Jerusalem.

At first the leaders of the synagogues affected tried to dispute with Stephen, but such was his inspiration and eloquence that they were quickly put to rout. Finally, seeing no other way to stop the daily defection of their own members to the sect of the Nazarenes, they joined in a common cause with Caiaphas, who overlooked no opportunity to harass the hated Nazarenes, and brought Stephen before the Sanhedrin on a false charge of having spoken blasphemous words against Moses and against God.

Only two witnesses were required to swear to the charge for an accused to be brought before the Sanhedrin and condemned, but Stephen's enemies took no chance that moderate men upon the court like Gamaliel would succeed in freeing him. The required two witnesses duly perjured themselves by swearing to a charge of blasphemy, but though the accused spoke eloquently in his own behalf, the same rabble the temple authorities had sought to loose upon Jesus seized him and dragged him from the palace of the Sanhedrin.

Peter was at Bethany for a brief rest and a visit with Mary, Martha and Lazarus, so he knew nothing of what was happening. After the bickering between the conservative faction of the church, led by James, and the liberal faction for whom Barnabas and Stephen were spokesmen and toward whose convictions Peter himself leaned, it was pleasant to sit in the lovely garden at Bethany and talk to his old friends about the days when Jesus had stayed there upon his visits to Jerusalem for the religious festivals. Together they spoke of the Master's love for the quiet house across the mountain from bustling, brawling Jerusalem; how he had gently chided Martha when she had complained because Mary did not help her with serving; of their agony when Lazarus died and their joy when he was raised from the dead.

Mark was with Peter at Bethany, and when they approached Jerusalem at the day's end, both the apostle whose hair had become almost entirely gray over the years and the slender, intense lad with the eager eyes of a scholar were happy and content. As always, the Holy City was startlingly beautiful with the golden glory of the temple dome shining in the afternoon sunlight. The cheerful voices of men and women returning to their homes after working in the fields and orchards during the day were just as musical as they had been upon a hundred other occasions when Peter had trod this path before. And as always, whenever he left the upper room that was his center of activity, small groups stopped him along the way, beseeching him to tell again the wonderful story he never tired of telling.

Then, like the bolt of lightning that had torn the veil of the temple on the day Jesus was crucified, an alien sound rent the quiet air. It was the voices of men shouting in anger, a sound Peter would never hear again without being reminded of the night when he had passed through the valley of fear and shame to find strength and forgiveness on the other side.

Before the startled eyes of Peter and Mark as they looked across the Kidron Valley toward Jerusalem, a crowd of people burst through the open gate of the city opposite them, fanning out like water forced through a narrow opening. In the midst of the crowd they could see the slender figure of a man who somehow managed to hold himself erect against the spiteful buffeting of those shouting for his death, though they swarmed about him like wasps about an invader of their nest. Peter could not make out the identity of the mob's target at that distance, but Mark's young eyes were sharper.

"Simon!" The youth's voice was shrill with horror. "It is Stephen! They are taking him to the place of execution."

The traditional manner of executing those found guilty of crimes deserving death under Jewish Law was by stoning at a place of execution designated by the elders of each city and village—usually in a corner of the city's wall. After many years of usage, such spots became easily identifiable by stains from the blood of victims spattered upon the wall by the impact of the stones against their bodies.

For Jerusalem, the place of stoning was near the gate through which the crowd had burst with its victim but still some distance from where Peter and Mark had stopped to watch. At Mark's cry of recognition they started running, but since they were forced to cross the Kidron Valley, the execution had already begun before they reached the outskirts of the milling crowd.

Customarily, the witnesses who had sworn to the charge of blasphemy were allowed to cast the first stone, while an officer of the court watched over their cloaks lest they be stolen in the excitement of the execution. Traditionally, however, every man was required to cast at least one stone, making the act of execution one in which the entire community took part, for a sin justifying the capital sentence was considered to be a reflection upon everyone, requiring—according to the lex talionis of Mosaic Law—an act of vengeance by each man affected.

The press of the crowd made it impossible for Peter to work his way to where Stephen had already been battered into insensibility, but he could see the representative of the

Sanhedrin who was guarding the cloaks of the witnesses and serving as an official observer.

It was Saul of Tarsus!

II

The pushing and shoving by those trying to reach the front of the crowd and cast their stones before the victim was declared dead and they were deprived of their vengeance, the hoarse shouting and cursing, the smell of blood from the bruised and torn body already battered to the ground by the hail of missiles, made Peter feel for a moment a twinge of the old fear that had sent him reeling away from the courtyard of the high priest on that night several years before when he had seen Jesus led from the palace and had heard the cry of the rabble raised in the night air. He conquered it immediately and strove to push his way through the crowd, but the press of bodies about him was so great that he could barely move and was forced to stand and watch while the hail of stones continued until Stephen's frail body was beaten into a bloody pulp.

A surge of the crowd finally carried Peter near the spot where Saul of Tarsus was standing. The apostle was startled to see what seemed to be a look of revulsion on the shorter man's face, though whether at the task he was forced to carry out or at being so near the ghastly reality of death under the stones, Peter could not tell.

"Stop the stoning!" he shouted indignantly at the agent of the Sanhedrin. "Don't you see that he is already dead?"

Peter's words seemed to make up Saul's mind. He spoke sharply in Aramaic, ordering the stoning to cease, but the blood lust of the crowd had been raised to fever pitch and he was forced to shout again and again before the stoning finally ended. At his order the crowd parted so he could approach the spot where Stephen lay, stepping carefully so as not to touch with either his sandals or his foot any of the spots where the victim's blood had spattered upon the ground. For a moment Saul looked down at what had been a living man, but Peter could see no sign of pity or compassion upon his face.

"The blasphemer is dead!" he announced finally. "Stone him no more, for fear of defiling yourselves."

"Lord, do not lay this sin to their charge." The words were only a whisper, but they came from Stephen's lips with the last faint breath of life.

Saul of Tarsus had been turning away to where the witnesses were now putting on their outer garments. But at the sound of Stephen's whispered prayer he whirled and took a step toward the body once again, looking down at it with a puzzled frown upon his face.

A murmur of anger rose from the crowd, because they had been stopped before death had claimed the victim. Peter knew that in this ugly mood their anger could easily turn against Saul himself, but the shorter man seemed unconcerned by any such consideration. Ignoring the muttering of the crowd as it began to break up and drift away from the place of execution, he continued to look down at Stephen with a strange expression in his eyes. Almost, Peter thought, it was a look of admiration for a man who could forgive his tormentors, even at the moment of death. But it could be—he realized when Saul raised his eyes and met his—a look of uncertainty, too.

The crowd had thinned enough for Mark to force his way to Peter's side, only a pace or two away from where

Saul was standing. The boy was crying, for like everyone in the congregation of the Nazarenes, he had loved Stephen very much.

"Murderer!" he spat at Saul of Tarsus, and would have attacked him if Peter had not put his arm about his shoulders, restraining the youth.

Saul did not speak, but again Peter was surprised to detect that strange look in one whose eyes, on every other occasion when he had seen him before, had burned with the hot fires of a fanatic. Peter knew he should feel anger toward the man who had officiated at the execution of his friend, but somehow he did not. Rather he sensed the other's uncertainty, and having experienced much the same thing more than once himself, could not help feeling a sense of compassion for him.

"This man was my friend—and innocent of any wrongdoing," Peter said quietly to Saul of Tarsus. "I pray you let me remove his body for burial."

Saul glanced down at Stephen once again, but this time his gaze lingered upon the broken body only for a moment. "Take him," he said with a shrug, and turned toward the gate leading to the city.

Peter saw Barnabas' tall form pushing through the rapidly thinning crowd toward where he and Mark were standing. It seemed for a moment that the Cypriot intended to block Saul's way, but when Peter called to him, Barnabas stepped aside to let the short man pass and came over to where the two were standing.

"It was the rabble," he said angrily. "Caiaphas loosed them upon Stephen so the Sanhedrin would not have to ask Pilate for permission to execute him."

"Would the verdict have been different if the court had acted?" Peter asked, and Barnabas shook his head.

"Stephen had no friends on the Sanhedrin today—nor did

244 § UPON THIS ROCK

we. The high priest saw to that before he brought him before the court. From now on it will be a war to the death between him and us."

"With Saul as the executioner?"

"That is the word I hear in the market place," Barnabas
said. "They say Caiaphas has sworn to destroy all who believe in Jesus of Nazareth, and that Saul of Tarsus is anxious
to please him in every way."

"Who is this Saul?" Peter asked.

"A member of the synagogue of the Cilicians. Once he
was a student of Gamaliel, but of late he has joined his
brother Cilicians and Caiaphas in seeking to destroy us."

Peter knelt and lifted the battered body of Stephen in his
arms, unmindful of any defilement. "We will bury him on
the slope of the Mount of Olives where the tombs are," he
told Barnabas. "Go into the city and tell our brethren, so
we may mourn him together."

III

Barnabas, it developed almost immediately, had been right
in his surmise that the arrest of Stephen was actually a test
by Caiaphas of just how far Pontius Pilate would let him go
in persecuting the Nazarenes. The moodiness of the Roman
governor, his discontent with being left so long in the relatively minor post of governor of Judea and Samaria—though
he was married to a member of the highly placed Julian family
from which had come several emperors of Rome—all were
known to have changed Pilate from a relatively efficient if
ruthless administrator into a disgruntled, fuming man who left
the duties of his office largely to subordinates.

Just how much guilt Pilate felt for his part in the death of Jesus, no one knew. But Claudia Procula, his wife, was known to have pleaded with him to have nothing to do with the attempt of the temple authorities to destroy Jesus, and it was common gossip in Jerusalem that she felt Pilate had been wrong in condemning the Nazarene.

Whatever Pilate's feelings, he did not bring the high priest to task for the death of Stephen, and emboldened by their initial success, Caiaphas and Saul swept through the Lower City as the angel of death had swept through Egypt when Pharaoh had refused Moses permission to lead his people from the land. Under the swift forays, the beatings and goadings of their tormentors, the congregation of the Nazarenes began to shrink rapidly.

Again and again Peter and John sought to have themselves arrested, intending to denounce before the Sanhedrin the reign of terror which Saul, in particular, had loosed against pious Jews whose only sin—if it could be called that—was their conviction that the promised Messiah had already come. But neither Caiaphas nor Saul dared to risk a direct attack upon Peter and John in disobedience of the court's decision when Gamaliel had spoken in their favor, so the apostles were denied this recourse.

During those terrible days Peter was a tower of strength for the rapidly waning congregation, but soon even he could not deny that if the church was to be preserved and Christ's teachings spread widely abroad, a new and radically different strategy must be put in effect. Fortunately, just such a plan had been developing in his mind for many months. Now he broached it to the leaders of the group.

"The time has come to carry the good news elsewhere," he told a meeting of the elders called at his request. "Before even the spark is quenched here."

"But Jerusalem is the very wellspring of our faith," James protested. "If we leave it and the temple, we will be putting a thousand years of the Law behind us."

"There must always be a church in Jerusalem," Peter agreed. "And you, James, should head it, for even Caiaphas respects your learning and your piety. Most of the trouble that assails us has arisen because the other synagogues hate us for taking their followers. It is time we sent people out into other parts of the world, preaching the gospel and establishing new churches."

"What of the apostles?" someone asked.

"We should stay here for the moment," Peter said. "Though later I think all of you should go out—as Jesus sent us to teach and heal when he was still alive."

"Who will go now?"

"Most of the deacons and others who have been strong in the faith," Peter said. "As many as are able and willing."

"What about you?" Barnabas inquired. "Someday soon Saul may think himself strong enough to attack even you."

"Until that happens I shall stay in Israel," Peter said. "Or until other churches have been established which I can visit and strengthen."

Since the only alternative seemed to be imprisonment and perhaps death at the hands of Saul of Tarsus, few posed any objection to Peter's order that the leaders of the Jerusalem congregation be scattered abroad, there to plant the knowledge of Jesus in new and fallow soil, hoping it would thrive as did the seed in the parable the Master had loved so well. Those who were of the Diaspora, Peter encouraged to return to their own cities and preach to the Jews there, establishing new synagogues wherever they could. Some went to Phoenicia, others to Egypt, still others to Damascus, Babylon,

Petra and other population centers where there were substantial Jewish colonies.

In Jerusalem, the practice of sharing everything they owned begun in the early days of the church had to be abandoned, since the congregation was forced to meet now in secret lest Saul sweep down upon them. These were parlous times indeed for the young church, and but for the rocklike faith and confidence of Simon Peter, it might have been destroyed completely. All through this period of terrible persecution Peter stood steadfast, encouraging all who would to leave Jerusalem and spread the good news of Jesus abroad, while almost singlehandedly holding together the little band that remained as what came to be called the Mother Church. Nor did he cease to speak from the Porch of Solomon daily as a living reminder to Caiaphas and Saul that they had not stamped out the faith of the Nazarenes entirely.

Gradually, as the Jerusalem congregation grew smaller and less important, the intensity of the persecution began to decrease. Barnabas had gone to Cyprus when the leaders were scattered at the height of Saul's harassment, but now he returned at Peter's suggestion, bringing with him the young scribe Mark and some encouraging news about the various places to which the faithful had been scattered. Tired and weary from the long period of work, Peter was glad to see the two and to have Barnabas again as his right hand.

"In Cyprus I heard that a strong church is being established in Antioch," Barnabas reported. "And they say that Nicanor and some others have had good success in Damascus."

"Philip sends glowing news of the work in Samaria," Peter said. "The Lord has indeed favored us by letting the seed fall on fallow ground."

"The Lord has favored us, but mainly by building his church upon a solid rock named Simon Peter," Barnabas said. "Who else would have turned Saul's own sword against him by sending those who fled before its blade to build anew elsewhere?"

"The Lord guided me," Peter said simply.

"One day I shall thank Saul of Tarsus for doing us a favor when he sought to destroy us," Barnabas said grimly. "What are you going to do, now that the persecution has begun to wane, Peter?"

"Continue to build as we have done before."

"Here in Jerusalem?"

Peter shook his head. "It is hard to persuade new converts to join us when they know Saul and Caiaphas may attack if the congregation starts to grow again. I think our greatest future now lies outside Jerusalem."

"Where?"

"The Master has not yet revealed that to me," Peter admitted. "But Philip wrote from Samaria recently, asking that we come there and baptize those who have believed. That may be the start."

"James will not like your bringing Samaritans into the church," Barnabas warned. "You know he believes the Master commissioned us to preach only to the lost sheep of Israel."

"Those of Samaria may be among the lost sheep. Remember the parable Jesus gave us about the Good Samaritan who helped the Jew left for dead by robbers. He said then that the Samaritan was more of a neighbor to the injured man than were his own people who passed him by."

"Many will still speak against you if you offer them the salvation promised by Jesus," Barnabas insisted.

"I shall not decide that, Barnabas. The Lord will speak

through the Holy Spirit if it be his will for them to receive eternal life."

"And if he does not?"

"There is always Galilee—and Peraea. We can start anew at Capernaum—if we must."

"Take Mark and me with you to Samaria," Barnabas begged, but Peter shook his head.

"I need you here to watch Saul," he told them. "And to warn James and the others if he tries to take them while I am away. John and I will go together."

The district of Samaria lay north of Judea, with the boundary only a short distance from Jerusalem. But though both were governed as part of the same territory by Pontius Pilate, and though, as Peter had reminded Barnabas, the people of both areas worshiped the same God, they were far from being the same country. More than five hundred years earlier, when Israel had been invaded by Assyria, the tribes making up the northern kingdom had been carried away into captivity, leaving only Judah to the south. And in order to destroy Israel's potential as a nation, the Assyrian king had imported many thousand of foreigners into the area now known as Samaria.

The worship of the Most High had never been carried out as religiously in northern Israel as in the southern kingdom of Judah, and intermarriage with heathen—particularly the Phoenicians—had been common there. With so many immigrants in what had formerly been the northern kingdom of Israel, the region had quickly become populated with a people who were not pure Jews as those in Judah—later called Judea—considered themselves to be. And though most of the newcomers took up the worship of the Most High, the Judeans had always regarded the Samaritans—as they came to be known by the name of their capital city—almost as they did

Gentiles. The Samaritans, on the other hand, had erected a temple of their own on Mount Gerizim, claiming that theirs was the true faith, and something like an armed truce existed between the two parts of Pontius Pilate's district, creating considerable difficulty for the Roman governor.

It was late on the second day of a journey by foot northward across the central range of hills forming the spine of what, in the time of Moses and Joshua, had been called Canaan, when Peter and John approached the city of Samaria —renamed Sebaste about fifty years earlier by Herod the Great. Though the palace fortress erected first by King Omri and defended by his son Ahab had been leveled centuries before by Assyrian invaders, it was still easy to see why the center of government for Israel's ten northern tribes had been built at Samaria. The hill upon which the city stood was an isolated, rocky mass rising several hundred cubits above the valley floor and commanding a wide area of fertile plains.

Philip met the two apostles when he saw them coming up the street to the house where he was staying, and the three men entered a cool court around which the house was built. There they were served refreshments by the women of the family while Philip told how he had preached Christ and his Resurrection to the people of Samaria, healing the sick and casting out evil spirits, and how great numbers had believed and asked to be accepted into the Kingdom of God.

"You have done well," Peter commended his friend. "Perhaps we can accomplish here what we have not been able to do in Jerusalem."

"Then the persecution of Saul continues unabated?"

Peter nodded soberly. "Our people are scattered abroad, and only a few remain besides James and the family of the Lord. Just before I left, word came that Saul has been given a commission by the high priest to seek out the followers of

Jesus in other cities and destroy them. He might even come here."

"I think not," Philip demurred. "Saul is a Pharisee, and few in Samaria follow the old ways. The only trouble I am likely to have is with a magician named Simon Magus."

"We have heard of him in Jerusalem," John said. "Is it true that he performs miracles through sorcery and the works of the devil?"

"He appears to perform miracles," Philip admitted reluctantly. "But he claims that his power, too, comes from God."

"Have you proof that it does not?" Peter asked.

"No. But when the people heard me speaking of Jesus and saw how I healed the sick and cast out evil spirits, many left off following the magician and came to me."

"Then you have triumphed over evil. Why should such a thing leave you uneasy?"

Philip gave him a quick look. "You sensed it, then?"

"From the moment I saw you."

"I would feel better if Simon Magus continued to oppose me," Philip explained. "Instead, he now claims to be converted, and has been baptized."

"It is far better to have saved him," Peter said, remembering his own experience with Ananias and Sapphira.

"I would agree if I could be sure that I had," Philip said. "But somehow I still cannot bring myself to trust him."

"Are you certain your prejudice against the magician has not blinded you to the truth?" Peter asked.

"No. But how can I be sure?"

"If the man is sincere, the Holy Spirit will come upon him when we lay hands upon him with your other converts. If not, it will be absent from him and we will know."

"I had not thought of that." Philip's troubled face cleared.

"The congregation here is anxious to hear you and John speak, so I will arrange a service for tomorrow. Then we will learn whether Simon is lying when he says he wishes to follow Jesus."

Philip had not exaggerated the number of those he had converted, Peter saw when they gathered the next day. People of all levels were represented, from the highest to the lowest, but none stood out like the magician called Simon. Tall and handsome, he was richly dressed and went out of his way to be pleasant to the visitors. Yet Peter was somehow reminded of Judas Iscariot, for the two men had the same hawklike look and the same coldness in their eyes. He rigorously put the thought from him, however, lest he be prejudiced in his evaluation of the other man's sincerity.

After telling once again many of the parables of Jesus, including that of the Good Samaritan, Peter and John prayed and lay their hands upon Philip's converts in the traditional ceremony by which the Holy Spirit was conveyed to those who believed. Dozens were filled with it, but though both apostles put their hands upon the bowed head of the magician, they could see that the divine gift was withheld from him.

Peter made no mention of the lack, but Simon Magus brought it up of his own accord after the service. "Give me this power that on whoever I lay hands he may receive the Holy Spirit," he said ingratiatingly, taking a purse from his belt and dangling it casually by the strings.

Peter felt a surge of anger at this obvious attempt to bribe him but repressed it, for he had resolved never again to let that emotion control his actions. "Your money shall perish with you because you believed the gift of God could be purchased with it," he told Simon sternly. "Your heart is not right in the sight of God, so repent of your wickedness and pray that the thoughts of your heart may be forgiven you."

The magician was taken aback by Peter's stern manner and his air of authority. "Pray to the Lord for me that none of these things you have spoken may come upon me," he begged. But though Peter prayed with him again, and once more Simon Magus professed to believe, there was still no outpouring of the Holy Spirit.

This was the first time in Peter's experience that the gift of Jesus's favor had been withheld from anyone claiming to believe in the Master. He was glad that he and John had come to Samaria, for he realized now that some men would seek to use the power given to the apostles for their own benefit. But what he could not know then was that his own path and that of the magician called Simon would cross again in another—and far greater—city.

Peter and John did not remain in Samaria long, for word came to them that Saul was still harassing the believers in Jerusalem, and Peter did not want to leave the congregation there very long without the support of his strength. Upon his return, he saw at once that his absence had only served to increase the influence which James, as the nearest kinsman of Jesus, exerted over the congregation. In fact the Jerusalem group had become little more than simply another synagogue within the city and was rapidly losing the militant spirit which Jesus had given it and which Simon Peter had nurtured.

When John and Peter reported that the Holy Spirit had been poured out upon converts in Samaria, even the most conservative among the congregation could hardly deny that it was the will of the Master for Samaritans, at least, to be accepted into the large structure of the church encompassing all who believed in Jesus, wherever they were. But when it came to admitting Gentiles, even the advice of the Master to "go and teach all nations" could not immediately overcome the reluctance of the Jerusalem congregation to break laws which all Jews had obeyed for more than a thousand years and which they were convinced had kept them pure as a separate people.

Peter had been very much impressed by the outpouring of the spirit he had witnessed in Samaria. And when Philip came to Jerusalem with the additional report that a similar thing had happened to a man from Ethiopia—the keeper of the treasury for Queen Candace of that land—whom he had met on the road, Peter was convinced that the time had come for the activities of the church to enter upon a far wider sphere.

Wishing to avoid strife when the congregation was almost too weak to continue existence in the Holy City, however, Peter did not press the matter over the objections of James and the more conservative leaders of the church at Jerusalem. Instead, he chose to wait and see how the will of God would be revealed. But when that occasion finally came, it was through such an improbable event that at first Peter himself could hardly believe he had heard aright—the startling news that, on the road to Damascus, Jesus had appeared to Saul of Tarsus.

IV

For the apostles at Jerusalem and the leaders of the church there, the news of Saul's conversion was as hard to believe as if the devil himself had suddenly become a follower of Jesus. In order to be certain of the truth, Peter sent Barnabas to the Syrian city to investigate. When he returned after an absence of about a month, the congregation gathered to hear his report.

"The whole thing happened as you have all heard," Barnabas informed them. "Just as we were told before Peter went to Samaria, Saul had applied for a commission from Caiaphas to seek out the followers of Jesus in Damascus and other cities and persecute them, as he did here in Jerusalem. The commission was granted, but as he traveled to Damascus a great light shone suddenly from Heaven at a place beyond the Sea of Galilee, blinding him. In the midst of it, Saul saw Jesus and heard his voice telling him to go to the house of Judas, whom we all know, on the Street called Straight, in Damascus."

"How did you learn all this?" John demanded.

"From the lips of Saul himself."

"He was lying," John said triumphantly. "A man who would persecute innocent people and put them in prison could not be depended upon to tell the truth."

"I doubted him at first," Barnabas agreed, "so I made other inquiries. Judas himself told me that Saul was blind when he reached his house. And the story Saul told him is the same that he told me."

"We all know the Cilician is clever," John said bitterly. "If he had made up a tale beforehand to deceive us so he could gather evidence against our brethren in Damascus, he would hardly vary his story from one telling to another."

"I thought of that, too," Barnabas said. "Until I heard the testimony of our brother Ananias in Damascus."

"What testimony?"

"You all know that this Ananias is a just man and not like that other who died with a lie upon his lips when he held back the money from the sale of his land," Barnabas said. "Even before Saul reached Damascus, the Lord warned Ananias in a dream of his coming. And when Ananias protested in the dream that Saul was an enemy, the Lord told him: 'Go your way, for he is a chosen vessel to bear my name before the Gentiles and kings and the Children of Israel. For I will show him what great things he must suffer for my name's sake.' "

Peter somehow felt no surprise at the news of such a startling change in the man who had been the bitterest enemy of the church in Jerusalem. Long ago, when he had first seen Saul of Tarsus during his own and John's trial before the Sanhedrin, he had experienced the strange conviction that somehow their paths would cross again. And though that event had not yet taken place, he was sure the happenings on the road to Damascus were a part of some plan for whose working out he must wait.

"As soon as Saul's sight was restored," Barnabas continued, "he gave testimony in the synagogues of Damascus —the same to which he had been sent as an agent of the Sanhedrin. And when he told of the death and Resurrection of the Master and how he had seen him on the road, a great company came to believe. I talked to some of them and can vouch for the fact that they received the gift of the Holy Spirit."

"From the hands of Saul?" James demanded incredulously.

"Yes. I saw it happen a number of times myself."

"Are you certain the gift of the Holy Spirit was poured out upon Saul's converts, Barnabas?" Peter asked. "Without any of our brethren in Damascus laying hands upon them?"

"I am certain. But because I knew some among you would still doubt, I brought the written testimony of Ananias and Nicanor." From his robe Barnabas took a small scroll and laid it upon the table. "You can see for yourself—if you still doubt."

Peter did not doubt his friend's story for a moment, unbelievable though it was that Jesus would reveal himself to one who had been the bitterest enemy of his church, while withholding a similar revelation from its earthly head and his own disciples. James, however, unrolled the small scroll, read it carefully, and rolled it up again.

"It is as Barnabas says," he confirmed. "Nicanor was a deacon of the congregation here in Jerusalem, and Barnabas is one of our most trusted brethren, so we cannot but accept their testimony. Yet it is still a hard thing to believe."

"Where is Saul now?" Peter asked.

"When his preaching moved so many, the very synagogues he was sent to visit conspired to kill him," Barnabas explained. "To save his life, our brethren in Damascus let Saul down over the wall in a basket by night and he fled into the desert."

"And no one has heard from him since?"

"No one."

"Perhaps that is the last of him then," one of the elders said, and from the murmur of approval following the words, Peter could see that, in spite of the startling conversion of the man from Tarsus, most of those present would be quite content to hear no more of him. Peter, however, did not consider such a prospect. Remembering how he had been called when the draught of fish in his nets had almost swamped his boat on the Sea of Galilee, he was sure that Jesus must have some special purpose for Saul of Tarsus and that it would be revealed in time.

"Did you learn anything else in Damascus, Barnabas?" James's question brought Peter back to the present.

"Yes. Our brethren Simeon, Lucius of Cyrene, and Manaen, have started a new *ecclesia* in Antioch. Travelers from there say it is already much larger than we are here in Jerusalem."

For Peter, this was good news indeed and further proof that he had been carrying out the will of the Master when he had sent so many of the believers in Jerusalem away so they might give testimony elsewhere.

"I am convinced that this whole affair must be part of the working out of Jesus's commission to us to preach to all nations." Barnabas echoed Peter's thought.

"Surely not the affair of Saul," James protested. "Don't forget that he was present at the death of Stephen, and many of our brethren have suffered because of him."

"We have seen how the Samaritans believed on the Lord and received the Holy Spirit," Peter pointed out. "And the same thing happened with the Ethiopian baptized by Philip. The way Saul of Tarsus was called must be Jesus's way of showing us we must now carry the gospel elsewhere."

The meeting ended on that note, but Peter did not delude himself that all there agreed with him. Nor could he put aside a feeling of disappointment that the Master had chosen to appear to Saul of Tarsus and not to him, though he comforted himself with the knowledge that, even through so unlikely an agent, Jesus had once again indicated the direction the work should take. Acting upon that conviction, he sent Barnabas to Antioch to support those laboring there and was heartened by the regular reports sent back by his old friend, describing how the new church was flourishing in the capital city of Syria.

As for the congregation at Jerusalem, it continued to exist, largely because, with his most conscientious agent gone, Caiaphas appeared to lose interest in it. Then, almost as dramatically as he had escaped from Damascus nearly six years before, Saul of Tarsus appeared in the Holy City, causing a controversy within the congregation there that threatened at first to do what the persecution he had directed had not been able to do—destroy it completely.

V

Almost nothing had been heard of Saul during the years since his dramatic conversion on the road to Damascus and his narrow escape from death in that city. Rumor said variously that he was living as a hermit in the desert, that he was carrying on missionary activities in Petra, the capital of the Nabateans south of the Dead Sea, and that he had journeyed as far to the east as Babylon. But when he appeared in Jerusalem, he seemed to be none the worse for his experience, and his request to be consecrated as a teacher both in the Holy City and abroad was like a torch set to dry tinder.

A burst of anxiety and resentment flared, particularly among those who had suffered personally at Saul's hands, and all of Peter's tact and wisdom were required to keep some of those who had been close to Stephen from attacking the former agent of the Sanhedrin. Fortunately, Barnabas had come with Saul to support him in his effort to gain the approval of the Jerusalem congregation, and the two convinced the others that Saul should at least be given a hearing.

The meeting was held in the upper room, with only the apostles who were in Jerusalem and the elders of the congregation present, since both Peter and James feared that Saul might be attacked bodily if it were an open meeting. Looking at Saul as he waited for the questioning to begin, Peter was struck again by the dynamic force which seemed to actuate the man in everything he did, a force so alive and so potent that it stirred others to enthusiasm—or to resentment—merely by his presence. And even though, like the others, he had been prepared to suspect Saul's motives in returning to Jerusalem, Peter found that he could not help being drawn to the other man.

It was not entirely because of physical appearance, Peter decided. For, as he had noticed during the trial of the Sanhedrin and again at the death of Stephen, Saul was short, bandy-legged, and already a little bald, though still a young man compared to most of those present in the chamber. Rather, Peter thought, the impression Saul made upon those seeing him for the first time must come from the majestic and almost godlike appearance of his head, the broad and mobile mouth, and the deep-set eyes burning with a fanatic zeal that was still undiminished, even though he was facing men whose first instinct would naturally be to regard him as an enemy and yet who held the final power of approval or disapproval over his further work as a follower of Jesus, both in the Holy City and abroad.

James the Just—as the kinsman of Jesus was often called— opened the hearing. Though he was rigidly courteous to Saul, his disapproval even of the other man's presence in the chamber was obvious in the frosty tone of his voice, the set look of anger upon his face.

"We are gathered to consider the desire of Saul of Tarsus to join himself with us in preaching the Word," James announced. "If anyone has testimony to give concerning this matter, let him speak now."

John opened his attack before Saul could speak in his own behalf. Intense and fiery, he and his brother James had been dubbed affectionately the "Sons of Thunder"—not without reason—by Jesus. But John was also often called the "Beloved Disciple," because the Master had committed the care of his mother Mary to him in one of his last utterances from the cross. And after Simon Peter, no man was more respected in the whole church than he.

"Why should we accept as a worker in the vineyard of the Lord one who consented to the death of Stephen and persecuted the faithful here?" John demanded heatedly. "We even have evidence that Saul obtained letters from the high priest, authorizing him to persecute our brothers in Damascus."

Peter was watching Saul but saw no sign of flinching. He knew that courage of a high order had been required to return to Jerusalem and face the leaders of the church he had persecuted—men who were certain still to distrust him and his motives—and Peter could not help admiring Saul for it. At the same time, he could not shake off the premonition that the short man standing before the council was destined to play a considerable part in the growth of the young church.

Perhaps, it occurred to Peter—as he listened to the verbal assault made by one after another of the apostles and elders upon the former agent of the Sanhedrin—Saul's role might even come to rival his own, for the Master had called the man of Tarsus in a strange and startling way, whose retelling by Saul, Barnabas had already warned Peter, had tremendously moved listeners wherever the other man had spoken of it. Moreover, Peter knew well that, should he throw the weight of his own influence against Saul, the latter would almost certainly never reach a position of importance in the church.

Not once, however, did Peter feel any temptation to follow the easy course by letting James, John and the others who were attacking Saul keep the floor while he remained silent, damning the man of Tarsus by his very failure to speak. Ever since the day when he had left this same room after Mark had brought word that Jesus was crucified, he had not considered the welfare of Simon called Peter in any choice with which he had been faced. Instead he had always asked himself what Jesus would have him do, and the answer to that question he had already felt in his heart.

"Brethren, we are not here to decide by ourselves whether Saul of Tarsus shall be joined with us in the work of the Master," Peter reminded the group finally, after everyone else desiring to speak had been given his say. "But to seek the will of God in this matter."

"Would you have us take to our bosoms the viper that killed our brethren?" John demanded heatedly.

"Do not forget that the Master said: 'I came not to call the righteous but sinners to repentance.' " Peter rebuked his fiery friend. "And when we were passing through Jericho on the road to Jerusalem for the Passover, the Master forgave Zaccheus, though he was a publican and a sinner."

"All of us heard Zaccheus repent of his sins," John snapped. "But Saul of Tarsus was a known enemy until he suddenly turned his coat, claiming that the Lord appeared to him on the road. Even his former associates would have none of him afterward and forced him to flee, we know not where, since nothing has been heard of him for, lo, these many years. How do we know he is not conspiring even now to worm his way into our confidence so he can accuse us before the Sanhedrin and gain the favor of the chief priest once again?"

"We cannot know unless we hear Saul's story," Peter said. "Even the most hardened sinner deserves to be heard."

Saul had been listening intently to the interchange, his eyes going from one to the other while Peter and John were speaking. Now he began to speak.

"You know that I was once in Jerusalem, breathing out threatening and slaughter against the followers of Jesus Christ and that I consented to the death of Stephen," he said quietly. "Yet if you ask me why I did this, I cannot tell you —except that it seemed to be the will of the Most High at the time."

"Are you a prophet then, that you speak the will of God for others to follow?" John demanded scathingly.

"I am a Jew, even as you are, born in Tarsus of Cilicia." Saul maintained the same quiet dignity that had characterized him during the entire hearing. "I came to Jerusalem and studied at the feet of Gamaliel, where I was taught the Law as you were—and obeyed it."

Even the most vitriolic among his accusers was silent now, held in the spell of a voice that was like a great harp, which once struck, continues to vibrate. Through appealing to the reverence of James and the more conservative faction in the congregation for the Law of Moses, Saul had wisely chosen the only way in which he might impress them.

"When I departed from Jerusalem for Damascus," he continued, "my purpose was to bring those who followed Jesus of Nazareth back here in bonds, to be punished. But as I drew near Damascus, a great light from Heaven suddenly shone around me. I fell to the ground blinded, and as I lay there I heard a voice from Heaven say 'Saul, Saul! Why do you persecute me?' "

"Did you recognize the voice?" James asked.

"No. But when I asked 'Who are you Lord?' the voice answered 'I am Jesus of Nazareth, whom you persecute. It is hard for you to kick against the goad.' "

A murmur of surprise went through the room, for even the bitterest among them could hardly fail to sense the deep sincerity in the speaker's voice, or be impressed by the fact that the Lord had spoken directly to Saul.

"What happened then?" James asked, but in a less frosty tone.

"The same voice said to me 'Arise and go into Damascus and there you shall be told of the things appointed for you to do.' "

"How were you able to see Jesus if you were blinded?" John demanded.

"It was the vision of the Lord himself in all his glory in Heaven that blinded me," Saul explained. "Afterward, I was led to the Street Called Straight in Damascus, where a devout man named Judas took me into his home. I was blind for a time, until one of our brethren called Ananias lay his hands upon me and said 'Brother Saul, receive your sight.' Then I was immediately able to see again."

"Did Jesus say anything else to you?" John inquired.

"Not on the road to Damascus," Saul said. "But Ananias told me: 'The God of our fathers has chosen you that you should know his will and see the Just One and hear the voice of his mouth.' Since then the Lord has often spoken to me in my heart, telling me what to do when I was uncertain of my course."

Peter was sure Saul was telling the truth, for he had often heard the same reassuring voice in his soul, strengthening him when he was confused and uncertain about what course the Master would have him follow.

"Why did you come to Jerusalem now?" James asked.

"It was I who advised Brother Saul to appear before you," Barnabas interposed. "I believe the Lord has selected him for a great purpose. And since the Master revealed himself to him, I feel that he should be consecrated as one of us."

"As an apostle?" John asked.

"Yes."

"But can we really be sure that he saw Jesus?"

"I both saw and heard Jesus of Nazareth," Saul said firmly. "Everything happened exactly as I have told you."

There were only a few more questions, and finally James looked at Peter, who had remained silent, except during the brief interchange with John. "What is your feeling in this matter, Simon?" he asked.

"When word first came that our bitterest enemy had suddenly become a servant of the Lord, I, too, hesitated to believe it," Peter admitted. "But we have all heard how the Master asked Saul why he kicked against the goad, and since I have some knowledge of that, I believe him."

"Surely you, of all people, have never doubted," Barnabas protested.

"I denied Jesus, not once but three times," Peter reminded him. "And before that I was loath to follow him, for I had believed in another messiah and had been disappointed, once almost losing my life. But the same goad of which Saul has spoken was pricking me, and in the end I could not help but see the truth—as he did on the road to Damascus. The Lord spoke then for all of us, so we can only obey his will."

After that the vote was only a formality and the former persecutor of the congregation of the Nazarenes was welcomed into their midst, though still with some reservations by John and James and a number of others. Finally the room was empty except for Peter and Saul.

"You could have made it very hard for me just now if you had wanted to, Peter," Saul said quietly. "Long ago when I watched the cloaks of those who cast the first stones at Stephen, I saw condemnation for me in your eyes. Why did you give your approval today?"

"Because it is obviously the Lord's will that you join in our work."

"But in what field? He did not tell me that on the road to Damascus, and I still do not know."

"When the time comes, you will," Peter assured him. "Tell me this: are you sure you have no regrets?"

"For what?"

"For all that you gave up when Jesus called you. You would not have been given the commission of the Sanhedrin to persecute our people in Damascus if the members of the court had not expected you one day to become a high official. Now they cannot afford to let you go unpunished, so they will surely seek to arrest you and bring you to trial if you remain in Jerusalem."

"I *was* already well on the way to obtaining the high position you speak of before I departed for Damascus," Saul confirmed. "In fact, I persecuted the followers of Jesus because I knew I would gain approval from Caiaphas and the others."

"Do you feel any remorse?"

"I was wrong," Saul admitted frankly. "But as I said just now, I was carrying out the Law as it had been taught to me and as I saw it then. Only on the road to Damascus did I learn a new and better way."

"Are you sure it was only on the road to Damascus?"

Saul smiled, and a warmth that was to enrich their relationship for many years to come was kindled between the two men. "You, too, have felt the pricks, so you know what it is to be uncertain deep within your soul," he said. "Perhaps they began to goad me when I first saw you and John standing on the Porch of Solomon, fearlessly preaching that a man shamefully crucified as a common criminal was actually the Messiah and the Son of God. Or it may have been when I saw Stephen go to his death without fear, praying that the Lord would forgive those who took his life."

Saul turned to look out the window through which came the many sounds of a city that make up its inner voice: the soft chatter of women on the way to the well; the creak of a cart wheel bumping over a rocky street; the tinkle of a silver-

SAUL OF TARSUS § 267

smith's hammer; the hum of a potter's wheel; the cry of a beggar asking for alms. He had given up all this, as well as the praise and admiration of men in high places, Peter knew, for the uncertain future that those who followed Jesus shared. And Peter himself could not have blamed him for feeling a certain longing for what was behind him.

"My boyhood was spent in Tarsus of Cilicia, a seaport city where many ships came and went." Saul turned to face Peter once again. "I learned to speak Greek as early as I did Hebrew, and often watched ships at their piers, loading and discharging cargo. More than once I wished that I, too, could travel to distant parts of the world, places like Rome, Ephesus, Antioch, Alexandria, Spain or even Britain. But most of all I wanted to see Jerusalem and the beauty of the temple and to worship at the Holy Altar."

"That was my greatest ambition, too, as a boy," Peter agreed. "But when I came to Jerusalem, the War of Varus began and I almost lost my life at Sepphoris."

"Even as I cut and sewed fabric and made it into tents, learning my trade," Saul continued, "I was following caravans in my mind along the road through the Cilician Gates to Pisidian Antioch, Derbe, Lystra, and sometimes even on to Thyatira and northward to Bithynia on the shores of the Pontus Euxinus. As a boy I was taught to read the writings of the Greek philosophers as well as the scrolls of the Law and the Prophets. And when I came to Jerusalem, I was a student of the greatest of the teachers, the Rabban Gamaliel, who saved you and John from death before the Sanhedrin. One day I would have been a member of the ruling council of the Jews and could have journeyed as an emissary to our people everywhere in all the far-off cities of the world. Are you surprised that I sometimes wonder how I could have exchanged all of that for the life of a fugitive?"

"All of us who followed Jesus had to make that choice," Peter reminded him.

"But can a man change his beliefs and his entire life in an instant?"

Peter shook his head. "Much goes before—and after—such a drastic change. That was what Jesus meant when he spoke of the goad. Even before you were struck blind on the road to Damascus, you must have heard the call of a purpose for you even higher than your ambition as an officer of the Sanhedrin. And you listened because deep inside you the voice of the Lord himself was telling you that only in this way could you find eternal life."

"And peace?"

"There is no peace, as most people name it, for those of us who serve the Christ. Yet ours is the greatest peace that can come to any man, the peace to live without fear, the peace to know one's course is set and that whatever befalls us, we will one day be with him forever. Do you think that is enough, Saul of Tarsus?"

"I have chosen the way of the Nazarene and I would not go back if I could," Saul answered, without a moment's hesitation. "I only pray that my courage and my strength shall prove as great as the man Jesus named the Rock upon which he would build his church."

Book Eight

THE CENTURION CORNELIUS

*"There was a certain man in Caesarea called
Cornelius, a centurion of the band called the
Italian band."*

THE ACTS 10:1

I

BECAUSE of the danger to Saul from the vengeful temple authorities, he and Barnabas departed shortly after the hearing before Peter and the others in Jerusalem. Peter had assigned Barnabas to the church at Antioch, and Saul was going on to work in his home city of Tarsus until such a time as the further purpose for him was revealed. As for the church in Jerusalem, James and the others were content to be merely another congregation among the hundreds in the city—but not Simon Peter.

The visit to Samaria and the realization that the Holy Spirit could be poured out even upon a people whom the Jews had traditionally hated for centuries had materially broadened Peter's viewpoint concerning the direction the church should take in the future. Ever since, he had been filled with a restlessness that would not let him be content with the day-to-day activities at Jerusalem. Finally he decided to visit other cities in the area where members of the Jerusalem congregation had been sent to escape the persecution by Saul some six years before. His first choice was Lydda, about two-thirds of the way from Jerusalem to the seaport city of Joppa.

At Lydda, the Roman road between Jerusalem and Joppa came down from the hills to the rolling plain called the *shephelah*, lying just inland from the sandy dunes of the seacoast. The ground around the town was fertile, and with an ample water supply from numerous wells, the whole area was like a garden—in striking contrast to the forbidding hill country lying eastward toward Jerusalem.

It was spring when Peter made the journey, always the

loveliest season in Judea, and he was cheered as the road wound through groves of almonds, pomegranates, olives, apricots, mulberry and sycamores. Between the trees, scarlet anemones formed a bright blanket over the fallow earth, with saffron, ranunculus and wild flowers growing in vividly colored patches. Protected by the low hills of the *shephelah*, Lydda was like an oasis, and after the hustle and bustle of Jerusalem and the constant threat of persecution by the temple authorities, a place of peace.

The lovely Plain of Sharon—as the northern extension of the *shephelah* was called—stretched as far as Mount Carmel, the jutting headland marking the beginning of Phoenicia in ancient times. From that region had come the artisans who had fashioned the glorious temple of Solomon, as well as the sturdy shipbuilders who had constructed the high-decked "Ships of Tarshish"—so called because the Phoenicians sailed them on long voyages to Tartessus, or Tarshish, in Spain, at the western end of the Great Sea. Built at the port of Eziongeber on the Red Sea, these great ships had sailed eastward as far as the coast of India, bringing back a treasure trove of exotic goods to swell Solomon's coffers during one of the most glorious and prosperous periods in Israel's history.

As soon as Peter reached Lydda, a man named Aeneas, bedded for eight years with paralysis, was brought to him. The apostle lay his hands upon Aeneas, and when the sick man rose, took up his pallet and walked from the house, word of the miracle and Peter's presence in Lydda spread rapidly. Large numbers of people flocked to hear him speak, many of them turning to the new faith. And since the area was one of the most beautiful in all of Israel, Peter was content to remain there for several weeks.

From Lydda to Joppa, Peter's next stop, was less than a day's journey by foot. The beautiful seaport city was located upon a sloping hill that descended, terrace by terrace, to the level of the shore. As a port, however, Joppa left much to be desired, since the sea was so shallow for a considerable distance offshore that the great biremes and triremes with which Rome carried on commerce with the far corners of the empire were forced to anchor well out in the sea when loading and unloading.

Joppa had long been a favorite summer resort for rich people from Jerusalem. Its groves were a shady paradise with a constant breeze from the sea stirring the palm fronds and sweeping through the houses. Wells needed to be dug only a little way into the earth to obtain water, and tall wheels turned by animals plodding in a patient circle lifted it to a network of canals by which the surrounding orchards and groves were irrigated.

One of the major industries of Joppa, besides its importance as a landing place for pilgrims on the way to Jerusalem, was the tanning of leather. The abundance of water, the large groves of trees in the hills, from whose bark the reddish fluid for tanning could be obtained, and the warm sun for drying the leather, all made Joppa an opportune place to work. Peter went directly to the house of a prominent tanner named Simon who was a friend and believer of long standing, but was not allowed to rest. Almost immediately word came that a former member of the Jerusalem congregation named Tabitha, or Dorcas, was at the point of death.

Tabitha had been an indefatigable worker, turning her talents at sewing to fashioning clothing for children, until driven from Jerusalem by the persecution instituted by Saul. She had continued her work here in Joppa, Peter saw when he hurried to the room where she lay—already immobile in death—for garments in all stages of completion were scattered about.

The room was filled with women weeping and mourning with loud cries for their friend, but Peter gently ushered them out and closed the door. Alone with the dead woman, he knelt beside the bed to pray, and once again felt the reassuring sense of power from Jesus that so often came to him in times such as this.

"Tabitha, arise," he said confidently, and at once the woman opened her eyes and sat up to greet him.

This was the first time Peter had raised a person from the dead, and he could not help feeling a little awed by it. But his own awe was nothing compared to that of the city's inhabitants when news of the miracle spread abroad. Soon great crowds—reminiscent of those which had followed Jesus in the early exciting days of the Galilean ministry—thronged about him wherever he went, begging to hear the story of the Christ in whose name the miracle had been performed.

Peter quickly came to love Joppa, for though the vast reaches of the Great Sea spreading endlessly westward were far different from the much smaller lake where he had grown up, it held much of the same lure for him. On the sandy beach he watched the fishermen embark at dusk, running their boats out by wading as far as they could in the shallow water, then leaping into them and seizing the oars to row away from the shore before a wave could sweep them back upon the beach—just as he and Andrew had so often done at Capernaum.

At night, he could lie upon a pallet spread out on the rooftop at the home of Simon the tanner and watch the bobbing torches of the boats fishing well out to sea. And in the morning, with the rising of the sun, he was often awakened by the voices of the fishermen and the scream of the sea gulls as the boats were beached upon the shore and the catch piled into baskets to be carried to the fishhouses where they were

cleaned and split for drying in the bright sunlight, and ship-
ment to other cities.

Sometimes, at night, Peter would take torch and spear, wading into the shallow waters and spearing a fish with a quick,
expert stroke when its outline was revealed by torchlight
against the white sand of the sea bottom. Or again, to help fill
the larder of his friends, he would wade out and cast with a
small net, using the old skill accumulated during his years as
a fisherman upon the Sea of Galilee. Most of the time, however, he was busy with the ever-increasing affairs of the
rapidly growing church at Joppa.

Because the city was a seaport through which many thousands of people passed in both directions each year, mainly
going to and from Jerusalem for the religious festivals, fresh
crowds gathered daily to hear Peter's teaching. Rich Jews
from Alexandria and the cities of Egypt preferred to land at
Joppa—even though forced to endure the discomfort of being
carried ashore upon the shoulders of fishermen—rather than
to continue one or two days' sail northward to Caesarea, the
Roman port that was also the site of government for the district of Judea and Samaria. Besides, the journey to Jerusalem
from Caesarea required travelers to cross Samaria, with the
constant threat of being robbed by the Samaritans, who hated
the Jews, or by bands of brigands who infested the wild
country north of Jerusalem.

As busy and as productive as his mission to Lydda and
Joppa turned out to be, Peter should have been happy, for
both the work he was doing and the contacts with those going and coming from other parts of the world were stimulating
and satisfying. Yet he found himself afflicted, after a few
months in the seaport city, with the same restlessness that had
plagued him in Jerusalem. By now, however, he recognized it
as a part of the divine discontent stirred by the Master in all

who truly followed him, though where it would take him next he did not yet know.

Meanwhile a subtle change was taking place in Simon Peter, a change of which even he was not as yet fully aware. Through the years since he had first met Jesus, the Galilean fisherman called Simon of Bethsaida had gradually expanded his viewpoints and his understanding of the world about him. And though Joppa, unlike Caesarea to the north, was primarily a Jewish city, the constant coming and going of people from the Diaspora, with their broader knowledge of the rest of the world and the contact with Greek thought and customs which exerted the strongest influence in forming the culture of that world, inevitably had its effect upon him.

At Joppa, too, he was thrown more in contact with Gentiles than he had ever been before and came to know them, not simply as pagans to be abhorred by a pious Jew, but as people with the same emotions he experienced and the same need for peace and assurance in their souls. But though he vaguely perceived the change that was going on within himself in preparation for his next venture in the service of the Master, Peter came to a full realization of it only when—like Saul on the road to Damascus—the direction in which Jesus wished him to turn next was revealed to him in a dream.

It was Peter's custom to return to the house of Simon in the late afternoon, following a day spent in the market place and on the shore where the ships unloaded, talking to all who would listen to the thrilling story he had to tell. There he would go to the housetop where the cool breeze from the sea swept over the city and pray alone for a while before joining the tanner's family in the evening meal. While he was praying one afternoon, he experienced an extraordinarily vivid dream or trance—he could never be sure just which—though he had no doubt of its source.

Before his eyes in the dream, the heavens seemed to open and he saw a great sheet tied together at the four corners very much as the people in that region tied their belongings in a cloth when moving or carrying things to be sold in the market. In the dream, the sheet was lowered rapidly toward the earth by unseen hands. And when it came near, he saw that it contained many kinds of animals, including pigs and other living things which a devout Jew could not touch under penalty of defilement according to the Law.

Peter naturally recoiled from the sheet and its forbidden contents, even when he heard a familiar voice say, "Rise, Peter. Kill and eat."

"Not so, Lord!" he cried in horror. "I have never eaten anything that is common or unclean."

"What God has cleansed, do not call common," the voice answered, and now its accents were like thunder.

Three times this extraordinarily vivid experience was repeated, each time with the final admonition: "What God has cleansed, do not call common." Then the sheet was drawn up into the heavens, which closed after it.

Peter awoke, greatly troubled about the meaning of the vision. Deep in his heart he sensed what it was, but everything in his life as a Jew who obeyed the Law naturally rebelled against such an interpretation, and for the moment at least, his mind instinctively rejected it. Simon the tanner had not yet come home, so he had no opportunity to talk of it with him. Nor, he knew, would anything be gained by going to Jerusalem and discussing the experience with James and the elders there, for they would certainly reject summarily the conviction which was slowly beginning to develop in his heart.

While he wrestled with his own conscience on the housetop, Peter heard voices below and went to the edge of the roof to look down. Three men stood before the door: one was a Roman soldier and the other two were dressed as servants. Peter could think of no immediate reason why he should be arrested, unless Caiaphas had heard of his success in Joppa and Lydda and had decided to hale him before the Sanhedrin again. And even then, a Roman soldier would hardly have been sent to seize him when he had broken no Roman law of which he had knowledge. While he debated what to do, he heard the soldier speak to the tanner's wife.

"We are seeking one Simon called Peter," he said. "They told us in the city that he is here."

The woman hesitated, and sensing that she was afraid to reveal his presence there lest danger come to Peter, another of the men added, "We have come from the Centurion Cornelius in Caesarea, and mean no harm to him."

"I am the man you seek," Peter called down from the housetop and descended the stairway to where they waited.

The servant bowed low, as if Peter were a nobleman. "Cornelius has been instructed by God to send for you so he may hear your words," he said.

Though Cornelius was a Gentile and a Roman, Peter remembered him well from that day at the foot of the cross when the Roman officer had kept him from attacking those who had been throwing dice there for Jesus's robe. He had not seen Cornelius since, but he knew that some of those who had escaped from Jerusalem during the persecution by Saul had gone to Caesarea and had been befriended by the Roman officer, so he felt himself to be in no danger there.

"Come in and rest," he told the men. "I will go with you in the morning."

It was only after the evening meal that a connection occurred to Peter between his dream that afternoon and the coming of the men from Caesarea. But when he questioned them, he learned that they had left the district capital several days before, obviously ruling out any such relationship. Accompanied by several members of the church at Joppa who hoped to preach in Caesarea, Peter left the following morning, reaching the Roman district capital late on the afternoon of the second day of travel.

II

Under Herod the Great, Israel had become one of the most important nations at the eastern end of the Mediterranean Sea and a powerful bulwark for Rome against the rebellious Parthians farther to the east. Lovely though it was, the Plain of Sharon extending southward from the foot of Mount Carmel had been only rolling pastureland before Herod, with no cities of any importance and no natural harbor south of the Phoenician ports. At a place called Strato's Tower, some twenty miles south of Mount Carmel, however, a rocky ledge projected out into the ocean, and upon this foundation Herod had chosen to build a seaport.

Some twelve years was spent in constructing the beautiful city that rose upon the ledge and the shore behind it. Broad quays extended out into the ocean to break the waves and form a double harbor about two hundred paces each way, with a pier more than a hundred and thirty paces in length, built of huge stones and raised out of water twenty fathoms deep. Upon an elevated spot beside a temple of polished stone close to the shore, Herod had erected a large statue of the Emperor Augustus as Jupiter Olympus. Visible far at sea, the statue served as a guide for ships putting in there on the route between Antioch and Egypt along the regular circuit of the Mediterranean followed by Roman shipping.

Great aqueducts brought water into Caesarea from a small river and from springs bursting out of the hillside near the foot of Mount Carmel. Upon the slope north of the city, a large amphitheater had been constructed capable of containing twenty thousand spectators, while a hippodrome for chariot races occupied a location somewhat to the east of it.

Caesarea was a far more pagan city than any Peter had visited in his missionary travels. As he and his companions approached it they could hear shouts of approval and disapproval from the excited crowd in the great amphitheater and see gladiators fighting for their lives within the arena. They could also easily hear the roaring of the lions kept in cages beneath the amphitheater for the sport called *venatio*, in which condemned criminals were thrown to the beasts as entertainment for the bloodthirsty crowds.

Cornelius' home was located near the base of the great mole that extended out into the sea as a breakwater, forming a fairly safe anchorage except in times of severe storm. A considerable number of the officer's kinsmen and friends had gathered to await Peter's arrival. When the party from Joppa came into the outer court, Cornelius started to prostrate himself at Peter's feet but the apostle took him by the arm and stopped him.

"Stand up," he said gently. "I myself am also a man." Peter did not, however, immediately enter the main part of the house where the others were, for to do so was a defilement under the Laws of Moses.

"How did you happen to send for me?" he asked Cornelius as they stood in the cool atrium of the Roman dwelling. A fountain played in a small pool there and the furnishings were luxurious, for Cornelius was a wealthy man and the Italian Band, of which he was the commander, one of the most respected military organizations making up the Roman army.

"I have been a follower of Jesus of Nazareth since shortly after the day he was crucified," Cornelius said.

"Do you know just what brought you to him?"

Cornelius nodded. "I was not on duty when the Nazarene was arrested and taken before Pontius Pilate, but one of my fellow officers told me later what happened. When Pilate asked Jesus whether he was King of the Jews, the Nazarene answered: 'My kingdom is not of this world. If my kingdom were of this world, then my disciples would fight that I not be delivered. To this end was I born, and for this cause I came into the world, that I should bear witness to the truth!' "

"John has told me of it," Peter said, and a spasm of pain crossed his face. "I was hiding away in fear at the time."

"But you were not afraid when you came to the foot of the cross," Cornelius reminded him. "If I had not held you back, you would have seized the Lord's garment from the soldiers and been thrust through for your pains. At the time, I did not know what it all meant. Only when my friend told me Jesus's words before Pilate did I dare to hope that he might be my Saviour, too."

"I still don't understand why you sent for me at this time."

"I and my band are soon to be transferred to Rome," Cornelius told him, "and I wanted to speak with you about Jesus before we go. Four days ago, as I was praying in the afternoon, I saw a vision like a dream in which an angel said to me: 'Your prayers and your gifts have come before God for a memorial. Send men to Joppa and call for one Simon, whose surname is Peter. He lodges at the house of Simon, a tanner, by the seaside, and he will tell you what you should do.' "

"Did the angel say more?"

Cornelius shook his head. "As soon as the vision ended, I called two of my servants and sent them to Joppa with a soldier."

Peter had been troubled in his mind during the journey from Joppa to Caesarea, not only concerning the meaning of the extraordinarily vivid dream he had experienced just before leaving but over what he would say to the centurion. Now, he realized, his quandary had been solved, for if the Lord had spoken to Cornelius even before he had to him, it could only mean that the two events were connected and that once again Jesus had clearly outlined Peter's course for him. This time, however, Peter realized that he had been moving toward that course ever since he had seen the Holy Spirit poured out upon the Samaritans, whom every pious Israelite was brought up to hate.

"You know it is unlawful for a Jew to keep company or to come near anyone of another nation," he said, searching for a way to explain to Cornelius the great truth which had just illuminated his mind—like the sun breaking through the clouds after a storm.

"I do not wish you to defile yourself," the centurion said quickly, before Peter could go on. "I have only told you what was spoken to me in the vision."

"What I am saying is that God had already shown me I could not call any man common or unclean," Peter explained. "It happened in a dream just before your servants and the soldier arrived, but I did not fully understand its meaning until now."

"I can only be thankful that you were willing to come at all," Cornelius said humbly.

"We are present here before God to hear all things commended by him," Peter told him. "Let us go inside."

The people gathered by Cornelius were Romans, for the

most part: his wife and children, the members of his own household, several soldiers and servants, and a few others whose garb identified them as minor officials. All were Gentiles—under Jewish Law—but none of them would have been there, Peter knew, if they had not already shown an interest in the teachings of Jesus. And when he saw their eager faces uplifted to him, he knew what he should say.

"Of a truth," he began. "I perceive that God is no respecter of persons. But in every nation, he who fears him and works righteousness is accepted by him. You know already the word God sent to the Children of Israel, preaching peace by Jesus Christ, the Lord of all, for it has been published throughout all of Judea, beginning from Galilee after the baptism preached by John. That word told how God anointed Jesus of Nazareth with the Holy Spirit and with power, and how he went about doing good and healing all that were oppressed by the devil. For God was with Jesus and we apostles were witnesses of all he did."

Peter paused, and as his eyes swept the faces before him he was filled with a surge of pride that he had been chosen by the Master as the first of the apostles to carry the good news freely to Gentiles.

"God raised up Jesus on the third day and showed him openly," he continued, his voice deepening with the fervor that filled him now. "Not to all people, but to witnesses chosen before God, even to us who did eat and drink with him after he had risen from the dead. He sent us to preach to the people and testify that it was he who was ordained by God to be the judge of the quick and the dead. And to him all the prophets witnessed that through his name whoever believes in him shall receive remission of their sins."

Peter's final words were all but drowned out by something that was already familiar to him—though until a few days ago he would have sworn it could never happen in a gathering of Gentiles. Once again he heard the familiar rush of sound like a great wind blowing through the room and saw his listeners seized by the Holy Spirit, as he and the others had been on the day of Pentecost.

The Jews who had come from Joppa with Peter were astonished at what they saw, but there was no mistaking it or its significance. In the weeks that followed, Peter went about the beautiful city of Caesarea, speaking to any who would listen, whether Jew or Gentile, pagan or worshiper of the Most High. He was joined in this effort by Philip, who now lived in Caesarea. And, moved by the fervor of the two men, many joined the new faith and were given the gift of the Holy Spirit.

Peter's actions in Caesarea could not long go unnoticed in Jerusalem, however, for the Holy City was only two days' journey away. Soon a message came from the elders of the congregation there and the other apostles, ordering him rather peremptorily to return and give a report of what he had done.

III

When Peter came into the upper chamber in Mary's house where the leaders of the Jerusalem congregation were gathered to hear his report, he was reminded of another scene that had taken place in this same room not so long before when Saul of Tarsus was called upon to defend himself before this very same group. Peter knew from the grim faces of James and many of the others that they were already prepared to condemn his actions in Caesarea, but a new world had been opened to him upon a rooftop in Joppa and again in the house of Cornelius, a world whose horizons were endless. For the sake of the church, he was prepared to make every effort to ameliorate the objections of James and the others, but he had no thought of giving in to them and returning to the old ways. Caesarea had marked a great turning point in the spread of the Master's work. From now on there would be no going back, as far as his personal ministry was concerned.

"You associated with men who were uncircumcised, and ate with them," James accused him sternly as soon as the meeting began.

"I did it upon the instructions of the Lord himself," Peter answered calmly, and a murmur of indignation and disbelief swept through the group.

"Have you forgotten that Jesus himself said 'Go not into the way of the Gentiles and do not enter any city of the Samaritans, but go rather to the lost sheep of the house of Israel'?" James demanded.

"I myself heard those words spoken by the Master's lips." Peter could have reminded the kinsman of the Lord that James and the rest of Jesus's own family had opposed his work at first and that only after the Master's death and Resurrection had James himself come to take an active part in the church— largely at Peter's own request. But nothing would be gained, he knew, by widening the chasm that had threatened to split the church from its very beginning. For, once the followers of Jesus began to fight among themselves here in Jerusalem, it would be folly to hope that groups in other cities would not be drawn into the same conflict, causing the work everywhere to suffer.

"I, too, believed at first that the teachings of the Master were only for Jews," Peter admitted. "But you were with me in Samaria, John. You saw the Holy Spirit come upon those who believed."

"The Samaritans worship the same God we do," John pointed out. "But you baptized Gentiles in Caesarea."

"What about the eunuch from Ethiopia? Did not the Lord speak to Philip?"

"Philip did baptize the eunuch," James admitted, "but the Queen of Sheba came to worship the Most High in the time of Solomon before returning to her people, and many of our ancient scholars believe there have been worshipers of the Most High in that land ever since. The eunuch must have belonged to that group. Remember, he was reading from the Book of Isaiah on the road from Jerusalem to Gaza when Philip found him."

"It was the Lord himself who directed me to go to Caesarea and speak to Gentiles there," Peter insisted, and went on to tell of the vision of Cornelius, his own dream at Joppa, and his visit to the centurion's home, ending the account with the final and irrefutable proof that Jesus himself had ordained the spreading of the gospel to Gentiles—the pouring out of the Holy Spirit upon those who had been converted. When this occurrence was vouched for by the men from Joppa who had accompanied Peter, James and the others had no choice except to agree, however reluctantly, that it was indeed the Lord's wish that the gift of eternal life not be denied to Gentiles if they repented and believed in Jesus as the Christ.

Had Peter's experience in Caesarea been the only evidence of the widening sphere of the work to which Jesus had committed his followers, it might not have impressed the elders at Jerusalem quite so much as it did. But shortly before his return to the Holy City, a report had come from Barnabas in the great Syrian capital of Antioch that the work was progressing rapidly there—to such an extent, in fact, that Barnabas had obtained permission to bring Saul from Tarsus to help carry it on.

Emboldened by this news and the decision of the apostles and elders that Gentiles might now be brought into the church, Peter traveled northward through Israel and Samaria, preaching the Word everywhere and baptizing those who gave themselves to the new faith. He was accompanied on the leisurely journey by the young scribe John Mark, and as they walked the roads Peter spoke of the things Jesus had said and taught, while Mark stored in his memory these sayings of the Master.

And then quite suddenly the small church at Jerusalem suffered what for a while threatened to be a fatal blow—a resumption of the persecution which had come so near to destroying it at the hands of Saul of Tarsus.

IV

Aristobulus, the son of Herod the Great who had ruled Judea and Samaria for a few years when Simon Peter was a boy, left five children at his death—the strongest of them a youth named Agrippa. In profligate and depraved Rome, where he had spent most of his life, the young prince charmed himself into the favor of Drusus, eldest son of the Emperor Tiberius, and the somewhat younger Claudius, generally regarded as a half-wit because of his retiring ways and his difficulties in speech.

At the death of Tiberius a few years after the Crucifixion of Jesus, one of Agrippa's closest friends, the already insane Caligula, became emperor, and Agrippa was named tetrarch of a small district in the northern part of what once had been Israel. Herodias—the wife of Herod Antipas who had earned him the denunciation of John the Baptist—envied Agrippa, however, and persuaded the aging Antipas to go to Rome and seek a larger kingdom. In so doing, they had played directly into the hands of the clever Agrippa, who accused Antipas of wanting to become an independent monarch. Caligula then obliged his friend by banishing Herod Antipas to Gaul and making Agrippa ruler of Galilee and Peraea.

The young Herod's initial good fortune was only the beginning of his almost meteoric rise to power, however. Happening to be in Rome when Caligula was assassinated after a few years of rule, Agrippa handled the negotiations whereby his other friend, Claudius—regarded by most Romans as a moron —became emperor. And to reward him, Claudius changed the former status of Judea and Samaria from that of a district governed by a procurator to part of the domain of Agrippa— as king.

Agrippa had one advantage over many others in the star-crossed house of Herod the Great; his mother had been Mariamne, of princely Jewish heritage in the Hasmonean family. He was therefore able to achieve what few of his house had ever managed before in being acceptable not only to the Romans but also to the Jews. To ingratiate himself further with the ruling hierarchy of priests in the temple and convince everyone that he was at heart a pious Jew, Agrippa made great sacrifices and decreed that any Gentiles who might marry into his own family must hereafter be bound by all the laws and customs of the Jews. And as a final means of gaining favor with the temple authorities, he arrested James, the son of Zebedee and the younger brother of John, and had him beheaded in the beginning of a new campaign of persecution against the congregation of the Nazarenes in Jerusalem.

Peter was not in the Holy City when the tragedy occurred. He could have protected himself by remaining away, but he had given up running away long ago on that night when he had fled from the palace of the high priest to Mary's house and the upper room. Knowing that now, more than ever, the small congregation at Jerusalem must be kept alive as the heart, so to speak, of the Nazarene faith, he returned there at once, without going on to Antioch as he had originally intended. And there, as he spoke from the Porch of Solomon according to his custom, Peter was arrested.

This time Peter was not taken to the so-called "hold" of the temple, the small prison where malefactors were often locked up pending trial before the Great Sanhedrin; instead he was placed in the Roman fortress of Antonia. The arrest had taken place just before the Passover, and from his captors Peter learned that Agrippa was determined to make a public spectacle of his execution immediately following the religious feast. Many pilgrims would still be in the city then, and the king could be sure that news of Peter's death would spread rapidly to other parts of the world, discouraging the followers of Jesus everywhere.

The fact that he had been taken to the Roman prison warned Peter that he would almost certainly be tried before Agrippa himself and not before the Sanhedrin, as he had hoped. He was not, however, concerned primarily for his own safety; on that day when Jesus had sent him back to Jerusalem with the command to "Feed my sheep," he had put his future in the hands of the Lord. But he was gravely concerned about the fate of the harassed congregation in Jerusalem and what the new persecution by Herod Agrippa might hold out for them, as well as for the other apostles who were still in the Holy City.

Had he been able to reach his fellow apostles, Peter would have sent word to them to flee from Jerusalem, but at the moment he was in prison, with no means of reaching them. Obviously, too, the temple authorities who had sought so long to destroy him had already warned Agrippa of the miraculous power he possessed. For, not only was he forced to stand or lie between two soldiers, bound by a chain to each, but two additional guards were posted at all times outside the gate of the cell in which he lay. Peter's only hope, therefore, was that he might somehow get a message to the others when he was brought to trial and given an opportunity to defend himself, as all prisoners were guaranteed under Roman law. Comforted a little by this hope, he finally fell asleep between his two guards.

It was sometime in the early hours of the morning when Peter was awakened by a touch on his shoulder. He turned upon his back, feeling the chain attached to his right wrist tug against that binding him to his Roman guard, and peered up at the visitor, but did not recognize him. That the other man was not a soldier, Peter could easily see, for he wore a white robe.

"Rise up quickly," the visitor said. And to Peter's amazement, when he rose to his feet the chains binding his wrists and ankles fell to the floor, though without making any sound. Nor did the guards between whom he had been sleeping show any signs of awakening.

"Gird yourself and put on your sandals," the visitor commanded, and Peter dressed quickly, still with the feeling that this must all be a dream. But when the guide crossed the cell and opened the door, he did not need the command "Follow me" to hurry after the young man in the white robe.

The guards outside were sitting beside the door with their backs to the wall. But, like everyone else in the prison, they, too, seemed to be asleep and paid no attention to Peter and his guide as they hurried through the corridor toward the outer door. There the massive iron gate also opened at the touch of the young man, although Peter did not see him use a key.

The street outside the prison was narrow, ending in one of the stairways leading downward to the Tyropean Valley and the lower part of the city. Hurrying to keep up with his guide, Peter was startled when he turned a corner and found himself alone, with no sign of the man who had so miraculously released him from the Roman prison. He did not waste time trying to understand how such a thing could have happened, however. Certain now that he had been released through divine means, he knew he must place himself as quickly as possible beyond the reach of Herod Agrippa.

V

Through the deserted streets Peter moved with long, swinging strides; here and there a dog barked and a cock crowed, but he met none of the night guards who patrolled Jerusalem during the religious festivals. When he came to the house of Mary and Mark, he was not surprised to see chinks of light showing through the tightly drawn blinds and to hear the murmur of voices inside praying—he could be sure—for his deliverance.

Stepping into the shadows of a terebinth tree growing beside the door, Peter knocked upon it. There was no response, but he could still hear the voices of those inside, so he knocked again; finally the door was opened a mere crack, enough for him to recognize a girl named Rhoda, who often served with Mary, peering out at him.

"It is I, Rhoda," he said. "Simon Peter."

The girl gasped and disappeared, but when Peter tried to push the door open he found that it was guarded by a chain.

"It is Peter," he heard Rhoda telling those inside. "He stands before the gate."

"You are mad," someone said.

"I saw him, and he spoke to me!" the girl protested.

"It must be his spirit," another voice said. But when Peter knocked again, one of the deacons came to open the door and he was surrounded at once by a happy group, eagerly asking questions about his escape.

"The Lord sent an angel and delivered me out of the hands of Herod," Peter explained. "But I must leave at once, lest the king come and punish all of you. Go tell these things to James and to the others of the brethren."

"Where will you go?" John Mark asked. "Agrippa will surely send soldiers to bring you back."

"Syria is the nearest district ruled directly by Rome. Even Agrippa cannot take me there."

Mark's face brightened. "One of the Italian Band commanded by Cornelius in Caesarea came to Jerusalem yesterday in a chariot. He was very much concerned when I told him you had been arrested."

"Do you know where he is?" Peter asked quickly.

"Not far away, at the home of a kinsman. If he will take you to Caesarea in the chariot, Cornelius can find a ship there to take you on to Antioch."

"Hurry and find him," Peter directed.

While Mark went for the soldier, Peter ate hurriedly, giving instructions all the while to the other apostles to leave Jerusalem at once before Agrippa could vent his wrath at Peter's miraculous escape upon them. The excited people who had waited there praying for him were still asking questions when Mark and the soldier from Caesarea arrived with the chariot. And only a little more than an hour after his release, Peter and the soldier departed by way of the Water Gate, which was left open at night for any who might need to bring water from the pools outside the walls.

From Jerusalem, the travelers took the central highway leading northwestward to Antipatris, and thence along the Via Maris, traversing the lovely Plain of Sharon on the seaward side of the district of Samaria. From Pirathon, they again turned westward to Caesarea, reaching that city toward midnight.

Peter had no desire to bring down the anger of Agrippa upon Cornelius and his other friends at Caesarea, so when a ship was not immediately available, he pushed on north by foot along the shore, heading for the Phoenician cities on the coast where he could be sure of finding a ship for Antioch. A few hours' walk took him over the border of the district beyond the reach of Herod Agrippa, but he continued across Mount Carmel to the protected bay of Accho and the port city of Ptolemais, southernmost of the Phoenician centers.

By waiting a while at Ptolemais, Peter could have taken a boat northward directly to Antioch, but decided instead to continue up the coast by foot, visiting the Phoenician cities and stopping to preach in each of them before coming at last to the Syrian capital. He was welcomed joyfully by Barnabas, Lucius of Cyrene, Manaen and many others from Jerusalem who had been driven to Antioch by the persecution of Saul. And he was especially pleased to learn that the apostles who had been in Jerusalem at the time of his arrest had also escaped, along with John Mark, who was now in Antioch. James, the kinsman of the Lord, however, had remained in Jerusalem to head the small congregation still left in the city.

VI

Barnabas insisted that Peter join him and Mark in a house he
had rented in Antioch, and after the evening meal on the day
of Peter's arrival, suggested that they take a walk about the
city. The way led along the south bank of the Orontes River
that divided Antioch in half—except for an island, or *insula*,
in the middle of the stream, where the Roman government
buildings for the province were located. The streets here in
the poorer section of the city, where paved at all, were of
rough cobblestones, and pools of dirty water from a recent
rain stood here and there, forcing the two men to pick their
way. Dirty children were playing in the pools, and occasionally one of them would spit the sullen word "Christian!" at
them.

"Pay no attention to them," Barnabas advised. "Those who
hate us in Antioch gave us that name."

"Christian." Peter repeated the word thoughtfully. "It has
a pleasant ring somehow and comes easy to the tongue."

"Our enemies use it as a term of derision," Barnabas explained.

"Then turn their own tongues against them. To Gentiles,
the word Nazarene has little meaning, since they do not know
Nazareth as we of Galilee do. As followers of the Christ,
however, we can all proudly call ourselves Christians."

"But we have always ignored those who call us by that
name here," Barnabas protested.

"Then ignore them no longer," Peter said firmly. "By naming ourselves Christians, we will defeat those who would de-
ride us."

Barnabas nodded slowly, a thoughtful look in his eyes. "I remember when you and John were brought before the Priestly Council, after you healed the paralyzed man in the temple. You said then of the Master, 'The stone rejected by the builders has become the head of the corner.' Perhaps, as you say, we can change the word Christian from a curse to a badge of honor."

Peter soon realized that Barnabas was not simply taking him on a casual walk. Near the river, they stopped before a large building in the Jewish area of the city, with a seven-branched candlestick chiseled into the wood above the door identifying it as a synagogue. When they entered, they found the building almost filled and were forced to take seats at the back.

The arrangement, Peter saw, was strictly according to Mosaic law, with a raised pulpit in the center visible from all sides. A group of benches upon a lower platform, reserved for the elders of the congregation, was now filled, and shortly after they took their seats the service began. As usual, it was opened by reading from the scrolls of the Law and the Prophets, first in Hebrew and then in Greek. At the end of the reading the scrolls were replaced in the cabinet or ark, and the *chazan*, or cantor, who was directing the service, stepped to the pulpit. Speaking in Greek, he gave the traditional invitation to any who might wish to address the congregation.

Peter looked inquiringly at Barnabas, wondering why his friend had not warned him if he expected him to speak, but Barnabas shook his head. "We will arrange for you to address a service on the Sabbath, Peter," he said in a whisper. "Tonight I want you to hear someone else."

While Barnabas was speaking, a short man rose from one of the front benches. Even before he climbed the steps leading up to the platform and the raised pulpit upon it, Peter recognized Saul of Tarsus.

"Our friend Paulos will speak to us again," the *chazan* announced, quite as if it was customary for Saul—addressed here by his Greek name of Paul—to speak before this congregation frequently. Peter remembered now that Barnabas had asked and received permission from the church at Jerusalem to call Saul from Tarsus for work in Antioch, and understood that Barnabas had brought him here tonight to hear the man who was now known as Paul.

"Men and brethren," Paul began, and, with the audience, Peter was caught up at once by the rhythmic flow of his words, the compelling timbre of his voice and—though he had told it himself many times before—the always enthralling story of a new hope and a new joy for all men. "I have spoken to you before of the events that happened in Galilee and in Jerusalem, telling how Jesus of Nazareth, the Messiah of God, was born in Bethlehem of the line of David and began his ministry with his baptism by John the Baptist in the waters of the Jordan. Moreover, brethren, I declare to you the gospel I have preached and you have received and upon which you stand. By it you may be saved if you keep in memory what I have preached to you, unless you have believed in vain. For I gave you first of all what I also received: how Christ died for our sins, according to the Scriptures, and was buried and rose again the third day; how he was seen by Cephas, by the Twelve, and by more than five hundred brethren at once, of whom the greater part are presently alive.

"Later, this same Jesus Christ was seen by James," Paul continued, "then by all the apostles, and last of all by me also, as one born out of time. For I am the least of the apostles, one who is not really fit to be called an apostle, because I persecuted the Church of God. But by the grace of God, I am what I am, and his grace, which was bestowed upon me, was not in vain."

The large hall was now completely filled, and Peter could see many people standing outside, listening through the windows and the open doors.

"It has been like this ever since he came from Tarsus to work with us here," Barnabas whispered to Peter. "I wanted you to hear him so you would know we did right in supporting him before the elders at Jerusalem."

"Now if it be preached that Christ rose from the dead, how is it that some say there is no resurrection from the dead?" Paul continued. "If there be no resurrection from the dead, then Christ is not risen, and if Christ is not risen, then our preaching is in vain and your faith is also in vain. Yes, and we are convicted as false witnesses of God because we have testified that God raised up Jesus Christ. Yet he could not have raised him up—if the dead do not rise.

"Now, brethren, it has been said among you that I speak too simply, that I do not teach from the Law and the Prophets as others do, and that therefore my teaching is of naught. But I teach only Christ and of his Crucifixion that all the world might have eternal life. For all those who follow Jesus Christ believe only one thing; that he came into the world to give his life as a ransom for many, and that ransom having been paid, all of those who believe in him are certain of eternal life and the strength to carry them through periods of adversity.

"But why should the Son of God come to earth and suffer torture at the hands of men, even the agony of the cross and the tomb? When Christ was still here on earth, he told the lawyer Nicodemus of Jerusalem, whom many of you know to be a just and upright man, the reason for his coming. This I heard from the mouth of Nicodemus himself in the words of our Lord and Master when he said: '*God so loved the*

world that he gave his only begotten Son that whoever be-
lieves in him shall not die but shall have eternal life.' "

"Brethren," Paul's voice rose now and he seemed to grow
taller. "What greater love could God have for man than to
give his own Son? And what greater love could that Son have
than to lay down his life for us and our sins? Therefore, if
Christ so loved the world that he gave his life for us, it be-
hooves us to love one another with a love which passes anything asked of us before.

"Though I speak with the tongues of men and of angels
and have not love, I have become like sounding brass or a
tinkling cymbal. Though I have the gift of prophecy and
understand all mysteries and all knowledge; though I have all
faith so that I could move mountains, but do not have love, I
am nothing. And though I bestow all my goods to feed the
poor and give my body to be burned, yet have not love, it
profits me nothing.

"Love suffers long and is kind. Love does not envy, does
not vaunt itself, is not puffed up. It does not behave itself
unseemingly, does not seek its own, is not easily provoked,
and thinks no evil. It does not rejoice in iniquity, but rejoices
in the truth. It bears all things, believes all things, hopes all
things, endures all things.

"Brethren, if a man is overtaken in a fault, you who love
one another must restore him in a spirit of meekness, lest you
also be tempted. You must bear one another's burdens in order
to fulfill the Law of Christ. If a man thinks himself to be something when he is nothing, he deceives himself. So let us not be
weary in well-doing, and as we have opportunity, let us do
good to all men, especially to them of the household of the
faith.

"Finally, my brethren, be strong in the Lord and in the
power of his might. Put on the whole armor of God that you

may be able to stand against the wiles of the devil, with your loins girt about with truth and wearing the breastplate of righteousness. Above all, take the shield of faith with which you shall be able to quench all the fiery darts of the wicked, the helmet of salvation, the sword of the spirit—which is the Word of God. For God showed his love toward us in that, while we were yet sinners, Christ died for us."

A deep silence filled the room as Paul stepped away from the *luach*. Then a man sitting near the front rose, and tottering upon uncertain feet, moved down the aisle between the benches to fall upon his knees before the small elevated platform where Paul stood. And, as if his action were a signal, dozens of others also converged upon the pulpit, surrounding the speaker with a bank of petitioners, their faces uplifted to him as they begged to receive the salvation promised to those who believed upon Jesus Christ as the Son of God.

As he watched, it seemed to Peter that he could hear once again the rush of wind through the building, as he had heard it upon that day at Pentecost when he had told the same thrilling story the speaker had told tonight—though, he admitted in a moment of deep humility, not with the same eloquence. For somewhere, perhaps in the blinding light which from his own account had shone upon him on the road to Damascus, Saul of Tarsus had become another man—fittingly with another name—a trumpet whose notes of praise to God and his Son would, Peter was sure, never be uncertain.

The pressure of Barnabas' hand upon his sleeve brought Peter back to the present. Paul was moving about among those who knelt before him, laying his hands upon them and praying that they might be given the gift of the Holy Spirit and the salvation that accompanied it.

"Do you want to speak to Paul now?" Barnabas asked, but Peter shook his head. Tonight was a personal triumph for the man who not long ago had been called Saul of Tarsus; a triumph well deserved, for never had Peter heard so eloquent a voice lifted to tell the story that had begun in Galilee long ago.

Outside, the air from the nearby river was dank and cool, making Peter shiver a little and draw his robe closer about him. Having been for so many years the acknowledged leader of those who followed Jesus of Nazareth, with authority even over the believers at Jerusalem—though he rarely used it there in order to avoid a conflict with James and the more conservative group who dominated the church—it was hard for Peter to admit that anyone else might surpass his own efforts in serving the Lord.

And yet, as he had listened to Paul's brilliant oratory while the man of Tarsus marshaled facts to support his text that God, out of his great love, had sent his own Son to earth to die, thereby showing all men the way to eternal life, Peter could not but admit that with his limited education, his lack of experience and understanding of the great world outside Israel, it was extremely doubtful whether he would be able to bring such powers of oratory and logic to bear upon listeners as Paul had done tonight.

Only for a brief moment did Peter feel doubt and perhaps a little envy. Then in his heart he seemed to hear a familiar, gentle and beloved voice speaking across the years and saying once again "You are Peter, and upon this rock I will build my church and the gates of hell shall not prevail against it. I will give to you the keys of the Kingdom of Heaven. Whatever you shall bind on earth shall be bound in Heaven. And whatever you shall loose on earth shall be loosed in Heaven."

The words and the memory of the occasion upon which they had been spoken reminded Peter once again that he must never envy others their part in the work the Lord set for them. Exactly where Paul's role lay in the future of the church was yet to be determined, but for Simon called Peter there was always the certainty that his own role had been outlined long ago by the Master himself.

"How long has Saul—Paul—been in Antioch?" Peter asked as he and Barnabas walked homeward through the now largely deserted streets.

"Less than a year. When I saw the need here for one who spoke Greek fluently and was of the Dispersion, I went to Tarsus and brought him back with me. He has led many thousands to the faith since then."

"If tonight's sermon is a sample of his preaching, I can understand why the Holy Spirit favors him."

"And why he was called on the road to Damascus," Barnabas agreed.

"I was not one of those who doubted the call given to Saul, even in Jerusalem," Peter reminded his friend.

"I know," Barnabas said. "And I have prayed daily that the Lord would grant me your tolerance and humility. But I am only human, and sometimes—like tonight—I am guilty of the sin of envy."

"I, too, envied Paul for a moment," Peter admitted. "But then I remembered that Jesus chose an unlettered fisherman of Galilee to lead his church, and surely the change in Saul of Tarsus on the road to Damascus was no greater than that."

VII

Peter was delighted with the thriving church at Antioch when he met with its leaders the next day and heard their report. It reminded him very much of the exciting time when he and the other disciples had first returned to Jerusalem after the

Ascension of Jesus, and several thousand new believers had been added to the church in a single day. There was a zest and a joy of serving in Antioch, qualities which had almost been stamped out lately in Jerusalem, strangely enough by the very man who was now the mainspring of the work here. Peter enjoyed particularly the chance to meet old friends and companions who had settled in Antioch, sowing seeds which, in the words of Jesus himself, had fallen "Into good ground and brought forth fruit, some an hundredfold, some sixtyfold, some thirtyfold."

Paul showed an undisguised pleasure at seeing Peter again. And remembering the other man's honesty and candor when they had talked in Jerusalem after his retreat into the desert, Peter could not help feeling a little ashamed of the twinge of envy he had experienced toward Paul and his eloquence the night before. Much of the day was spent in discussing the affairs of the church at Antioch with its leaders and in an account by Peter of the many recent happenings in Jerusalem and his visits to other cities in Judea, Samaria and Caesarea. At the evening meal, they partook of the Sacrament of the bread and wine, which Jesus had first shared with them in the upper room at Jerusalem and which was now customary when followers of the Master met together.

"Barnabas and I feel that the Holy Spirit has called us to carry the word into other lands," Paul said to Peter when the meal was finished. "But some of the brethren here in Antioch think we should keep on with the work which has been so fruitful."

"It does no good to kick against the goad, as you and I both well know," Peter told Paul. "If the Lord has called you, there is no escaping the call. Where do you hope to go?"

"First to my old home of Cyprus," Barnabas explained. "I have kinsmen there, and some of those who were at

Jerusalem are teaching in Salamis. They will make us welcome, and we will be able to speak in the synagogues of that
city."

"It should be a fruitful mission," Peter agreed.

"But what of the work here in Antioch?" Lucius of Cyrene,
who had been one of the founders of the church there, asked.
"Paul is our most eloquent teacher."

"You forget that a new voice has come among us," Paul
said. "How long do you plan to be in Antioch, Cephas?"
Like many of those who knew Peter well, he sometimes used
the nickname Jesus had given the rocklike disciple.

"Until the Lord calls me back to Jerusalem—or elsewhere."

"Would you direct the work here while Barnabas and I are
gone?"

"I go wherever the Holy Spirit sends me," Peter said. "Until
there is another call, I shall be happy to remain in Antioch."

"Then it is settled. Tomorrow Barnabas and I will arrange
passage to Cyprus."

"And after that?" Peter asked.

"Who knows?" Paul said, and Peter recognized the look in
his eyes, for he, too, had experienced that same feeling when
he had stood upon the shore at Joppa and watched the sun
setting in the farthest reaches of the Great Sea. Already, letters were coming in from many cities of the empire where
the good news had been taken, telling of the work being done
by converts there. In Rome, a healthy and growing church
had been in existence for some time, and Peter had received
requests to help with that work, too. But with the church in
Jerusalem again subject to persecution, this time by Herod
Agrippa, Peter did not feel safe in going so far away. Now it
seemed that Paul would be the one to carry the good news
abroad.

"We cannot know where the spirit will lead us—until it

speaks in our hearts," Peter said. "But wherever it calls us, there we must go."

Peter had been happy when he found John Mark in Antioch with Barnabas. But when Barnabas invited Mark to accompany him and Paul upon the missionary journey to Cyprus, Peter gladly gave the young scribe his blessings. In the weeks that followed, he was busy with the work that had occupied both Barnabas and Saul in Antioch. And with the church constantly expanding there, he felt a considerable satisfaction in his stewardship.

Then two things happened that changed sharply the course of Peter's life. From Caesarea came word that Herod Agrippa had died while addressing a great gathering during the gladiatorial games in the stadium there. And about the same time, Mark returned alone, having left Barnabas and Paul when they crossed over from the island of Cyprus to the mainland district of Pamphylia, after a remarkably successful mission in Cyprus where they had almost converted the Roman governor.

"Paul would have taken you on a far journey, Mark; perhaps as far as Pisidian Antioch," Peter said in greeting his young friend. "Why did you choose not to go with him?"

"I wanted to be with you," Mark answered, but Peter could see from the young man's troubled manner that this was not the whole answer.

"Did something happen between you and Paul?"

"He did not want me to leave—but Barnabas understood."

"Understood what?"

"Paul does not teach as you do," Mark blurted out. "He does not tell the sayings of the Master about seeds sown on rocks and barren soil and about virgins who did not fill their lamps with oil."

"Paul did not know Jesus as we did," Peter reminded Mark.

"He would have no way of knowing such things, except as he has heard them from others—particularly Barnabas."

"That makes it even more important for me to be with you, so I can write down the sayings of Jesus—as you promised me I could," Mark said.

Peter smiled. "I haven't kept that promise very well, have I? With the persecutions and the work in Samaria and Joppa and Caesarea, there hasn't been much time."

"I will write them here in Antioch," Mark offered. "Then when people can read about Jesus and know what he was really like, they will soon come to love him as all of us did."

Peter gave the young man a keen look. "Are you saying that Paul portrays the Master differently?"

"He preaches that Jesus died to remove from all men the burden of complying with the Law, and that they can achieve eternal life only through the Master's blood," Mark said. "He even likens Jesus to a sacrificial lamb, slain to atone for our sins."

"The Master spoke of himself that way."

"I know. But Jesus was always gentle and kind. He even forgave Judas for betraying him."

Mark's words recalled for Peter the days when he had first sat at the feet of the Master in the warm sun of Galilee and had drunk in the words with a joy that sometimes filled his heart so full that he could hardly speak. He had tried to transmit this joy to others, along with the message of Jesus's purpose in coming to earth, as it had been revealed to him. But he could not help wondering now whether his failure to emphasize the sacrifice of the Master for others might not account for the fact that, particularly when it came to the Gentiles, he did not seem to stir listeners as Paul did.

"Look into your heart and tell me the truth, Mark," Peter

said. "Wasn't your real reason for returning because you felt that Paul was taking over my authority?"

"You should see the way the people who are converted by Paul worship him." The words tumbled out in a rush, now that the real reason for Mark's concern had been revealed. "Why, he acts almost as if he were more important than even the Master himself."

"I saw something of the same thing the first night when I arrived in Antioch," Peter agreed. "But that is the fault of the people. Paul never exalts himself, Mark; he preaches only Christ crucified and risen from the dead. The Lord must have felt his gifts were badly needed for our work to have called him on the road to Damascus."

"Then you think I was unfair to Paul?"

"A little—but you were driven by loyalty to me, and I forgive you. Each of us must serve the Lord in his own way, Mark—with the gifts that are given him. Paul possesses a rare eloquence to move men and inspire them, so they naturally look to him for leadership. My own work lies in another sphere, and yours may even be more valuable in the end than either of ours—if you write down the sayings of the Lord for all to read. You remember the parable of the talents, don't you?"

"Yes."

"Jesus asks each of us to use what has been given us to the best of our own ability. If we do that, God will reward us in keeping with the way we use our own particular skills."

"Should—should I go back to Pamphylia, then?" Mark asked.

"No," Peter told him with a smile. "Now that Agrippa is dead, I can begin a journey of my own and I will need you with me."

VIII

The succeeding months were among the most pleasant Peter remembered since those early days when he and the others had walked with Jesus along the roads of that green and fertile land called Galilee. With Mark, he set out upon a journey southeastward, visiting the familiar places where Jesus had taught: Nazareth, Magdala, Capernaum, Bethsaida—the beautiful city of Tiberias built by Herod Antipas upon the Sea of Galilee—and many others. In each locality, Peter showed Mark where Jesus had walked and described the events that had taken place, recalling as best he could the particular teachings of the Master associated with each city or region, while the young scribe made notes of what was done and said.

Leaving the lake, they moved northward again to the area around Caesarea-Philippi, so Peter could show Mark the very spot upon Mount Hermon where Jesus had proclaimed him the leader of the disciples. Peter had always loved the mountainous country of Northern Galilee with its forest-clad slopes, its turbulent streams, and its vineyards and olive groves surrounding the villages. And as they journeyed northeastward in the shadow of Mount Hermon, following—in reverse—the ancient route by which Abraham had come into Canaan some two thousand years before, he shared Mark's thrill at the beauty of Damascus seen from a hilltop a few hours' journey away.

Lying on the south bank of the River Barada, also sometimes called the Abana, Damascus was a low-walled square of white buildings gleaming in the sunlight between the green of the trees that partially hid the roofs. Southward and westward stretched the broad reaches of the desert, but set in the foothills of the anti-Lebanon range, Damascus was like a green jewel, with flowering trees everywhere. The church there was a busy one, having been started by some of those who had fled from Jerusalem at the time of the earliest persecution. It had been given a new life by the impassioned preaching of Paul immediately after his conversion, and Peter and Mark were shown the very wall over which the fiery man of Tarsus had been lowered while fleeing for his life.

The two were busy in Damascus for several weeks, much of the time spent in convincing those who still clung to the conviction that the new faith must be preached only to Jews, by recounting Peter's own experiences in Samaria and Caesarea and the success that had attended the work of Barnabas, Paul and the others in Antioch. Again and again the reluctance of Jews brought up to follow strictly the Laws of Moses was a stumbling block around which Peter was forced to lead the new congregations by telling again of the vision that had come to him and the decision of the church at Jerusalem that the gospel could be brought to Gentiles as well as Jews.

Their mission in Damascus completed, Peter and Mark set their faces toward Jerusalem once again, traveling by way of the desert center of Petra upon the eastern slope of the Arabah, south of the Dead Sea, where Paul had preached following his escape from Damascus. They remained in that region only a short time, however, for word came from Jerusalem that another of the controversies which had so tortured the church was in the making, and Peter was forced to hurry back to the Holy City to resume once again his role of peacemaker.

Paul and Barnabas had returned to Antioch not long before the arrival of Peter and Mark in Jerusalem, after a journey that had taken them as far north into Asia Minor as Pisidian Antioch, and thence eastward to Iconium and Derbe in

Galatia before retracing the route they had traversed on the outward journey. In every city they had been heartened by an immediate response to their preaching of the new faith. Yet, as in Jerusalem, they had encountered resistance on the part of Jewish congregations already in those cities against opening the church to Gentiles.

Because he, too, had been brought up with a devout respect for the Law, Peter was able to understand the feeling of those who opposed Barnabas and Paul. Many of the earliest converts had been Pharisees, devout men who had longed for the coming of the Messiah but found it hard to accept without reservation the concept, preached by Paul in particular, that through his death Jesus had freed everyone from the burden of the Law.

Knowing Paul, Peter could understand how the impetuous and ardent "Apostle to the Gentiles," as Paul had named himself, would be impatient with what he must consider the slowness of James and the others to come to his point of view. But Peter could also appreciate the convictions of those who had lived through Saul's persecution of the church and the later attacks upon it by Herod Agrippa, when the Lord himself had saved Peter from death.

The meeting between Paul, Barnabas, the apostles who were still in the city and the elders of Jerusalem, was held in the synagogue of the Nazarenes—as it was still known in the Holy City. As he looked about the group, Peter noted that many familiar faces were absent. John was there, as was James, the kinsman of the Lord, but John's brother James was dead at the hands of Herod Agrippa. Philip, the deacon whose work had been so important in the early days of the church, was now living in Caesarea with his family, guiding the churches in that region. Many others had fled to Antioch and to more distant parts of the world until—of the original Twelve who had followed Jesus throughout Galilee—only Peter and John were present.

As he had done for many years in his capacity as leader of the Jerusalem congregation, James presided over the meeting. No sooner had he stated that the purpose of the gathering was to decide whether or not Gentile converts must be circumcised according to the Laws of Moses, than a babble of controversy arose. Listening to the arguments, often heated, Peter realized that the question they were debating had long since been decided—with Paul himself as the agent bringing about the decision.

Until the death of Stephen and the persecution that had followed, Peter and the other apostles had been content to remain at Jerusalem, and the congregation there had been just another sect within the Jewish faith. But the very vigor of Saul's persecution had scattered the faithful abroad, like seeds sown by a sower in the parable Jesus had loved to tell; and landing in ground made fallow by the eagerness of men everywhere to achieve eternal life, new growth had sprung up quickly.

Some of these new growths—notably the great church at Antioch—were now actually more important for the spread of Jesus's teachings than the congregation of Jerusalem, and inevitably, in becoming a faith open to the whole world, the Church of Christ had broadened its concepts and its appeal. It was a little saddening for Peter to realize that those glorious days after Pentecost were a thing of the past, never to be revived here where Jesus had given his life upon the cross. And yet, he could see that the promise of the work already done by Paul, Barnabas, himself and many others, was far greater than had been that early growth in Jerusalem.

"Go and teach all nations," Jesus had commanded, and be-

cause Peter himself had taken the first real step to carry out
the command, he knew that he must not let a small group of
stubborn men in Jerusalem hamstring the glorious future
offered for the further spread of the gospel by shackling it
with restrictions that Jesus himself had long ago removed.
Therefore, when the debate had proceeded for some time
without any sign of a meeting of the minds, Peter rose to his
feet.

"Brethren, you know that a good while ago God made a
choice among us that the Gentiles should hear the word of
the gospel through my mouth and believe it," he said, speaking with the simple, earthy logic that was such a vital part of
him. "God, who knows the heart of everyone, bore witness
concerning them by giving them the Holy Spirit, even as he
did to us, and put no difference between us and them, purify-
ing their hearts by faith. Now we believe that through the
grace of the Lord Jesus Christ, we shall be saved even as they.
Why, therefore, do you tempt God to put a yoke upon the
neck of our brethren, when neither our fathers nor we ourselves were able to bear it?"

Never had the essence of Jesus's doctrine been put more
simply and more concretely. In the face of Peter's logic, no
one could argue against him, for not one of those listening
could truthfully say that he had not found the Law a burden
and had not, upon many occasions, broken it.

When Peter sat down, Paul rose to tell of the journey he
and Barnabas had made to Cyprus and the mainland of Asia
Minor. With his usual eloquence, he described the longing of
people everywhere to hear the teachings of Jesus and the
good news that, through his death upon the cross, the Master
had ransomed them all and given them the gift of eternal life.

Ordinarily James could be expected to side with the more
conservative faction among the Pharisees of the congregation.

But the kinsman of the Lord was often called James the Just, and it was said that his knees were calloused from praying in the temple that he might be guided by God's will in managing the affairs of the young church in Jerusalem. When finally he spoke, his words were slow and thoughtful, carrying with them the conviction of deep piety and grace which was needed to heal this first serious division within the new church.

"Simon Peter has declared how God at first visited the Gentiles to select people from them for his own name," James said. "To this, the words of the prophets agree, for it is written: *'After this I will return, and will build again the tabernacle of David, which is fallen down. I will build again the ruins thereof, and I will set it up, that the residue of men might seek after the Lord, and all the Gentiles, upon whom my name is called.'*

"Therefore my decision is that we do not trouble those who have turned to God from among the Gentiles, but that we write to them, asking that they abstain from pollution by idols, from fornication, from things strangled and from blood."

It was a shrewd, perhaps even inspired, solution to the problem—one that would not offend either warring faction. By quoting from the highly revered writings of the prophets, James had established an authority for the spread of God's mercy to Gentiles, a mercy which must certainly include the greatest of all divine gifts, the Messiah who had laid down his life upon the cross for all. At the same time, the kinsman of the Lord had insured that Gentile converts would still obey some of the stricter provisions of the Laws of Moses. For the worst sins of all were the eating of meat from animals sacrificed to idols, adultery, the eating of things strangled, and contamination by blood. Thus the conservative faction of the church was not offended and at the same time Paul and Barnabas were left free to make converts among Gentiles wherever they went.

IX

Simon Peter was getting to be an old man now and was content to remain in Jerusalem for a while, resting from his travels and enjoying the quiet life there now that the district was once again ruled by a Roman procurator, following the death of Agrippa, and the congregation of the Nazarenes was free from persecution—at least for the moment. But soon the divine discontent of the desire to be once again about the Master's business stirred in him once more and he decided to return to Antioch, where Paul and Barnabas were preparing for a second journey to visit churches they had established in their first missionary effort.

Peter had thought the controversy over circumcision was settled by the Council of Jerusalem, as it had come to be called. But when he arrived in Antioch after a leisurely visit to congregations in Samaria, Caesarea and Phoenicia, he found himself the center of a new and disturbing conflict, one that threatened again to tear the whole church apart. Equally startling was the change in the Antioch church, now by far the largest in the world.

Acting forthrightly upon the authority given him by the Council of Jerusalem to convert Gentiles upon an equal basis with Jews, Paul had enlarged the Antioch congregation remarkably since Peter had last visited the city. One aspect of this rapid growth troubled Peter, however, as it did many of those who had been instrumental in beginning the work in the Syrian capital. It was the same thing that had troubled Mark on the first missionary journey with Barnabas and Paul and had made him return to Antioch—the fact that the Gentile members of the congregation seemed to consider Paul alone as their mentor and recognized little connection with the church at Jerusalem or with the apostles.

Word of all this had come to James while Peter had been traveling leisurely northward toward Antioch, and a delegation had been sent from Jerusalem to inspect the Antioch church and determine to just what extent its members were obeying the decisions made at the Council of Jerusalem. Nor did Paul seem to be doing anything to lessen the separation from the Mother Church, Peter saw, for he boldly preached that he had been especially called by the Lord for what he termed the "Apostleship to the Gentiles," a considerable departure from the charge Jesus had given Peter to be leader of all those who followed him.

Hoping to avoid any more disruption of the Antioch congregation than had already been brought about by Paul's somewhat peremptory methods and the resentment of his faction against the appearance of the representatives from James, Peter sided with neither. Instead, he planned to discuss the whole matter with Paul and Barnabas and the various elements in the group, seeking to harmonize them as he had done at Jerusalem.

He was not able to see Paul immediately upon his arrival, however. And so he did not realize that, with so many looking only to the dynamic little apostle for leadership and following few of the traditional Laws of Moses, which Peter and the earlier workers in Antioch still obeyed most of the time, a crisis had already developed—in Paul's mind, at least.

Traditionally, the Christian congregations often partook of a common meal before the Sabbath service, observing the

Sacrament of bread and wine which Jesus had given them upon the evening before his death. With so much change in the church at Antioch since his last stay there, Peter felt almost like a stranger, and naturally chose to sit with old friends, including some of those who had been sent from Jerusalem by James, rather than with people he hardly knew.

Perhaps Peter was also expressing unconsciously a certain degree of disapproval for Paul's rather highhanded assumption of leadership. But he would have been the last to imply that he or any of those who had worked to further the church differed from the Gentiles in the sight of God or his Son. Only when the service began and he saw the flush of anger in the cheeks of Paul—who had been sitting with some of the more recent converts—did it occur to Peter that the man of Tarsus might put an entirely different interpretation upon his presence among the more conservative faction. And by then it was too late.

When the customary invitation to address the congregation was given, Paul rose—without waiting to see whether or not Peter desired to speak first. His eyes were burning with anger, and Peter was reminded of the time long ago when he had first seen the dynamic, intensely zealous young man, who as an agent of the Sanhedrin, was bent upon persecuting and destroying the new Nazarene sect.

The years and the recurrent bouts of fever to which Paul had been subjected upon his journeys had taken their toll. Nor had he recovered completely from injuries sustained during his journey through Galatia, when he had once been stoned and left for dead. Nevertheless, his head still had its leonine cast, and his eyes—though afflicted by a persistent inflammation—still burned with the same hot fire of fanatic devotion to the cause that had become his whole life.

Paul had become more bald through the years and his

beard was thinner and tinged with gray, just as Simon Peter's was almost snowy white, since he was much older than Paul. But the long, flexible fingers of the artisan had lost none of their grace and dexterity, for Paul worked at his trade of tentmaker even in Antioch. And as he talked they moved constantly like the brush of an artist—a characteristic gesture which Jesus, too, had possessed, Peter remembered—painting in gestures as well as words the thought being expressed.

Peter was sitting quietly in the elevated space where, in all Jewish synagogues, the "rulers" had their places. Among the new *ecclesia*, the spiritual leaders of the congregation were often called by the term *presbyter*, or somewhat more formally, by the Greek word *episkopos*—meaning overseer or bishop. When Paul began to speak, his voice lashed the congregation like a whip, bringing people sharply upright in their seats.

"Brethren," he said. "I speak to you today because certain people have come among you seeking to unsettle your faith, the same faith I have taught you and through which you have placed your trust in me. I say to you that if anyone is preaching a doctrine contrary to the one you received from God through me, a curse be upon him."

These were strong words, for no two teachers ever used exactly the same theme or the same interpretation of a particular doctrine of Scripture.

"You all know that not long ago Barnabas and myself journeyed to Jerusalem because then, as now, false prophets had come among you," Paul continued. "They preached that men could not be saved, as God revealed to me, by believing in the Lord Jesus Christ and his Resurrection, but needs must be circumcised and keep the Laws of Moses. At Jerusalem, I laid before James and the elders the way of salvation I preached to you here in Antioch, and also to the brethren in

Galatia, Cyprus and Cilicia, and which all of you have believed. When the leaders at Jerusalem saw that I had been entrusted with the charge of taking the truth of Christ to Gentiles and the heathen, just as Peter was entrusted to take it to the Jews, these same leaders gave to Barnabas and me the right hand of fellowship, with the understanding that we should go to the heathen and they go to the Jews."

Barnabas started to interrupt, for the Council of Jerusalem had not limited Peter's work at all. In fact, the question of restricting the jurisdiction he had always exercised over the whole church had never arisen, either at Jerusalem or elsewhere. Peter did not wish to fan any further the controversy which already threatened to get out of hand, however, so he shook his head at Barnabas, and the tall Cypriot relaxed in his seat.

"Peter knew this, and when he first came to Antioch, he ate and associated with everyone, whether Jew or not, whether circumcised or not. But recently, other false prophets have come from Jerusalem, saying that the Jews should not eat with the uncircumcised, and Peter has joined them." Paul turned to face Peter directly for the first time. "So I say to you now before this congregation: if you are living like a heathen and not like a Jew, although you are a Jew yourself, why do you try to make the heathen live like Jews?"

The question was directed at Peter, but Paul did not give him an opportunity to answer.

"We ourselves are Jews by birth, and yet we know that a man does not come into right standing with God by doing what the Law commands, but by simple trust in Christ," he continued. "Through the Law, I have myself become dead to the Law, even as you who have accepted Christ with me have done, so that I may live only for God. I have been crucified with Christ, so I myself no longer live, but Christ is living in me. The life I now live as a mortal man, I live by faith in the Son of God who loved me and gave himself for me. Therefore, if right standing with God came only through the Law, as the false prophets have told you, Christ died for nothing.

"But Christ did not die in vain, for all of you are the sons of God through faith in him." Paul's voice rose like a trumpet. "And all of you who have been baptized into union with Christ have clothed yourself with him. There is no room for Jew or Greek, no room for slave or freeman, no room for male or female. For you are all one through union with Jesus Christ, whose whole law is summed up in one thing: '*You must love your neighbor as you do yourself.*'

"Brethren, practice living by the spirit, for the products of the spirit are love, joy, peace, patience, kindness, goodness, faithfulness, gentleness and self-control. There is no law against such things. If we live by the spirit, let us also walk where the spirit leads. Let us stop being ambitious for honors, challenging one another and envying one another, for if anybody thinks he is somebody when really he is nobody, he is deceiving himself."

Now Paul's voice rang out over the hushed crowd in a veritable paean of triumph. "May it never be mine to boast of anything but the cross of our Lord Jesus Christ, by which the world has been crucified to me and I to the world! Now peace and mercy be on all who walk by this rule, and let nobody trouble me after this, for I carry on my body the scars that mark me as Jesus's slave."

When Paul took his seat, all eyes turned to Peter, for what had happened in Antioch that night had never occurred before in the history of the church. One apostle had condemned another publicly, and moreover, the one condemned was the man recognized by all—until now at least—as the very Prince of Apostles, designated by Jesus himself to be the rock upon which the church was founded.

Peter knew he had every right to rise and refute Paul's accusations, particularly the claim that the world had arbitrarily been divided into two parts—one for the Gentiles and one for the Jews, with jurisdiction over the former assigned to Paul and over the latter to Peter himself. He knew that Barnabas and probably the rest of the apostles and the early members of the Antioch Church felt that it was his duty to do just that in order to leave no doubt in the minds of any listener that he and he alone was the earthly head of the church, designated by Jesus himself for that honor.

But Peter was asking himself, too, what would be gained by humbling Paul publicly in order to salve his own pride? How much confusion would he create in the minds of those who had been converted by Paul? And how much would creating that confusion undermine their faith? A debate here and now, over the same issue that had plagued the very life of the young church from that first day when the twelfth apostle had been elected to succeed Judas, could do nothing but damage to the congregation that had become the greatest bulwark of the faith in this part of the world. And the preservation of the great Antioch church, to which he had given so much himself, Peter knew to be far more important than for him to humble Paul by a show of his own authority.

Without speaking, he got to his feet and left the building, while a dead silence held the congregation in its grip until he was gone.

X

As he had often sought communion with the man he served
in the garden on the Mount of Olives, Peter stopped now
beside the river, a little distance away from the meeting place,
and prayed that Jesus would speak to him again within his
heart, telling him where his own immediate duty lay in this
controversy threatening the Antioch church and in fact the
whole body of those who followed Jesus. No answer came,
however, so he turned back, still deeply troubled, toward
the house where he was living with Barnabas, Mark and some
other leaders of the Antioch congregation. Troubled as he
was, he did not notice a cripple lying in the doorway of a
house, seeking to alleviate some of the pain in his twisted
body with the warmth of the sun. Nor did the man call out to
him, but as the apostle passed the afflicted one, his shadow fell
upon the pain-wracked body.

"God be praised! I am healed!" The shout of joy startled
Peter, and he looked around momentarily, seeking its source.
Like the paralyzed man who had been healed on Peter's first
visit to the Porch of Solomon with John, the cripple here
in Antioch leaped to his feet and began to caper joyfully
about, shouting the good news over and over.

"How did it come about that you were healed?" Peter
asked.

"Master, I know not," the man answered. "Except that, as
I lay in the doorway, your shadow fell upon me and at once
I was made whole."

All of Peter's uncertainty and doubt vanished in that instant, for he knew now that Jesus had spoken to him as
clearly as if he had heard the Master's own voice assuring

him that he was following the course Jesus himself would have him follow.

"Tell no man of this," Peter instructed the former cripple. "The Lord has made you whole. Go and give thanks to him for his mercy." But in his joy the man ignored the instructions and ran on, shouting the news of his healing, so Peter was forced to turn aside into another street, lest a crowd gather because of it. He was almost at Barnabas' house when he heard Mark call to him and turned to see the youth hurrying to catch up with him.

"I wanted to follow you when you left the synagogue," Mark said, "but Barnabas thought you would rather be alone."

"I needed time to commune with the Master," Peter admitted.

"Did Jesus speak to you?"

"Not in words. But as I walked along the street, my shadow fell upon a cripple lying in the doorway, and immediately he was healed."

Mark's face brightened. "Paul will lose some of his arrogance when he hears of this. Let me be the one to tell him first."

Peter shook his head—a little sadly. "Have I taught you so little, Mark, that you still want to humble another man?"

"But Paul reprimanded you publicly! You—the one upon whom the Lord's mantle fell!"

Peter put an affectionate arm across the youth's shoulders as they walked through the narrow street toward the house. "Once when I was with Jesus, a controversy sprang up among the disciples concerning who would be greatest in his kingdom," he said.

"I remember your telling me about it."

"And do you remember Jesus's answer?"

Mark frowned—then his face brightened. "I have it written down, but I think I remember it, too. Wasn't it: 'The one who is lowliest among you all is really great'?"

"You remember the words correctly," Peter approved. "Do you understand the meaning?"

"Yes. But Paul still had no right—"

"Paul has been chosen by God for a great work, Mark; perhaps a greater work than my own, for I am old and often easily wearied. By answering him publicly, I could have justified myself through humbling him, but Jesus told us we should humble ourselves instead."

"What are you going to do, then?"

"Do?" Peter smiled. "The Lord's work—as I have always done. If I am ever to visit the great church at Rome it must be soon, for I am an old man. Besides, many still have not heard of Jesus, and even our brethren who have will need comforting in times of peril."

"Let me go with you," Mark begged.

"I thought you were going to accompany Paul and Barnabas upon their next journey."

"Paul doesn't want me."

"Why? You apologized to him for leaving before, didn't you?"

"Yes. But he still refuses to let me go. I—I think he's afraid I would be a spy for you."

Peter was not surprised a few days later when Barnabas told him he and Paul had come to a parting of the ways and that Silas, who had been one of the stalwarts in the congregation at Jerusalem, would accompany Paul upon the forthcoming journey, while Barnabas went another way. Nor did Paul make any attempt to see Peter after the denunciation before the congregation.

Had he known that he would never see Paul again, Peter would willingly have humbled himself and gone to him, assuring him that he felt no resentment because of what had happened. But by that time Peter himself was already busy with plans of his own, plans that were to carry him farther from Jerusalem and Antioch than even Paul had yet journeyed.

Book Nine

NERO CLAUDIUS, IMPERATOR

*". . . but when thou shalt be old, thou shalt
stretch forth thy hands, and another shall gird
thee, and carry thee whither thou wouldest not.
This spake he, signifying by what death he
should glorify God."*

JOHN 21:18, 19

I

T WAS still summer in Antioch, but already Simon Peter was beginning to dread the coming of winter, though here at the eastern end of the Great Sea even the cold season was relatively mild. Age had stiffened his joints as it had whitened his hair and beard to a snowy hue. Each day he found it harder to push himself into the round of duties expected from the head of the great Church of Antioch and one of the few apostles still alive. The going was especially difficult in winter, though Mark—now a man in his forties—helped as much as he could to take the load from Peter's bent shoulders.

Through the open window where the apostle stood, the warm sunshine flooded the room, reminding him of Galilee, but it had been many years since he had visited his old homeland, for of late other tasks had occupied him. Besides, he knew things would be changed markedly there, just as they had changed everywhere.

Beginning at Antioch long ago and spreading abroad in an ever-widening circle—of which Peter himself had been the first architect in Samaria, Lydda, Joppa and Caesarea—the work of the church had made rapid progress under Paul's aggressive leadership during several missionary journeys. Enthusiastic and growing congregations now existed in such far-off places as Ephesus, Philippi, Berea and Corinth. And Peter himself had helped to nourish the church at Rome during a stay of several years in the Imperial City.

The empire, too, had been undergoing a change in recent years, following the death of the Emperor Claudius. The elite

Praetorian Guard had originally installed Claudius as emperor after the assassination of Caligula, because he seemed to be a harmless fellow whom the military forces could rely upon to do their bidding. But Claudius had turned out to be one of the best rulers in Rome's history, and his armies had pushed back the frontiers of the empire, even reconquering Britain. Also, both political and religious freedom had prevailed through his strict enforcement of the law of Associations, decreed by the Emperor Augustus.

The Law of Associations had stated that all organizations, whether religious or political in nature, were prohibited from meeting unless they registered with government authorities and received permission. Once this was given, however, they could be sure of freedom from harassment as long as no treason was preached. Under it, the many Jewish congregations in Rome—making up in all around thirty thousand people—had registered and were free to worship. And since the Christian congregations were regarded as merely another Jewish sect—like the Essenes and the Therapeutae, whose major center was at Alexandria in Egypt—the authorities in Rome had not troubled them.

As a result, the church in Rome had grown steadily, and Peter could look back upon his years there with pleasure and satisfaction. In fact he had only decided to return to Antioch and Jerusalem—having visited many of Paul's great new churches on the way to Rome and established others by his own preaching in Cappadocia, Pontus and Bithynia—when word reached him of new and grave trouble impending in the Holy City, with the dynamic Apostle to the Gentiles at its center.

Paul had returned from his third missionary journey, bringing a collection gathered from churches along his route for the aid of the congregation in Jerusalem, which had been badly struck by famine. He had arrived at Tyre on a Phoenician vessel which had sailed directly there from Patara, bypassing Antioch, and had gone on to the Holy City. Unknown to Paul, however, sharp changes had been going on in the priestly hierarchy at Jerusalem, and a group who hated the very word Christian—as the followers of Jesus were known everywhere now—was in power.

Once again the priests used their favorite method of setting the rabble on an intended victim with a false charge of blasphemy. As he was undergoing the ritual of cleansing from defilement in the temple at the suggestion of James, Paul was set upon by the mob, escaping only when he claimed refuge in his Roman citizenship—by virtue of having been born in Tarsus—and demanded protection from the garrison of Antonia.

Peter had already left Rome for Jerusalem when word came that Paul was on his way to the imperial capital after a winter shipwreck on the island of Melita. The two apostles missed each other, and in Jerusalem, Peter found the Mother Church so weak that he went on to Antioch to keep up the work there, while Paul was in Rome awaiting trial before the emperor.

In Antioch Peter had first learned of the eloquent letters Paul had written during his imprisonment in Caesarea to the young churches he had established in Asia Minor, Macedonia and Greece, exhorting them to stand fast in their faith and keep on with the work which he, at the moment, was prevented from doing except by correspondence. And since Paul appeared to have an excellent chance of being released by the Roman authorities and the work at Antioch went well under Peter's wise and inspired guidance, the affairs of the church as a whole were in good order—for a while.

Then the small congregation at Jerusalem had been dealt

almost a death blow when Porcius Festus, the procurator of Judea and Samaria, died suddenly, and Ananus, a bitter enemy of all Christians, was appointed high priest. Without a strong-willed Roman governor in residence at the moment to control him, Ananus had immediately convened a new Sanhedrin and summarily haled James, the kinsman of the Lord, before it, along with most of the elders of the small congregation in Jerusalem. The sentence of death had been handed down and carried out in a single day by stoning, wiping out with that one blow all except a tiny remnant of the Christians in Jerusalem.

Stunned and saddened by the news from the Holy City, Peter could do little at Antioch but mourn for his friends and fellow workers, who, like James, the son of Zebedee, had given their lives for their faith. The only thing from which he could take heart was the fact that his wisdom long ago in sending out teachers and workers from Jerusalem to establish new congregations—like the one at Antioch of which he was now the leader—had not only expanded the sphere of activities of the original *ecclesia*, but had now preserved it from destruction.

In spite of that small comfort, however, Peter was saddened by the change he could see taking place in Israel—even from a distance. For a new element was growing daily in power, a dangerous and radical movement very much like that with which Judas and Simon the Zealot would have allied Jesus's own mission long ago in Galilee and Judea, had they been able to do so. New leaders, even more irresponsible and dangerous than Barabbas and Menahem, the son of Judas the Galilean, were stirring the people to violence against Rome. And though the actual rebellions which had broken out so far were still minor, Peter could see a dangerous pattern developing through the years, since as a boy he had witnessed the horrors brought on by the War of Varus.

Nor was the news from Rome much better now, except that Paul had finally been absolved of the false charges against him and had departed for Spain on a journey he had planned before his arrest in Jerusalem and subsequent imprisonment in Caesarea and Rome. Even before Peter had left the Imperial City, there had been evidence that Nero, successor to the Emperor Claudius, was becoming more and more depraved. The young emperor's tutor Seneca had managed to hold him in check for a while, but with his elevation to the throne, everything that was evil in Nero seemed to have come to the fore.

For years, the inhabitants of Rome had shut and bolted their doors at dusk as protection against the bands of highborn young ruffians—of whom Nero had often been a member—who roamed the streets, attacking any wayfarer unlucky enough to be out after dark. Now these ex-companions had become Nero's closest advisers, and the city was rapidly approaching the state of complete anarchy which had existed under Caligula until the Praetorian Guard had decided to assassinate him.

Perhaps the worst influence of all upon Rome's new ruler was a beautiful, intelligent and utterly unscrupulous woman named Poppaea Sabina, the wife of Otho. Encouraged by his new mistress—who became empress after divorcing her husband—Nero's love for the fantastic and the outrageous, symptoms of the actual insanity which soon could be doubted no longer, led him to greater and greater excesses.

Reading the latest letter from the elders at Rome in the relative peace and security of Antioch, Peter could not throw off the feeling of impending disaster that so often assailed him now. Putting down the scroll which had been brought from Rome on one of the great ships that regularly made the circuit of the eastern end of the Mediterranean, except during the storms of winter, he went to the window. But even here in Antioch there was much to remind him of the pagan forces that controlled Rome, and which now seemed marshaled once again in an attempt to destroy the Church of Christ.

The window looked down upon a broad colonnaded street that bisected Antioch, ending upon the lower slopes of Mount Silpius, the height overlooking the city. Peter could not help shivering—as he had shivered long ago at Bethabara when his eye had spied the metallic gleam from the wall of Herod's fortress of Machaerus—at the sight of the Roman castle built on one of the several summits of Mount Silpius, ostensibly to guard the city from invasion, but also reminding its inhabitants of the futility of revolt.

From the dour, brooding threat of the castle, it was almost a relief to turn his eyes to the beautiful Temple of Jupiter Capitolinus, on another crag—even though it was dedicated to a pagan god—and the luxurious baths and aqueducts built by Julius Caesar to commemorate his defeat of Pompey. But he instinctively averted his gaze when it touched the lush green beauty of the infamous grove of bay trees marking the suburb of Daphne, where the marble walls of the Temple of Diana gleamed in the warm sunlight, a picture of beauty and peace quite at variance with the depraved rites practiced there by devotees of the goddess.

By contrast, the Christian congregations of Antioch worshiped in buildings of every sort, but Simon Peter was confident that the doctrine being preached daily in hundreds of such centers throughout the Roman world was destroying the pagan faiths as surely as Roman military might had conquered the far-off reaches of empire. And even though the Church of Christ was barely alive in Jerusalem and under attack in Rome, he did not doubt that it would emerge—as it had from the persecutions of Saul and Agrippa—strengthened and girded for new conquest.

Turning back to the room, Peter went to the table and took up a scroll upon which Mark had been writing when they had stopped work the evening before. Knowing that his life was drawing to a close, the old apostle had spent much time with the scribe, who was like a son to him, dictating all the words and the actions of Jesus that he could remember. Fortunately, he was helped by the strange faculty granted to the aged of recalling the distant past with remarkable clarity. And under Mark's facile pen and stylus, the world in which Jesus had lived and taught during the few short years of his active ministry had taken form again—though still only in part, for Mark was far from being finished.

More recently, Peter had put aside the work upon the "Sayings," as they called the work Mark was doing, in order to dictate a letter to the churches he had established during his journey to and from Rome. Now he stood looking down at the words inscribed so skillfully in Mark's hand upon the parchment.

"I think it meet, as long as I am in this tabernacle, to stir you up by putting you in remembrance, knowing that shortly I must put off this, my tabernacle, even as our Lord Jesus Christ has showed me."

Mark had protested at the words, Peter remembered with a smile, not understanding that death had held no fear for him since that night when he had wrestled with his own fears in the upper room of Mary's house while the Master was being mocked before Herod Antipas and scourged by the Romans. In the upper room Peter had finally overcome his greatest adversary, and his courage and zeal had never wavered again.

"Moreover, I will endeavor that you may be able, after my death, to have these things always in remembrance. For we have not followed cunningly devised fables when we made known to you the power and coming of our Lord Jesus Christ, but were eyewitnesses of his majesty, for he received from God the Father honor and glory."

Peter put down the scroll and moved to the window again. Through it he could see the bustle of the busy city, and merely by descending the stairway to the street, could have become a part of it. But more and more often of late he had felt oppressed by a deep sense of loneliness, for of the Twelve who had labored so diligently in the vineyards of the Lord during the early days of the church, only he and John bar Zebedee were still alive, as far as he knew, and John was far away in Asia.

Peter's own brother Andrew had long ago traveled eastward toward the land of the Scythians, far beyond the Tigris and Euphrates, there—according to meager reports received later—giving up his life in the service of the Master. Barnabas, too, was dead and buried on Cyprus, his birthplace, while Paul, according to the last report, was in Spain.

A knock on the door brought Peter's thoughts back to the present. He called out permission to enter, and Mark opened the door. One look at the younger man's face told Peter that the news contained in the scroll he carried must be very bad indeed.

"A letter has just come from Rome," Mark said. "Paul is dead—beheaded by Nero."

II

Peter opened his eyes but could not remember how he came to be lying down, for the sun still shone brightly through the window. His head ached, and for a moment he had trouble seeing the various objects in the room clearly. Then Mark moved into his range of vision. The scribe's face was anxious, and he carried a cup of wine in his hand.

"Drink this," he said.

"How did I come to be lying down?" Peter asked, when he put down the cup.

"It was my fault. I should not have given you the news without warning."

"Then I must have suffered a fainting spell?"

"Only for a moment. I caught you before you fell, and guided you to the couch."

"Did you say Paul is dead?"

"The news just arrived in a letter from Luke. He sent it by one of the military galleys bringing dispatches to the governor."

Luke's name was quite familiar to Peter. He had known the Greek physician well before Luke had accompanied Paul on his second journey to look after the often ailing apostle's physical welfare. A convert of Paul's in Antioch, Luke had also accompanied Paul on the journey to Rome, though whether he had gone to Spain, Peter did not know.

"I seem to remember your saying that Paul was beheaded by Nero." Peter's words were slurred a little, for he seemed to be troubled with a thickness of his tongue. And when he lifted his right hand, for a moment the fingers refused to move, though they opened slowly when he exerted a conscious effort upon them.

"Perhaps you should wait a little while before hearing the rest of the letter," Mark suggested, but Peter shook his head. He was feeling better rapidly now; his vision was clearing, and though the thickness of his tongue still remained, he could open and close the fingers of his right hand with less difficulty.

"Tell me the whole story," he insisted.

Mark opened the scroll in his hand. "Rome burned a month ago, according to Luke. The fire started in a group of wooden shops near the Great Circus beneath the Palatine Hill."

From his years of residence in Rome, Peter was able to visualize the picture vividly. The Emperor Augustus had claimed that he had found a city built of brick and wood and left one built of marble, but the boast was far from true. On the Palatine Hill there were many great palaces, and the Forum area between the Palatine and Capitoline—the two most important of Rome's seven hills—did contain many buildings: the Basilica Julia, the palace of the Pontifex Maximus—in front of which the body of Julius Caesar had been burned—the house of Vestal Virgins, the temples of the state gods Saturn, Jupiter, Castor and Pollux—as well as the divine Caesar. But the *Subura*, as the slums between the Viminal and Esquiline were called, was packed with rickety wooden houses built wall to wall. And thousands of similar structures were to be found in the Transtiberina—the district across the river where many of the Jews lived—as well as in other scattered locations throughout the city.

Peter shuddered at the thought of how the fire must have burst from the Circus Maximus into the narrow, crowded streets of the city as the flames engulfed the flimsy structures where the artisans and the poorer people lived. Thousands undoubtedly had died, many of them people he had baptized into the faith himself. It took little imagination to create a picture of horror as those seeking frantically to escape the burning city choked streets and roads, blocking all progress and trapping many thousands inside the roaring furnace that was Rome.

"The traveler who brought the letter from Luke said nearly all the city was destroyed before the fire was controlled," Mark said. "Nero was at Actium when it happened. He hurried back as soon as he had word of it, but some still say he had Rome burned for his own entertainment."

The feat, horrible though it was, was not beyond Nero's capabilities, Peter knew from the depraved emperor's history. He was not concerned about guilt now; his thoughts were of the Christians who had suffered in the holocaust—for many of those making up the Rome congregations were from the poorer classes, whose houses had no doubt gone up in the flames. Most of all he was concerned by news of the death of Paul, whose eloquent voice had been the clearest bell ringing out the glad tidings for people everywhere—but which would be heard no more.

"Does Luke say how Paul became involved?" Peter asked.

"Apparently those around Nero needed a scapegoat to blame for the fire so the people would stop saying the emperor had ordered it set while he was at Actium. You remember how he was already beginning to persecute the Christians before we left Rome—because we would not worship him as a god—don't you?"

"Yes."

"Luke says Nero now blames our people for burning the city, and is crucifying them daily, tossing them to the lions during the games, or dousing them with pitch and setting them aflame. Paul was among the first taken, but since he was a Roman citizen, they beheaded him instead."

"Thank God he was spared the agony of crucifixion or

the torch," Peter said fervently, remembering the field of crosses he had seen so long ago on the slope before Sepphoris.

"Luke closes his letter with a prayer of thanksgiving that you were not there to suffer the same fate as Paul," Mark added.

"Does he tell how the congregations in Rome are faring?"

"At the moment I judge they are afraid to meet together. Luke says thousands have already been executed by Nero."

"Help me up." Peter held out a hand to Mark.

"You fainted just now!" Mark protested. "You should not be on your feet."

"I must be about the Master's business," Peter said. "Help me up."

Mark supported the aging apostle with his arm, and after a brief moment of dizziness, Peter was able to walk to the window. There he leaned against the opening, drinking in the fresh air that poured through it and feeling himself grow stronger by the moment.

"Surely you couldn't be thinking of—"

"Find out when the next ship sails to Rome," Peter interrupted, and now there was no slurring of the words, no hesitation in his voice. "We must go there at once."

"But Nero would like nothing better than to destroy you as he did Paul," Mark protested.

"Long ago, by the Sea of Galilee, Jesus told me to feed his sheep. More than any other place in the world just now, the flock in Rome needs a shepherd in this time of trouble. If I left them without a leader, I could never face the Master when he calls me to join him in Heaven."

III

On his previous visit to Rome, Peter had landed at Brundisium —eastern terminus of that portion of the Appian Way crossing the Italian peninsula—and traveled the rest of the way by foot, as did most wayfarers who used that route. But he was far too feeble now to make that journey, and besides, he hoped to encourage the faithful who had survived Nero's persecution by coming openly to the Imperial City. He and Mark therefore took passage from Antioch upon a ship bound for Ostia, the seaport of Rome at the mouth of the River Tiber.

They were more fortunate than Paul had been in his journey to Rome several years earlier when his ship was wrecked by the autumn storms upon the island of Melita and he was forced to spend the winter there. Peter's vessel, a trireme, had been built by the Greeks who in turn had learned the art of shipbuilding from the Phoenicians, the bold seafarers whose ships had sailed the length and breadth of the Great Sea even before the time of David and Solomon. Driven by three banks of oars manned by galley slaves and by great sails when there was a breeze, the large craft made good time to Ostia with its cargo of grain and other products from Alexandria and Antioch.

It was still early autumn and the weather was warm when Peter and Mark landed at the Roman seaport. There had been a Christian congregation in Ostia at least as long as there had been one in Rome, and being outside the Imperial City, it had not suffered as badly from the persecution. The brethren there immediately whisked them away to a hiding place, and when they did not succeed in persuading Peter against going on to Rome, arranged for him to be met outside the capital city the next day.

The brethren at Ostia had decided that the safest way for Mark and Peter to reach Rome was to travel openly to the outskirts, hoping no one would recognize the venerable apostle before he was safely hidden. Peter did not like the idea of acting as if he were a culprit needing to hide; he was much more accustomed to openly announcing his identity and his mission. But he had been warned that he would never reach those he sought to help if he were recognized by the authorities, so he agreed, however reluctantly, to the need for stealth.

The traffic grew heavier as they approached Rome. Noblemen and their ladies rode in richly upholstered sedan chairs borne by slaves, the curtains drawn against the brilliance of the autumn sun. A detail of legionnaires returning from military duty marched to their quarters inside the city. Peasants going back to their villages after selling produce in the city markets kept to the roadside to make room for the soldiers, while travelers like themselves hurried to reach Rome before darkness fell.

There were almost no vehicles on the road, for the law forbade the entry of such into Rome during the daylight hours, freeing the city from the terrible congestion of vehicular traffic that would have made its narrow streets almost impassable. Because of Peter's great age, he and Mark were forced to travel slowly, and it was late afternoon when they paused atop a hill from which they were able to see most of Rome.

Their first impression was one of total destruction; the buildings not destroyed by fire had been so discolored by smoke and soot that they seemed to be mere shells. It was an especially shocking sight to one who remembered the majesty and beauty of Rome only a few years earlier, a scene of destruction almost awesome in its terrible completeness.

Yet as they came nearer to the city they could see that Rome was still very much alive, for new construction was going on everywhere. Fresh buildings of brick, stone and mortar were rising from the foundations of the old, and great new palaces—particularly a massive building which they were told was the new home of Claudius Nero, Imperator.

The Circus Maximus was under construction again, too, for Nero loved spectacles dearly, and before the great fire, had even staged one there complete with naval fleets maneuvering upon an artificial lake and battling against each other. The roads as they neared the city were lined by rows of uprights, each with the charred and ghastly remains of what had been a human body, doused with pitch and set aflame to light one of Nero's processions, still hanging from the cross-arms.

"Luke told only half the story." Mark's voice was choked with horror. "I wonder if there is a Christian left in Rome."

They found the answer to that question before they reached the city itself when two men fell into step beside them and greeted them quietly. One was Apelles, a Roman nobleman who had become a Christian long ago; the other was Linus, one of those Paul had brought to Rome to help with his work there while he awaited trial before the emperor.

"The tomb of my family lies just outside the old walls," Apelles said. "We can enter the catacombs through it."

The brethren at Ostia had told Peter and Mark that the Roman Christians had been forced to go underground in order to escape the agents of Nero, who constantly sought for them. But neither of them were prepared for what they were shown by Apelles and Linus.

Centuries before the coming to Italy of the people who eventually were known as Romans, its former inhabitants, the Etruscans, had initiated the custom of burying their dead in chambers hewn deep within the soft *tufa granulare*, an easily worked kind of volcanic rock that formed the base, so to speak, for much of the area. Later, the burial of any person's remains within the city itself had been forbidden by law, so what was literally a City of the Dead had grown up through the centuries, mainly outside the walls in the area to the left of the Tiber as they approached from Ostia.

The road was lined almost solidly with tombs in this area, and at a point still some distance from the center of the city Apelles led them aside on a path winding through what had been a vineyard, for here and there vines still ran along crumbling walls. Presently they stopped while Apelles went on ahead a short distance to reconnoiter, but he came back moments later and nodded for them to follow. The way ran around another corner of the wall beyond which the dark opening of a mausoleum yawned before them.

Mark took Peter's arm to support him against the possibility of stumbling in the dim sunlight illuminating the outer chamber of the mausoleum. They soon entered a second chamber through a heavy door, however, and found candles burning in sconces along the wall. Apelles and Linus each took one of these, and with the way now lighted, they traversed a short passageway cut from the soft *tufa*, to a stairway, likewise hewn from the soft rock but with the individual steps formed by narrow slabs of marble.

Peter was conscious of a strange sound that seemed to grow louder as they descended the stairway, but they were almost at the bottom before he realized that he was hearing voices singing a hymn. The sound filled his heart with gladness; it could only mean that some of the stalwart Christians he had known here in Rome were still alive, enough at least from which to build another congregation. Moments later they saw lights ahead and came into a larger chamber where the people whose voices he had heard were now repeating the prayer given them by Jesus himself.

Peter and the others stood at the entrance of the chamber until the prayer was ended. When the small group realized the identity of the aged apostle, they fell on their knees before him, but Peter raised them up with the same words he had used to Cornelius in Caesarea: "Stand up. I myself also am a man."

IV

In spite of the circumstances and the danger to everyone if their presence in the tombs were known, it was a time of rejoicing. For not only was the earthly head of Christ's Church there with them in the Catacombs—as the labyrinthine passages used for the burial of the dead were called—but many who had played an important part in the growth of the church as well. Peter embraced Timothy, who had been almost a son to Paul, as Mark was to him. Priscilla and Acquila —whom Paul had sent to Rome to help with the work— came to greet them, and Phebe, who had brought Paul's eloquent letter to the Romans even before his own arrival to plead his cause before Caesar. And they were greeted warmly by Luke, the slender, now graying Greek physician who had been Paul's close companion on his latter journeys.

Linus was the leader of the small congregation still remaining at Rome, and that night they all celebrated together the Sacrament of the bread and wine which Jesus had given them, though Peter was too tired to address more than a few words to the faithful gathered there.

It was a strange sort of a place in which Peter and Mark

found themselves. The walls of the separate chambers were hewn from the soft stone and contained niches in which the members of Apelles's family had been buried for many generations, each with its small marble slab upon which was chiseled the name of the occupant. The steadily increasing need for burial space had led to the hollowing out of other levels until, they were told, three and even four existed in some places. And lest they be trapped in a single catacomb with no way of exit, the Christians had hollowed out passages between the tombs of Apelles's family and others until a considerable network of the underground havens existed here beneath the surface of what had once been an old vineyard on the outskirts of Rome.

The catacomb hiding places were not a very comfortable habitation, however. The air was often musty and the underground chambers cool and damp, for it was difficult to heat them without betraying their occupancy by living persons. Peter did not sleep well; the cold made his joints ache. In the morning his movements were even stiffer than they had been before, but he still insisted upon visiting the tomb of Paul who—in spite of the fact that the self-styled Apostle to the Gentiles had castigated him in Antioch—he knew to have been one of the most important agents in propagating the new faith of the Christians—perhaps, Peter admitted frankly, even more important than himself, though Mark argued with him over that.

At a place near the Via Ostia, the road whereby Peter and Mark had reached Rome the day before, Luke showed them where Paul's body had been buried hurriedly by the faithful after his beheading on the orders of Nero. Peter mourned for the fallen soldier who had worn so proudly the breastplate of righteousness, as he called it, and the helmet of salvation. And it seemed as he stood there that he could hear again the voice of the dynamic little apostle saying, as in his letter to the great church at Corinth, "If the trumpet give an uncertain sound, who shall prepare himself for the battle?" And he knew without asking Luke that Paul's trumpet had never been uncertain, not even when he faced the sword of the Roman executioner.

"How did the persecution begin?" Peter asked Luke and Linus when they were safely back in the Catacombs.

"I think it was really when Simon Magus came to Rome," Linus said.

"The magician of Samaria?" Mark asked.

"Yes. He preached that he was the son of God, and many who were foolish believed him—some of them in high places. Paul denounced him publicly for what he was, a charlatan. But because of that, those who believed in Simon sought to destroy the followers of Christ in Rome."

"Was that why Paul met his death?" Mark asked.

Luke shook his head. "His enemies here in Rome brought Paul before the authorities on a charge of supporting one who claimed to be a king of Judea—they have often used that weapon against us. Even before that, Christians here were already being seized upon trivial claims and tortured, however, and Paul not only gave them strength and encouragement, but denounced their accusers."

"That was ever his way," Peter said, remembering the night when Paul had attacked him before the church at Antioch.

"Had Paul been less brave, he might still be alive," Luke agreed. "But when he spoke, people always stopped to listen. Nero could not leave so eloquent a voice unstilled very long, especially when Paul denounced him and those who fawned upon him."

"What happened to Simon Magus?" Mark enquired.

"He suffered the fate that overtakes braggarts who believe their own boasts. In order to impress the people and gain a larger following, Simon announced that he would fly through the air from a tower. But the wires by which he planned to fool the credulous broke and he was dashed to his death upon the earth."

"Surely that one thing would not bring on such a persecution as you have experienced," Mark protested.

"No," Linus said. "Much of our trouble came from the temple at Jerusalem."

"But how?"

"The Empress Poppaea has been friendly for a long time with some of the leaders in the synagogue of Rome," Linus explained. "The High Priest Ananus, who put James and the others in Jerusalem to death, sent letters denouncing those of us who follow Christ, so they used their influence with the empress to turn her and the emperor against us. The harassment had already begun while Paul was still a prisoner here in Rome. When the people began to blame Nero for the fire, he needed a scapegoat, and Poppaea had little trouble in convincing him that we should be selected."

It was strange, Peter thought, how the bitter hatred of the Jerusalem authorities that had actuated Caiaphas in putting Jesus to death long ago had now reached across both the years and the Roman world to harass the Master's followers here in Rome. But he had spent much of his life in fighting that force on many another front, and he proposed to keep on fighting it here.

Peter had seen, so clearly that he could hardly believe the vision had not come from Jesus himself, that the church at Rome must be preserved at all costs, no matter how long those who followed the Master were forced to hide in the Catacombs. Rome was now the center of an empire that, with the conquest of Britain carried out under the Emperor Claudius, extended from far east of the River Tigris to the unknown reaches of the Western Sea. And with great numbers of people constantly going and coming through the Imperial City, Rome afforded the same means of spreading the Christian faith that Jerusalem had done in the early years of the church—this time on a world-wide scale.

Nero had dealt the church here a grievous wound, it was true, but Peter could remember when Caligula had ordered his own statue set up in the Holy of Holies at Jerusalem, only to lose his life before the order could be carried out. He did not doubt that Nero, too, would one day fall like Caligula and the latter's friend Agrippa, who had once sought to destroy Peter himself. And when that time came, Peter was determined that the church at Rome must be alive and ready to tell once again "to all nations" the good news of what had happened so long ago in Galilee and Judea.

V

In the weeks that followed, Peter was truly a rock for the beleaguered church at Rome and its leaders, a strong anchor that was badly needed, for these were parlous times indeed. Nero's insanity was becoming more and more evident as time passed. With it, the persecution of those who followed the man the Romans called "Crestus" became more intense.

By tunneling from one chamber to another, the Christians were able to open up more and more of the network of catacombs in which they had taken refuge and find new hiding places. But food and water had to be brought in, and spies were everywhere, occasionally among their own people, eager to point out each new hiding place for a monetary reward or for the assurance of freedom from molestation for themselves and their families.

Every day new victims were seized and taken away to serve as provender for the lions in the arena during the gladiatorial games, or as human torches to light Nero's way to some new and more depraved orgy. Peter did what he could to comfort those in constant danger through his presence with them and the assurance that all would meet together in Heaven, there to be with Jesus throughout eternity. But short of accompanying the victims to the cross and the torch, thereby revealing his presence in Rome and causing his own swift arrest and execution, there was nothing else he could do. Meanwhile, human jackals searched among the tombs daily, seeking to discover the hiding places of the hated followers of Crestus. And since their faith forbade them to turn the tables upon these scavengers and destroy them, the only recourse of the faithful was to burrow ever deeper underground.

As time went on, an undercurrent of revulsion against Nero's excesses began to develop in Rome, and it was obvious that even he would not be able to destroy completely the inhabitants of the Catacombs. New passages and galleries were constantly being opened up, each with its complement of the dead stored in small niches in the walls called *loculi;* in the larger chambers, usually with an arch carved out over the tomb to give it the appearance of a sarcophagus, called *arcosolia;* or in the larger vaults and chapels of the wealthier families, called *cubiculi.*

The dead troubled the living far less than the agents of Nero, however, and the *cubiculi* in particular became the favorite hiding places of the Christians. Fortunately, many of those who had been converted to the faith in the early days of the church belonged to the upper classes—who were appalled by Nero's excesses and the mass trend toward emperor worship—so a large number of the tombs were made available for use by the persecuted group.

Almost from the moment of Peter's arrival in Rome, the Christians there had pleaded with him to leave while a chance still existed for him to escape unharmed. The church had passed through its own Golgotha now, due no little to the new heart given the Christians of the city by Peter's having risked his own life to come to them in their hour of travail. Besides, great congregations had been established outside Rome in Corinth, Ephesus, Antioch, Philippi and many other cities of the empire, so Linus and Luke in particular argued that— with Paul, the man who had founded them, dead—it was Peter's duty to keep them strong with the visible symbol of his presence.

Peter, on the other hand, did not feel that the time had yet come for him to leave Rome, since to do so might seem to some a betrayal of those who had nowhere else to go. He was forced to change that decision, however, when Apelles returned one evening from a visit to the city where, being a Roman of an old family, he was less likely to be seized as a Christian, bringing grave news for Simon Peter—and them all.

"Nero has learned of your presence here," he told Peter. "A warrant has been issued for your arrest, and the tribute to anyone betraying your whereabouts has been doubled."

This was the one eventuality Peter had been afraid of, though not because of any fear for his own safety. With the authorities making a concerted effort to seize him, those who had given him shelter would be in danger and the attacks upon the Christians would inevitably be increased—solely because of Peter's own presence in Rome.

"Do you think they suspect where Peter is?" Linus asked.

Apelles shook his head. "Word that the warrant was issued

came from one I can trust. Peter is safe for the moment, but we must get him away from Rome before someone betrays him."

"Or before all of you are killed because of me," Peter added. "Tell me, Apelles: could this person you speak of arrange for Mark to go to Africa at once? We have a strong church at Cyrene, and he would be safe there."

"I cannot desert you!" Mark cried. "Who will go with you when you leave?"

"I will," Luke volunteered. "Peter is right, Mark. You have already written some of the Sayings of Jesus, but many are still stored up in your mind. Nothing is more important now than that they should be preserved."

"You must go where you can safely complete your writing, Mark," Peter agreed. "But I will not endanger Luke or anyone else by letting them accompany me."

All recognized the authority and the finality in his tone— as well as the truth of what he was saying—so none made objection.

"I will arrange for Mark's passage at once," Apelles promised. "Carts from my friend's farm outside the city bring produce to the market every night and return in the morning empty. The guards know them and will not examine an empty cart. You can escape from the city that way, Peter. But Nero will surely have warned the guards at Ostia to look for you, and if you try to board a ship there, you will be taken."

"Then I will go to Brundisium," Peter said. "They will not be expecting me there."

"It is a long way." Being a physician, Luke could say what the others hesitated to put into words.

"The Lord will give me strength—if it is his will that I go," Peter said simply. "As soon as Mark is safely on the way to take ship for Africa, Apelles can arrange for me to hide in one of the carts."

VI

It was only a little after dawn when the cart deposited Peter beside the road before turning off on a path leading to one of the villages outside the city. He was still not sure in his mind that he had been right in letting the others persuade him to escape, for a much simpler way to make life in Rome safer for those who worked in the service of the Lord there and elsewhere would be to surrender himself, thereby bringing an end to the hunt for him. But Luke had reminded him again that Paul's churches in Greece and Asia Minor, as well as his own in Cappadocia, Bithynia and elsewhere, would be helped by a pastoral visit from the Prince of the Apostles, tired though he was of hiding and now running, and Peter had finally let himself be convinced.

He started down the cobblestoned road leading away from Rome, but made slow progress, for the months he had spent in the Catacombs, where the air was damp and cool, had tended to make his joints stiff and painful. Limping a little, he trudged along, still only half convinced in his own mind that he was doing the right thing.

It was still half dark when he saw a man appear out of the shadows ahead, his body partly hidden by the morning fog that hung over the road. As the newcomer approached, walking toward Rome, Peter thought the slender figure in the brown robe looked familiar, but there was not yet enough light for him to make out any details of the other man's face.

"Whither do you go?" he called out, thinking by speaking first to allay suspicion that he might be escaping from the city.

"I go to Rome to be crucified." The traveler was almost beside him now, and although his face was still hidden by the cowl of the robe, the voice was very familiar.

"Let me go with you, Lord!" Peter cried joyously, and turned again toward the distant city to fall into step beside the Master. There was no answer, and when he looked again, no one was there. Yet Peter no longer felt any doubt concerning the course Jesus would have him follow; a sense of peace had come over him that it was all settled at last.

Like brave, eloquent and always dynamic Paul, who had given his life here in Rome, so must the humble fisherman to whom had been handed a sacred trust as Prince of the Apostles and leader of all those who followed Jesus give to the world his own final testimony by going fearlessly to his death in the service of his Master.

Peter's stride even quickened a little as he walked toward the city. Nor was he surprised, before he had gone more than a short distance on the way back to Rome, to hear the rhythmic sound of *caligae* marching upon the stones. A detail of soldiers—sent, he was certain, to arrest him—appeared out of the morning fog on the road ahead. As he strode unafraid to meet them, he seemed to hear Jesus saying once again, as he had said on the shore of the Sea of Galilee:

"When you were young, you girded yourself and walked whither you would. But when you shall be old, you shall stretch forth your hand, and another shall gird you and shall carry you whither you would not."

Peter had not fully understood the meaning of those words when they had been spoken, but he understood them now. The Prince of the Apostles would certainly die—as the Master himself had died—the most ignominious of deaths possible at the hands of Rome, nailed to a cross. But Peter dared to hope and to pray that his captors would grant his final wish to be crucified head downward in a final tribute of love and true humility to the Master he had served so long.